When the Going Gets Tough, the Tough Get Praying

Changing God's Mind through Prayer

Brother Andrew

When the Going Gets Tough, the Tough Get Praying

Changing God's Mind through Prayer

With Susan De Vore Williams

Marshall Pickering

An Imprint of HarperCollins*Publishers*

Marshall Pickering is an Imprint of
HarperCollins*Religious*
Part of HarperCollins*Publishers*
77–85 Fulham Palace Road, London W6 8JB

First published in the USA by Chosen Books 1990
First published in Great Britain in 1991 by Marshall Pickering
under the title *And God Changed His Mind*

Copyright © Open Doors International
16520 Harbor Blvd, Fountain Valley, CA 92708, USA, 1990

This edition 1998

10 9 8 7 6 5 4 3 2 1

Brother Andrew asserts the moral right to be
identified as the author of this work

A catalogue record for this book is
available from the British Library

ISBN 0 551 03152 2

Printed and bound in Great Britain by
Caledonian International Book Manufacturing Ltd, Glasgow

Unless noted otherwise, Scripture texts are from the Holy Bible, New
International Version, copyright © 1973, 1978, 1984 International Bible Society.

Scripture quotations identified NASB are from the New American Standard
Bible, copyright © The Lockman Foundation 1960, 1962, 1963, 1968, 1971,
1972, 1973, 1975, 1977.

Scripture quotations identified NEB are from The New English Bible,
copyright © The Delegates of the Oxford University Press and the Syndics of
the Cambridge University Press 1961, 1970.

Reprinted by permission.

Verses marked TLB are taken from *The Living Bible*, copyright © 1971 by
Tyndale House Publishers, Wheaton, Ill. Used by permission.

To the
Suffering Church

CONTENTS

Open Doors with Brother Andrew

If you would like to receive further information about "Open Doors with Brother Andrew" and its ministry to the Suffering Church worldwide, please write to us.

Upon your request we gladly send you – free of charge – our monthly magazine, which gives up-to-date news and information about persecuted Christians around the world.

Name: ....

Address: ....

Postal Code: ....

Place: ....

Country: ....

Forward this form to the office nearest to you:

Open Doors	Open Doors	Open Doors
P.O. Box 6	Box 27001	P.O. Box 53
Witney	Santa Ana	Seaforth
Oxon	CA 92799	NSW 2092
OX8 7SP	USA	Australia
England		

Open Doors International – Headquarters
P.O. Box 47
3840 AA Harderwijk
The Netherlands

1
We Are Not Helpless!

Some time ago I heard two Christian women discussing the plight of hostages being held by Middle Eastern terrorists.

"I feel sorry for those poor men and their families," one of the women remarked, "but really, this is God's problem, not ours. We have to remember that He has already decided how their stories are going to turn out."

The other woman sighed. "Yes," she said, "but it's frustrating! It seems we're all being held hostage by the evil people in the world—the terrorists and dictators, the drug dealers, the criminals. . . ."

The first woman smiled and patted her friend's arm. "Well, that's how it *looks*," she said comfortingly, "but we know God has His reasons for allowing these things.

Even when we don't understand those reasons, we can be sure that *nothing* happens outside His will."

As I listened, I felt indignation rising within me. I could barely control the urge to turn to them and say, "What's the matter with you? Why are you talking this way? You're not helpless! God has given you the power to change that situation! Why don't you use it? Why don't you pray?"

But sometimes I know when it's pointless to open my mouth, and this was one of those times. Those women wouldn't have understood what I wanted to say. Even so, I couldn't get them out of my mind, and their conversation continued to trouble me because it illustrated perfectly a problem that has caused a tremendous weakening of the Body of Christ in our time.

Those two very devout women were steeped in a false doctrine that has infected the thinking of an alarming number of Christians in our time. I call it—for lack of a better term—*Christian fatalism*. Without realizing it, those women had succumbed to a spiritual error that had all but neutralized their effectiveness as believers. If I had asked them, "My dear ladies, have you considered joining Islam?", no doubt they would have been outraged and offended. But the truth is, their beliefs about "God's will" would have fit very nicely into the Muslim religion, and into a number of other fatalistic religions, too, like Hinduism and Buddhism. There is, however, *no* place for fatalism in Christianity. Quite the opposite!

The Bible is full of powerful illustrations that prove it. In these pages we will highlight a number of them, because I believe that in our determination to submit to the sovereign will of God, too many of us have lost sight of a powerful truth: God never created us to be puppets. He made us in His own image, endowing us with the ability to make independent choices. In doing so, He in a sense restricted His own omnipotence by allowing us to say yes or no to His will.

In other words, God has given us the privilege of choosing how our lives (and our world) will turn out. And those of us who know God are elevated to a stunning position within this framework: We become God's partners and collaborators in writing the story of mankind. Not only that, but we are empowered to challenge the powers of evil that have been at war with God since the beginning of time. We can, through our own faith and our prayers, lift the world off its hinges—if only we *will!*

No, God isn't interested in puppets; He is looking for people who will say yes to His invitation and make a difference in the world. He is looking for people who understand that in making Himself susceptible to our influence, He has given us "the keys of the kingdom" (Matthew 16:19)—the power to change human history for the better.

"Anyone who has faith in me will do what I have been doing," Jesus said. "He will do even greater things than these, because I am going to the Father. And I will do whatever you ask in my name, so that the Son may bring glory to the Father. You may ask me for anything in my name, and I will do it" (John 14:12–14). He couldn't make a more explicit statement, could He? "Take up My cause!" Jesus is saying. "Look at what I have done, and do more! I have given you the power, so go for it!"

But still we hesitate. Still we don't believe it's our place to "tell God what we want Him to do with His world"—which is the way I recently heard a Christian man describe intercessory prayer. But why not? God invites us—even commands us—to do it! Shall we decline His invitation like good Muslims or Buddhists or Hindus, who out of false humility cringe at the thought of a God who is open to influence, whose plans can be changed? I pray that we will not, because God is depending on us—and so is our world. Unless we shake off our fatalistic apathy and use the power God makes available to us through prayer, the blood of many on this planet will be on our hands. We are responsible!

Yes, God wants us to be active, not passive. He wants us to resist—and ultimately defeat—the principalities and powers that have been holding the world hostage since the beginning of recorded history. And He gives us weapons more powerful than theirs to do it. "Whatever you bind on earth will be bound in heaven," Jesus declares, "and whatever you loose on earth will be loosed in heaven" (Matthew 16:19).

Incredible! The fatalist can only shudder at such words! But as Christians we should be electrified by them. They confirm that God has given us access to the unlimited power of Jesus Christ Himself—power far greater than that of any so-called "superpower" on earth. They also tell us that, contrary to what the two women I mentioned earlier believed, God has *not* "already decided how this story will turn out," any more than He has decided whom we will marry or what Gorbachev will be doing five years from today.

Mind you, I'm not saying that God has no plans for us, or that He has taken His hands off the world and is letting us spin out of control into our own self-made oblivion. Nor am I saying that we have ultimate control over God or that He has put us in charge of everything. He is a sovereign God, and we can and should know His will—and we should *do* it. Doing things God's way should always be our objective, and the Scriptures give us all the guidelines necessary for that task. But we must also remember that God's plans for us are not chiseled in concrete. Only His character and nature are unchanging; His decisions are not!

Yes, when we see things happening in the world that appear to be "acts of God," and we disagree with what God seems to be doing (or allowing), *we can ask Him to change His mind.* God is always ready to listen to our side of the story, and even if He has made plans to do something, He is open to changing those plans under the right conditions.

Moses understood this facet of God's character as few men ever have, and the Bible gives us plenty of examples to help us understand how we can relate to God the way he did. In Exodus we read that the Lord said to Moses, "I have seen what a stubborn, rebellious lot these people are. . . . My anger shall blaze out against them and destroy them all." Sounds pretty final, doesn't it? A fatalist might have responded, "Oh, boy, we're in for it now! It's all over!" But Moses didn't accept that. He "begged God not to do it. . . . So the Lord changed his mind and spared them" (Exodus 32:9, 11,14, LB).

Moses knew it was possible to change God's mind, just as most of the other heroes of the Bible did. Moses *knew God*, and as God's friend he understood that God's plans could be changed. In later chapters we will talk more about Moses and the others who changed God's mind, but for now it's enough to know that these were human beings just like you and me, and if they could change God's mind, so can we! It happens all the time.

One example that particularly thrills me involves the recent developments in the Soviet Union. Back in 1983 our organization, Open Doors, called for seven years of prayer for the Soviet Union. We were convinced that the evil conspiracy that had brought untold misery and torment to the Body of Christ worldwide was headquartered in one place: Moscow. Millions had died as a result of genocide in Communist nations, and hundreds of thousands were in prison for their faith. We decided to take the offensive against Satan by attacking his strongholds. Many Christians around the world joined us. We prayed particularly that the barriers that have kept God's Word out of Eastern Europe and Russia would be removed and that Christian prisoners would be set free.

Within a year we began to see results. We heard for

the first time about an obscure man named Gorbachev. We began to hear the words *glasnost* and *perestroika* instead of the usual Communist rhetoric. The winds of change we prayed for began to blow, and there was no holding them back. Finally, just under six years from the time we first began praying, the walls between East and West began to crumble. The Berlin Wall—a worldwide symbol of Communist oppression—came tumbling down. Prison doors began to open. Eastern Europe rose up against the powers that had held them in bondage.

In 1989, after more than thirty years of smuggling Bibles behind the Iron Curtain, I challenged the Russians openly to allow our organization to distribute a million Russian-language Bibles to Soviet churches. Incredibly, they said yes. And at this moment, still less than seven years after we began praying, we are able to report to our prayer partners the glorious news that *not a single Christian leader remains in a prison or concentration camp in the Soviet Union for his faith!* That, my friend, is what happens when we pray.

Yes, we do have something to say about the things that happen around us. We don't have to take life as it comes; we can have an earth-shaking impact on our world because God's mind and heart are open to us and His power is available to us. It's no wonder God gets exasperated when He sees how reluctant we are to use the power of prayer. "This is a people plundered and despoiled," He says in Isaiah. "All of them are trapped in caves, or are hidden away in prisons; they have become a prey with none to deliver them, and a spoil, with none to say, 'Give them back!' Who among you will give ear to this?" (Isaiah 42:22–23, NASB). Who, indeed? Who will stand up to Satan in our time and demand, as Moses did before Pharaoh, "Let My people go" (Exodus 7:16, NASB)? Who will be on the Lord's side?

Certainly it will not be the fatalists—Christian or otherwise. They will never challenge the powers that be. It should worry us that Islam is the fastest-growing religion on earth. The majority of the people on this planet today, in fact, belong to the fatalistic non-Christian religions, and their numbers are increasing at an alarming rate. And now the Christian Church is being infected as well with the paralyzing virus of fatalistic apathy. How can this be?

It isn't so hard to understand. There is no denying the appeal of fatalism to people who are "spiritually inclined"—people who long to be religious. The fatalist's attitude seems to reflect tremendous faith: "I refuse to question the will of God," he will say with pious humility. But does he actually mean that whatever happens in the world is all right with him—including war, famine, oppression, the breakdown of the family and society, the exploitation of the innocent and weak, the degradation of all that is holy and pure? "If God allows it, there must be a reason," he will say, "and I can't hope to understand God's reasons with my small mind, so I accept what He does by faith and 'praise the Lord anyway.' " And ignorant listeners to this kind of talk will respond admiringly, "What faith!"

This kind of "faith" has no power, however, because it is based on a false premise. Call it what you like— *karma*, destiny, fate, *kismet*—it amounts to the same thing regardless of the costume it wears. It says that we cannot change the script God has written and our duty is merely to "go with the flow" of God's program. It makes life so simple, doesn't it? Yes, and that's a good part of its appeal. Fatalists can relax because they are no longer responsible for anything. They don't have to obey God or actively resist evil; they can simply "let it be" (as the Beatles recommended in their hit song of the '60s).

Fatalism has other appeals as well. If a Christian can incorporate fatalism into his theology, his life becomes immeasurably easier and more comfortable. He will gain hundreds of extra hours each year for television viewing and napping when he no longer has to waste time on such fruitless activities as studying the Scriptures, getting to know God through prayer, interceding for his family and for the world, combating the forces of evil or reaching out to others for the sake of Christ. He won't have to lift a finger again. He can sit in his recliner and vegetate for the rest of his life, feeling perfectly secure in his "faith." He is ready to meet every calamity of life, from divorce to death, with an attitude of stoic acceptance.

There is nothing new about this, of course. Even some of the greatest heroes in the Bible succumbed occasionally to fatalism. Remember what Job said upon learning that his whole family had been wiped out and everything he owned was lost? "The Lord gave and the Lord has taken away. Blessed be the name of the Lord" (Job 1:21, NASB). Astonishing! What a statement! Indeed, it is these words that are often quoted at funerals today as an affirmation of faith in the face of devastating loss.

But is this attitude Christian? No! It is "scriptural" only in the sense that the words are found in the Bible. What we must recognize is that these words were uttered in absolute ignorance by a man who had no idea that God and Satan were using his body as a battleground. Job couldn't see that Satan was counting on fatalism as his most potent weapon.

But we can't be too hard on Job; he didn't have the Bible to help him understand God's character or the nature of the spiritual warfare that was taking place in his life. He had no way of knowing that it was Satan, not God, who had "taken away" everything he held dear. The miracle of Job's story is not that he accepted his suffering without question; it is that in spite of his mistaken ideas about who was causing it, he still refused to curse God or charge Him with wrongdoing. So we can admire Job for remaining faithful in spite of his misconceptions about the situation. But we have no business transforming his misconceptions into Christian theology!

Our response to Satan's devious tactics should reflect a far deeper knowledge of God than Job's, because we have not only the Scriptures to draw upon, but two thousand years of Christian experience as well. We also have the Holy Spirit to enlighten us. But too many Christians today are in the same boat with those two women I heard talking about the hostages. They are drifting along, contentedly going with the flow as though the revelation of God ceased during Job's era, the Holy Spirit never came and prayer was never given to us as a way of gaining access to the heart and mind of God. Sadly, they don't realize until it is too late that the current that seems to be offering a comfortable, secure ride is actually pulling them faster and faster toward a deadly whirlpool—and oblivion.

This has been one of Satan's fundamental strategies throughout history. He continues to employ it because it has worked so well for so long. But we cannot permit his strategy to succeed! We have the power to resist and overcome him, and God has placed the weapon in our hands that can do so. That weapon is prayer.

Nothing makes Satan quite so fearful as a Christian who understands the power of prayer, because he knows that God holds nothing back from His friends. As we know God and begin to understand all that He is and all that is His, we are no longer helpless victims who can be tossed about by the storms and waves Satan stirs up. We are, in fact, capable of doing what the devil and his demons cannot. Jesus tells us,

> "If you have faith and do not doubt . . . you can say
> to this mountain, 'Go, throw yourself into the sea,'
> and it will be done. If you believe, you will receive
> whatever you ask for in prayer." Matthew 21:21–22

No wonder Satan is desperate to keep Christians from serious prayer! He has no power compared to that. Through prayer, not only can we move mountains, we can defeat every one of Satan's evil plans. It is a life-and-death matter, you see—for Satan as well as for us. It should not surprise us, then, that he works overtime dreaming up schemes to neutralize our prayers. If he can do that, he has nothing to fear from us. He can pursue his unholy agenda unhindered.

This is why I am concerned about Christian fatalism. It is not merely an innocuous doctrinal interpretation that we can coexist with as we do in the case of minor variations in Christian theology. Fatalism is a paralyzing disease that has invaded the Body of Christ with disastrous consequences. It infects its victims with complacency and apathy that immobilize their will to resist evil while eroding their determination to accomplish the great work of Christ.

Unless this creeping paralytic disease is halted, the world is going to be in even more desperate trouble than it already is. The ultimate cost in terms of human suffering will be horrifying beyond our comprehension. The atrocities and oppression we saw in Hitler's Europe, Mao's China and Stalin's Russia will pale by comparison. Millions will continue to languish in isolation and despair all around the globe at a time when they ought to be able to count on us to come to their rescue. And if we believe for a moment that God will keep the evil that is engulfing the rest of humanity away from our doorsteps, we are tragically mistaken. He will do no such thing. If we hide from the truth by taking refuge in false doctrines, we deserve to experience the consequences. Believe me, God will not protect us from them. We are not exempt from suffering.

Make no mistake: Satan is not getting nicer or more genteel as time goes on. (We will look at his strategies and how to counter them in chapters 6 and 7.) He is becoming stronger and more monstrous every day. We have only to look at current headlines to know that. A friend of mine put it this way: "When I was young, a bad boy was someone who swiped an apple from the grocer. Now a bad boy is someone who murders his whole family so he can collect insurance money to buy drugs."

We all know this is no exaggeration. The boundaries of evil are expanding every day, and fatalistic apathy is enabling those boundaries to grow because it offers no resistance. But Christians *must* oppose evil; we were born for battle! Every Christian is a soldier, a "member of the resistance" in God's army, taking part in spiritual warfare. The moment we lose sight of this, we become aimless in our actions and fuzzy in our focus. We forget why we were born, forget what we have been trained and equipped to do on the battlefield, and we die without ever knowing why we lived. Most importantly, we never complete the mission we were sent to accomplish. Score one more for the devil.

You see, once we begin to understand the consequences of Christian fatalism, we can no longer tolerate it. We must fight it for all we are worth, because it is the most powerful weapon the enemy is using at this moment in history to defeat the purposes of God.

So where does this leave us? Is the situation hopeless? Or is it possible to reverse the paralysis that threatens the Body of Christ, regain the ground we have lost by default and turn back the enemy? It will not be easy, but I am convinced it can be done. This book will outline the steps we must take if we are going to do it. It will give you the knowledge you need to take the offensive against the powers of darkness—and win.

But I should warn you: Knowledge can be a dangerous thing. By the time you have finished this book, you will know things that will require something of you. You will be compelled to take action. You will pray and mountains will move. You will use the keys to the Kingdom to open prison doors and set men free; you will strike back at the enemy who has held the world hostage too long. This will place you in the thick of the spiritual battle for planet earth in ways you may not have experienced before. You may become a target for the devil's attacks in ways you cannot imagine at this moment. Your life will never be the same again, that I can promise you.

So if you are looking for a peaceful, predictable life, it might be better if you closed this book right now and gave it away to someone who is after a little excitement. Remember what Jesus said: "I did not come to bring peace, but a sword" (Matthew 10:34). Be prepared! If you finish this book and apply the knowledge it imparts, if you learn how to discern when God's mind is open to change, and if you believe He is waiting for our prayers in order to defeat the enemy, then all prospects for a conventional life will be gone forever. You will take up the sword of the Spirit and perform great exploits for God, fulfilling His eternal purpose in ways nobody else can. In the next chapter we will look at exactly how you can prepare to do this.

I ask you, my friend: How will you be remembered in history? Will your name be spoken in the same reverent tones as those of Abraham, Moses, David, Joshua, Elijah or Paul? Will you "subdue kingdoms" through your prayers? Or will you fade into obscurity without ever living up to your high calling in God?

The choice is yours.

2
Who Can Change God's Mind?

Have you ever wondered why most Christians today are not doing the "greater things" that Jesus said we would do? For that matter, why we are not even doing the *same* things Jesus did? We call ourselves Christians—meaning "little Christs"—but do we love as Jesus loved, live as He lived and, above all, pray as He prayed, and with the same earth-shaking results? I'm not talking about miracles now—it's obvious that most of us don't routinely raise the dead, restore sight to the blind or satisfy several thousand hungry people with five loaves of bread and a couple of fish. I'm only asking whether or not we are making the kind of difference in the world that Jesus said we should make, the kind of difference the apostles and early Christians made.

There are exceptions, of course, but I think we can agree that most Christians today are not. The reason is simple: We don't understand that we can have the kind of relationship with God that will produce such results. We don't believe God will do what we ask because we don't really understand who He is or the principles that guide our relationship with Him.

Strong words? Perhaps. But if we understood God as the prophets and apostles and early believers did, if we really knew how to pray, wouldn't we be doing the greater things that Jesus predicted? If we knew God as He wants us to know Him, we would automatically have all the faith required to pray with the unlimited power and authority of Jesus Christ. Nothing would be impossible to us.

But year after year, decade after decade, people who do things "the Jesus way" seem fewer and farther between. The prayer link between the Body of Christ and the Godhead has grown weaker instead of stronger. Our prayers, too, have often degenerated into tedious recitations of "wish lists" instead of exciting, two-way dialogues and strategic planning sessions with the Creator of the universe. We are not convinced that anything will happen when we pray, so it doesn't. No wonder we look for excuses to avoid it! Would any of us willingly spend even a few minutes a day with a friend who never responded to anything we said, and never lifted a finger to help us when we needed it?

Our God *does* respond, however, when we understand how to talk with Him. He will move heaven and

earth for every one of us, just as He did for Moses and
Elijah, if we grasp the scriptural principles that make it
possible. Even today we can look around us and observe some Christians whose lives reflect the intimacy
of their relationship with God. They pray and things
happen! They're not surprised. They know what God
can do, and they have enough confidence in Him to ask
for big things and expect an answer. But such individuals are rare these days, aren't they? We have reached
the point at which people living as Jesus told us to live
are nothing less than spectacles to the rest of us. We
would probably call them fanatics, meaning that they
love Jesus more than we do.

We are stunned by the dramatic answers to prayer
described in the Bible stories of the prophets and apostles, and we are inspired by modern examples like those
experienced by my old friend Corrie ten Boom, who
amidst the horrors of a Nazi concentration camp became
one of our generation's most effective and irresistible
prayer warriors. (I can remember praying with Corrie
and thinking, *This is a woman God could never refuse!*)

The problem is that we see such people as *different*
from ourselves. We imagine that they have a special gift
that sets them apart from ordinary Christians like us.
We place them on pedestals and call them "spiritual
giants" and "heroes of faith," and, indeed, they are in
one sense. But we miss the point: They are not different
from us at all. They simply understand one idea crucial
to intercession: The people who change God's mind are
the people who know two things about Him—His character and His will.

God's Character

One episode from Moses' dealings with the children of Israel helps us understand how knowing God's character can affect our prayers.

As Exodus 32–34 opens, we find Moses and the people of Israel in an unbelievable situation. While Moses is up on Mount Sinai receiving God's handwritten instructions, the Israelites waiting for him in the valley below decide they have been waiting long enough. They demand that Aaron make them other gods to worship, so he melts down earrings collected from the people to create a golden calf.

Meanwhile, as God concludes His instructions to Moses, He reveals that the Israelites, "a stiff-necked people," have been "quick to turn away" from His commandments and are worshiping a golden calf. Compounding their sin, they are even crediting the idol with leading them out of bondage in Egypt!

Understandably, God's patience has finally run out. He declares that He has made up His mind to destroy Israel. "Now leave me alone," God tells Moses, "so that my anger may burn against them and that I may destroy them" (Exodus 32:10). But notice that God finishes this statement with the words, "Then I will make you into a great nation."

This declaration presents Moses with a difficult personal choice. God is offering him the opportunity to really become *somebody!* Instead of being stuck with this bunch of ingrates and infidels who turn their backs on

God at every opportunity, Moses can start fresh and become the patriarch of a great nation. How many of us would say no to such an offer from God? *After all,* we might tell ourselves, *if God wants to wipe out these rebellious wretches and use me to build a nation that will glorify Him, who am I to argue?*

But Moses, the true intercessor, doesn't accept *a* word from the Lord as *the* word from the Lord. He understands God's character; he knows God to be reasonable, merciful and true to His word. So he says to the Lord, in effect, "God, You can't do this! What will the Egyptians say if they hear You've destroyed the very people You called Your own and led out of captivity? And besides, don't You remember Your servants Abraham, Isaac and Israel? What about the things You promised them? You can't go back on Your word!"

Now there is a man who knows how to pray with insight and authority! As a result, God mercifully "change[s] His mind and spare[s] them" (Exodus 32:14, LB).

But the story doesn't end here. After convincing God to give the Israelites one more chance, Moses comes down from the mountain—with God's handwritten Law under his arm—to find his people dancing naked before the golden calf. In a fit of outrage or perhaps in a futile attempt to destroy the accusation against them (of which he holds the only copy in his hands), he shatters the tablets of the Law and demands that Aaron explain how he could possibly lead the people into such terrible sin. Aaron's reply will surely go down in history as one of the most astonishing examples of quick thinking ever recorded.

"You know how prone these people are to evil," he tells Moses. "They said to me, 'Make us gods who will go before us.'. . . So I told them, 'Whoever has any gold jewelry, take it off.' Then they gave me the gold, and I threw it into the fire, and out came this calf!" (Exodus 32:22–24).

Now you have to give Aaron credit. On a moment's notice he is able to turn idolatry and debauchery into a miracle of God!

Amazingly, it is after this stunning confrontation that Moses goes back to God and prays the boldest prayer ever recorded (equaled only by the apostle Paul's prayer for Israel in Romans 9:3) in an attempt to make atonement for his people.

"Oh, what a great sin these people have committed!" he tells the Lord. "But now, please forgive their sin— but if not, then blot me out of the book you have written" (Exodus 32:31–32). Incredible! This time Moses takes a gigantic leap of faith. In essence he says, "God, I understand Your righteousness and I know something about atonement. I'm going to offer the only atonement for my people that might be acceptable to You. Here am I; blot me out of Your book instead of them."

Moses is not defying God. He isn't saying, as some have contended, "Lord, if You don't want Israel, You can't have me either." No, Moses presents himself as an atoning sacrifice for the sins of his people. He offers to do what Jesus will do. He acts and speaks by revelation, and with such perfect insight into God's character and purposes that hundreds of years later, God chooses Moses to go with Elijah to the Mount of Transfiguration and speak with Jesus about what His atoning death in Jerusalem will accomplish (Luke 9:30–31). So you see, in interceding for his nation instead of accepting God's plans as final, Moses changes history in more ways than one!

God's response to Moses' offer of atonement is this: "Who ever has sinned against me I will blot out of my book" (Exodus 32:33). The Israelites will have to pay the penalty their sin requires. Still, for Moses' sake, God does not utterly destroy them.

In the period that follows, Moses and God grow closer and closer. "The Lord would speak to Moses face to face, as a man speaks with his friend" (Exodus 33:11). What an astounding statement! Moses and God are talking things over just as you and I might at my front door!

In one of these conversations, Moses approaches God with a remarkable request: "If I have found favor in your eyes, teach me your ways so I may know you. . . . Remember that this nation is your people" (Exodus 33:13). Moses knows, of course, that he has found grace in God's sight. God would hardly be talking with him every day if he had not! So Moses appeals to God as his friend. He can ask God for *anything*, and predictably he asks for the one thing that matters most to him as Israel's faithful intercessor: "Help me to know You better," he asks, "so I can continue to be Your friend and ensure that this nation is truly Your people."

God responds to Moses' plea with a verbal embrace: "I will do the very thing you have asked, because I am pleased with you and I know you by name" (Exodus 33:17). This beautiful affirmation prompts Moses to ask one more big thing. It is something no one has ever asked of God before: "Now show me your glory" (Exodus 33:18). Or, as one scholar translates it: "Show me *Thine own self!*" (Helen Spurrell). Can you imagine how it must have touched God's heart that Moses would make such a remarkable request? God responds without hesitation: "I will cause all my goodness to pass in front of you, and I will proclaim my name, the Lord, in your presence" (Exodus 33:19).

Yes, God gives Moses what He has never given any man: There on Mount Sinai the Lord Jehovah passes "all His goodness" before Moses, hiding nothing but His face, for Moses' own protection—"for no one may see me and live" (Exodus 33:20). As this spectacle progresses God announces who He is, giving us another stunning view of His character: "The Lord, the Lord, the compassionate and gracious God, slow to anger, abounding in love and faithfulness, maintaining love to thousands, and forgiving wickedness, rebellion and sin" (Exodus 34:6–7).

Again God reveals His character by telling Moses the meaning of His name, which is God's way of saying, "Moses, you asked to know Me; this is what I am like:

—Tenderly compassionate, kind, understanding
—Patient, reasonable, slow to anger

34

—Faithful and true
—Righteous and just."

But God further expands Moses' understanding by announcing Himself with a doubly emphatic name, "The Lord, The Lord" (which can also be translated "The eternal God, Ruler of all things"). This reminds Moses of God's sovereign power and authority.

How does Moses respond to this stunning revelation of God? Predictably, the great intercessor loses no time in putting his new knowledge to work for his people. "God," he says, in essence, "when You call Yourself by these names and I see who You are, it gives me hope that You might forgive even the unforgivable sins of my people! So I ask You—in spite of everything—to restore us and make us Your own!" This is surely one of the most brilliant strategic prayers of all time.

It is also one of the most effective: "I am making a covenant with you," God replies to Moses. "Before all your people I will do wonders never before done in any nation in all the world. The people you live among will see how awesome is the work that I, the Lord, will do for you" (Exodus 34:10).

Do you understand what is happening here? Moses appeals to God out of a profound understanding of His revealed character, and God responds instantly by giving Moses everything he asks, and much more. He also gives the Israelites what they do not deserve—another chance.

Let's look at the things we know about God from this one small portion of Scripture. We know that God is not only the holy, sovereign, eternal King, but He is also our loving Father—fair, just, compassionate, forgiving and true to His Word. We see, too, that God does not want to hurt or destroy His people; He goes to incredible lengths to avoid it, forgiving not just once or twice, but "seventy times seven" before His righteousness finally demands payment of the penalty for sin. Nobody has ever been able to say to God, "You didn't give me a chance!" God always gives us more chances than we deserve to turn from sin and become His friends.

We see also that before anything else, an understanding of God's character and purposes is essential to everything we do in the spiritual realm. The answer to the question "Who is God?" is the basis of all prayer, because we cannot relate to God in anything but a superficial way until we know who He is.

When you begin any acquaintance, the first thing you do is observe and ask questions about the other person's personality and character. What is he like? Is he relaxed and patient or a finger-drummer and a toe-tapper? Is he rigid or open to new ideas? Does he listen with interest and respect or would he prefer to perform monologues? Does he meet you halfway or does he want a give-and-take relationship in which you do a hundred percent of the giving while he does a hundred percent of the taking? Does he make fair and reasonable judgments about people or does he condemn others regardless of circumstances? Is he kind or harsh? Can you believe what he says or does he exaggerate and mislead you, making promises he has no intention of keeping?

By asking questions like these, we decide how much potential there is for friendship. We build a foundation of assumptions upon which the relationship can continue. We can't be friends with someone who is totally unpredictable and unreliable. We have certain needs and expectations, and when those aren't met, it isn't possible to build a healthy or satisfying relationship. We must question and probe to find out the reasons this person behaves as he does, because those reasons will explain what we can expect in the future. When we don't understand something we ask, "Why did you do that? What were you thinking?" We stretch to comprehend guiding principles so we can anticipate how our friend is going to react to us and to the world. This is, of course, the same process we should follow to build our friendship with God.

What do we know about God? How does He act? What has He done before? How does He describe Himself? What is our experience with Him? These are essential questions that must be addressed before we can hope to influence Him through prayer.

Ask a Muslim, "Who is God?" and he'll answer by reciting a list of 99 attributes of God—not one of which is *Father*. That is another fundamental difference between our God and the gods worshiped by every religion on earth. The Christian can call God "Father," because Jesus told us that's who He is: our Father. He is even more than Father, however; He is *Abba*—the Hebrew language version of "Daddy" or "Papa." Our God is the Daddy into whose lap we can climb, like little children, knowing He loves us unreservedly.

So that's one answer to the question "Who is God?" God is not only *a* Father, He is *our Daddy*. But what else do we know about Him? The many-faceted revelation of God's character in the Scriptures emphasizes several other qualities that make Him different from the gods and "prophets" of any religion. One of the most important, of course, is that He is loving. We are creatures who cannot live without loving and being loved because we were made in the image of God. Our minds, spirits and emotions yearn for the love of God. We can never fully satisfy that yearning outside of God, because "God is love. . . . We love because he first loved us" (1 John 4:16, 19).

God defines Himself as the great Lover of mankind who longs to be loved in return. Dozens of Scriptures reveal the depth and tenderness of God's love for us, including the entire Song of Solomon—the most beautiful love song ever written. God expressed His love through Jeremiah by saying, "I have loved you with an everlasting love; I have drawn you with loving-kindness" (Jeremiah 31:3). He says elsewhere in Jeremiah, "I am the Lord, I show unfailing love, I do justice and right upon the earth; for on these I have set my heart" (Jeremiah 9:24, NEB).

But it isn't just God's words that are loving. His deeds are loving, too. There is no god in the history of mankind other than ours who not only claims to love us, but proved it by laying down His life for us. We can have no doubts about the quality or the limitless quantity of that love. As the saying goes, "I asked Jesus, 'How much do you love me?' and Jesus said, 'This much,' and He stretched out His arms and died."

Many people have taken issue with the idea that a loving God could have created a world in which there is so much pain and misery. That argument has raged for centuries, but Jesus settled it completely when He took our place on the cross. That was God's answer to pain and misery. As Christians we know as well that the pain and misery in this world are not God's doing or His choice. He suffers with us, and ultimately suffered for us, but He never wants to make us suffer. Out of love, He gave us the freedom to say yes or no to His just and righteous will, and to the extent that we've said no, we have permitted the forces of evil to wreak havoc upon our world. The suffering we experience is the natural consequence of ungodly behavior —either our own or that of others. As humans, we are the authors of our own misery. God alone is the author of love.

There are thousands of pieces of evidence in the Scriptures that exemplify God's loving, just, righteous and fatherly character. We can't go into all—or even a fraction—of them here, obviously. But we have seen a number of characteristics that will enable you to relate to God on a more intimate level. Beyond that, you have eternity to explore the unlimited riches of God's personality and Spirit!

There is one more characteristic I want to mention, however, and that is the subtle but extremely important quality of consistency. God proves by His actions that

He *is* all the things He calls Himself. You may find a certain irony in this: On the one hand God is consistent, and on the other—as the Scriptures clearly prove—He can and does change His mind! How can we have it both ways?

There is a profound truth in this apparent irony. God will always act in ways consistent with His revealed character and purposes. These do not change. He is who He is and there is no shadow of turning in Him. But He is at heart a compassionate, loving God open to the needs and desires of those who know Him. In other words, *God's character, nature and purposes are changeless, but His plans are flexible.*

That flexibility gives us the opportunity to alter the course of our world through prayer when we know how to meet God's conditions for change and it leads us now to the subject of His will. When we begin to know Him better, we begin to understand His plans for the world. Then when we follow scriptural guidelines and learn to pray in ways that are consistent with His loving, holy purposes and will, we become involved in carrying out—and sometimes changing—God's plans. This is, in fact, the way we glorify Him and become true participants in His creative work. A look at the prophet Elijah helps us understand how.

God's Will

Perhaps after reading the earlier story of Moses and the children of Israel you still tend to think that he was larger than life, that we could never be like him. Is that so? Then look at how the Scriptures describe this other great Bible hero:

> Elijah was a man just like us. He prayed earnestly that it would not rain, and it did not rain on the land for three and a half years. Again he prayed, and the heavens gave rain, and the earth produced its crops.
>
> James 5:17–18

Read that first sentence once more: He "was a man *just like us*"—subject to all the same types of fears, distractions, problems and doubts. Elijah even had handicaps that we don't: Jesus had not yet appeared on the scene, nor had the Holy Spirit come to empower believers. Yet he prayed and it did not rain for three years. When he prayed again, the rains fell. Why? Because Elijah knew God and understood His will. Thus, when he prayed God changed His mind.

This story, told in 1 Kings 17–18, helps us see the connection between knowing God's will and changing His mind. Let's look at it briefly and see what we learn from the way that unusual drought ended.

First, notice the harmony here between Elijah and God, as if two friends are working to accomplish a divine plan. Elijah had said the rain would come only "at my word" (17:1) and God let him know in the third year that it would soon be time for that word (18:1).

Then we read in 1 Kings 18:41–46 that Elijah was aware of the sound of heavy rain long before a cloud appeared in the sky. His response? Prayer. He "bent down to the ground," began to intercede, and sent his servant seven times to observe the sky in the direction of the sea. Finally a small cloud appeared and a drenching downpour followed.

This suggests to us that because Elijah knew God, he also knew two things: God wanted him to pray for rain and God would not have changed His mind about the drought—that is, ended it—had Elijah not prayed.

Although Elijah knew God's will and the word had already been spoken, it still needed intensive intercession for God to implement His plan. (Did you ever pray with your head between your knees on a rocky floor? Try it!) Failing to see this has brought too much suffering to the world. Where are the Elijahs today who will change God's mind?

Elijah was not "special." His friendship with God was the only thing that made him exceptional. Because of that closeness he knew how to intercede in a way that got results.

Who can change God's mind? Those close to Him, those who know Him well enough to understand His character and His will, those eager to believe that God not only welcomes our prayers to change His mind, but *wants* them. This gives you and me a great opportunity because God is looking today for another Moses or Elijah—men and women who will make friendship with Him the top priority of their lives. We have the same heroic potential—not to do the same work, but to have the same kind of impact on the world that they had because of their prayers.

You see, prayer is not only the great "elevator" that can carry every believer into the presence of the King; it's also the great "equalizer" that gives us equal access to God. Whatever our experiences, intelligence, bank balances, education, social status or family circumstances, you and I have the same access to Him that every "spiritual giant" in history has had. With Moses, Elijah, Abraham, Paul and many others we can share "the treasures of darkness, riches stored in secret places" (Isaiah 45:3) promised by God to His friends. When we are that kind of friend to God, there is no limit to what our prayers can do.

The question is, what are the prerequisites to building this dynamic sort of relationship? There's no mystery about it. As always, God has made the way plain, because He longs to be close to us. If we follow scriptural guidelines for praying according to God's will, we can have a spontaneous, honest, vital communion with Him that knows no boundaries. (We will discuss these guidelines in the next chapter.) Within that framework, we *will* do the greater things that Jesus talked about, through our actions as well as our prayers. We will go to God with tremendous assurance and enthusiasm because we'll know who He is. We will automatically pray "according to His will" because we'll know what His purposes are and discern His will in every situation—and our prayers will reflect it. That's how our relationship with God *should* work!

The apostles and prophets understood this. Every "hero of faith" has been a hero only to the extent that

He has developed true friendship with God. As the apostle Paul wrote to believers in Philippi:

> I consider everything a loss compared to the surpassing greatness of knowing Christ Jesus my Lord, for whose sake I have lost all things. I consider them rubbish. . . . I want to know Christ and the power of his resurrection and the fellowship of sharing in his sufferings, becoming like him in his death.
>
> Philippians 3:8, 10

What a statement! Paul was willing to give everything he had, including his life, so that he might *know Jesus*. That was his number one priority. It was also God's. The result? Today you and I are different people, living in a different world, than would have been the case if Paul had not known the Lord as he did. You see, the prayers of God's friends not only change the individuals who pray; they also have a ripple effect that carries on throughout subsequent history. And, yes, sometimes they change God's mind as well!

I can't stress enough that God doesn't reserve this kind of communication for the "super-spiritual" or those with a special gift. He wants to get through to us in a way we can understand. He has done everything imaginable—and infinitely more—to make that possible. Did you know that every religion in the world has gods that must be sought out by man, while our God is the only one who has come searching for *us*?

Beginning with Adam and Eve in the Garden, God

has always been looking for us instead of waiting for us to find Him. In the greatness of His love, He has always made the first move. He has called out to us through the prophets, made Himself accessible through Jesus Christ and, finally, sent the Holy Spirit to help us achieve perfect harmony and fellowship with Him. Our God relentlessly seeks closer union with us. We have only to respond to His offer of intimacy.

"Let not the wise man boast of his wisdom," the Lord says, "or the strong man boast of his strength or the rich man boast of his riches, but let him who boasts boast about this: that he understands and knows me" (Jeremiah 9:23–24).

Let me tell you a story, and I pray that this illustration is the right one. Not that the alternative is wrong—no, but it is painful. I can only get hurt to the extent that I let you into my heart. And isn't that also where we can hurt God?

Years ago, before anyone had joined me on my long journeys in Communist countries, I began to ask God for a wife and family. I felt then that a family would be an antidote to the loneliness that followed every long and hazardous trip.

God's answer, several times, was clear and unmistakable: "More are the children of the desolate than the children of the married" (see Isaiah 54:1).

I wasn't content with that answer, so I continued to pray, asking God to give me a wife and children. And God answered, bringing me a wife and five great kids who love the Lord and are serving Him. I received what

I asked, despite God's initial "no" answer (if I may call it that).

It's only now, in retrospect, that I can look back over these years and understand why God at first refused me. Only He knew the almost unbearable pain and suffering a family could bring me in the years ahead. Only He could see that they could become, in a very real sense, *burdens* that I had to carry on my dangerous and extended trips. My concern for "the folks at home" would create untold misery. Homesickness—which I had never experienced before—would plague me wherever I went.

Added to that would be the misery and anxiety my family experienced during my prolonged absences. Much of the time while my children were growing up I was far away, out of touch, unavailable even by telephone or postal service. When family crises arose, my wife had to handle them without my support or involvement. And because of the nature of my work, I have had to do the same.

Even now, as I write this, I am in the Shouf Mountains in Lebanon, surrounded by hundreds of gun-toting Druzes. I have just finished lunch with Walid Jumblatt, the undisputed leader of all the Druzes, in his palace. Nobody knows I am here, and I can share it with no one.

And I realize more than ever that intimacy with the Lord Jesus is the one thing that will make our lives count as they should count.

3
Asking According to God's Will

Now that we know the importance of intimacy in praying to change God's mind, we can begin to learn more and more about His will. The important thing is to grow in confidence that we know His will—and can even know when to ask Him to change His mind.

I have found, oddly, that the ones who question knowing God's will the most are the ones who are least likely to move forward in this area—particularly about issues on which God's will is stated clearly in the Bible. They ask two questions, and these questions seem to come up almost everywhere I speak on the subject of prayer: "How can I know God's will?" and "How can I be sure I am praying according to His will?" When I hear them I always suppress a little sigh, because I know that most of the time what people are really saying is, "I'm waiting for God to telegraph instructions from heaven before I do something in the spiritual realm."

It's all too easy to use our ignorance of God's will as an excuse for doing nothing. "I would go on the mission field," many Christians have told me, "if only I could be sure it's God's will." When somebody says this to me, I reply, "All right, then, I'll *tell* you what God's will is: 'Go ye.' Now—will you go?"

Sadly, they won't! When I say that, the response is usually a flustered, "Oh, I know Jesus said that, but how can I be sure this is God's will for me personally? After all, there are a lot of factors involved in this decision. I'd have to give up my job, and my children would be uprooted. And where would we go, exactly? It's dangerous in a lot of countries now, and I couldn't expose my family to that. No, before I could do something that drastic I'd need to have a word from the Lord saying it was His will for *me*."

The people who respond this way aren't really much interested in God's will, I suspect, because if they were, they would be out doing it instead of holding out for a more comfortable alternate. They've simply found a way to get around God's will while still sounding spiritual. After all, what could sound more spiritual than "I'm not going to make a move until God shows me it's His perfect will"? We could use that as an excuse to avoid doing almost anything.

"I would pay my taxes," a man might say, "but first I have to be sure it's God's will. Perhaps God would prefer that I give the money to the church, or use it for my family." If he did that, of course, the government would soon make all his decisions for him! But we who know God would never say such a thing in the first place, because we know what Jesus taught: "Give to Caesar what is Caesar's" (Mark 12:17). We know His will without having to ask Him to reveal it again every year. There may be rare exceptions to the rule, but normally we can act upon God's expressed will without waiting for new or revised instructions from heaven. God has spoken, and His character and principles are eternally the same. We can stake our lives on them.

Many Christians these days still don't understand this. They're always "waiting on the Lord" for a revelation of His will when—especially in the larger issues like evangelism or intercession—His will is already perfectly clear. And they will probably wait forever, because the dramatic revelation they are seeking isn't going to come. This will, of course, give them the excuse they need to avoid doing what they really don't want to do to begin with.

Harsh words? No, I think they are accurate. We need to recognize apathy and laziness if we're going to remove them from our lives and do what God has commanded us to do. God never intended that we should live in a state of suspended animation, forever waiting for a word from Him about what to do next. His purposes and will are not mysteries. In most cases, we can—and should—know them, as we know Him. He and His will are inseparable.

Think of it this way: We instinctively know what will please our human parents, don't we? We know the principles that guide them, know what they approve and disapprove of. We understand the rules, like: "You will never hit your sister" or "You will always speak respectfully to your parents." Beyond these specific rules, we also know the general principles we have learned from daily experience in our family. As children in school, for example, we didn't have to stop every five minutes and run to our parents to ask, "Now, is it your will for me to study today's arithmetic lesson? Should I finish the problems our teacher assigned?"

We didn't have to worry about things like that. We knew the principles our parents taught us, and we could assume from what we already knew that we were supposed to study hard and finish today's arithmetic lesson. Because we knew our parents, we knew what to do from hour to hour without asking constantly, "Is this really what you want?" Certain principles prevail, so we could act using those principles as guideposts. And we could feel sure that our parents would be pleased when we acted accordingly.

This gives children tremendous security. Without this basic knowledge, we would grow up at loose ends, too afraid of making the wrong decisions to make any decisions at all. We would be totally neutralized and incapable of making our way through life because we could never be sure if our actions would meet with our parents' approval or bring a reprimand. We would spend most of our time in a state of anxiety, wondering if every little thing we wanted to do might bring the world crashing down around our ears.

Some children, unfortunately, grow up in families in which parents never teach principles and never establish clear rules or guidelines. These children usually become adults who can't function in society. Their lives reflect nothing but the chaos and uncertainty of their early lives. But this is not the way God intended families to be. And it is not the way He runs His own family.

What, then, are the eternal principles and purposes that can help us understand and apply God's will in every situation of our lives? The Scriptures give us so much guidance in this area that we could devote an entire book to that question alone. But this is a book about prayer and changing God's mind, so we'll confine ourselves to the principles that will help us decide how to know we are asking according to His will. Until we're sure about that, we can't hope to pray effectively.

Here are seven points. In the next chapter we'll apply these principles to situations you and I face every day.

Number 1: Realize that God's will is something we get to know progressively, not instantaneously.

As our intimacy with Him grows, so does our understanding of His will. We can't expect to understand everything about Him *or* His will during our lifetimes on this earth. The only man who ever knew and obeyed Him perfectly was Jesus.

But we have an eternal destiny in Jesus and (as I noted in the last chapter) we will be exploring the richness of God's character forever. Right now we simply make a beginning. We are children getting to know our Father. We try to discover as much as we can about who He is so that we can enjoy our relationship with Him and grow closer throughout the ages to come. As our prayers draw us closer to God, He shows us more and more of Himself, and His will becomes our will.

Number 2: Remember that although we can know God's will most of the time simply by knowing and obeying His Word, there will be times when we need—and can expect—specific guidance about situations where His will is unclear.

We are not slaves to the Law of God; it is our schoolmaster, the Bible says. It points us to Christ because it teaches us that we cannot obey God perfectly all the time. We're human, and we need the grace, forgiveness and guidance of God. No matter how well we get to know God, and no matter how totally we surrender our lives to Him, there will always be those occasions when we aren't sure what God wants us to do. When we face this kind of problem we have a right to clear guidance, and God will always give it.

The trouble most of us have with this, of course, is that (as I said at the beginning of this chapter) we too often say we need a word from the Lord to tell us His will when He has already revealed it. So we should make sure, before we ask for special guidance, that we don't already have it.

I heard about a married Christian man who said, "I've fallen in love with another woman, and I'm thinking of divorcing my wife to marry her. I'm praying that God will give me a sign if I'm not supposed to do it." God is not going to answer this man's prayers; His will is already clear and there's no need for a voice from heaven to confirm it. The man is merely playing games with God, hoping to use His silence on the matter as an excuse to sin.

So here's a good rule to follow: If you're asking for special guidance and are not getting it, examine what you already know of God's will to see if you don't already have your answer.

There are legitimate circumstances, however, in which we cannot discern what we should do or how we should pray, and when that happens we can ask God to give special help. He will provide reliable guidance so we can stay in the center of His will. The Holy Spirit will work in a variety of ways to show us the will of God in specific situations.

As we thoughtfully observe circumstances and events in our lives, for example, we will often get clues about what God wants us to do. A woman might contemplate making a career change that would require a move to a distant city, and as she prays for God's direction she might find that people unexpectedly cross her path to encourage and help her make the move. This could be God speaking through the circumstances to reveal His will.

But the woman should not make her decision solely on that basis. She can also ask the Holy Spirit to confirm this direction in some specific way that would remove all doubts.

God is always willing to confirm His will to us, by the way, because our asking is evidence of faith. Some have said that Gideon sinned when he put out his fleece, asking God to confirm and reconfirm His will. But God gave Gideon exactly what he asked for! There's nothing wrong with asking for this kind of help when we really need it. More about fleeces and confirmation in chapter 5.

But it's wise to be sure, when we ask God for confirmation of His specific will, that we are ready to obey Him when He does it. If we use requests for confirmation as a delaying tactic, we're out of line. And if we hope to use *lack* of confirmation as an excuse to sin, the way the man we just discussed was doing, we're in big trouble. It is as we seek to know and pray for and *do* the will of God that the Holy Spirit will direct our thoughts and actions.

Number 3: Never pray, "*If* it is Your will. . . ."

Coming at prayer like that is a sure way to destroy its effectiveness. Although many think it is a biblical pattern, it is actually an insult to God!

When we say that, God tells us, "I don't want to hear that kind of talk! Don't you know Me well enough to know My will? If you don't know Me, why should I give you anything?" But Christians have been saying this for years. Why? They have taken a single verse (James 4:15) out of context and have built it into a doctrine that fits conveniently into the Christian fatalism we discussed in the first chapter.

In this case, the verse is part of James' reproof of men

who were boasting about how successful they would be in their business schemes. James says to them, in essence, "You don't even know if you're going to be alive next year, and you're boasting about how rich you're going to be? You should be saying, 'If the Lord will, we may do this or that next year.' " These men obviously forgot Solomon's words: "Do not boast about tomorrow, for you do not know what a day may bring forth" (Proverbs 27:1).

James was criticizing those men for two reasons: First, because they were bragging about things they had no way of knowing (which was arrogant), and second, because they did not take God's will into account (which was presumptuous). God never told us to become rich or successful; in fact, He told us again and again not to get caught up in the pursuit of this world's transient pleasures and treasures. If these businessmen had known much about God, they would have had a different attitude. They would have sought humbly to do God's will instead of puffing themselves up with pride over their own foolish plans. Not that God wants us to be failures! He simply wants us to seek *Him*, not the things that moths and rust will destroy.

At any rate, James' statement is a far cry from saying that we should always pray *"If* it is Your will." This is the only verse in the Bible, in fact, that suggests that anyone should ever say, "*If* the Lord will, we will do such-and-such." The rest of the Bible tells us we can, and should, know God's will by knowing God Himself and understanding His Word. Then we can live and pray with power and authority—not for our own selfish benefit, but for God's glory.

Sometimes Christians also use the words of Jesus in the Garden of Gethsemane to bolster the idea that we should pray "If it is Your will." You'll recall that in His prayer Jesus said, "My Father, if it is possible, may this cup be taken from me. Yet not as I will, but as you will." He also prayed, "Father, if it is not possible for this cup to be taken away unless I drink it, may your will be done" (Matthew 26:39, 42)

But was Jesus *really* saying, "Father, I don't want to die on the cross—but I'll do it if You insist"? I don't believe that for a moment. Remember, it was only a short time before this that Jesus said, referring to His coming crucifixion: "What shall I say? 'Father, save me from this hour'? No, it was for this very reason I came to this hour" (John 12:27). Obviously Jesus would not make such an emphatic statement and then do a complete about-face in the Garden and ask God to keep Him from the cross.

Then what *was* Jesus praying for in the Garden? I'm convinced that the "cup" He was asking God to take from Him was *premature death in the Garden* as a result of the crushing satanic pressure that caused Him to sweat drops of blood (Luke 22:44) as His soul was "overwhelmed with sorrow to the point of death" (Matthew 26:38). Jesus knew that if He died in the Garden as a result of this pressure, His ultimate mission on earth could not be accomplished. So His prayer was, in essence, "Father, let *this* cup pass: I don't want to die here in the Garden. If You have changed Your mind about the cross, I'm asking You to change it again. And if You have changed that plan, why did You not tell me? (*That was the greatest reason for His agony.*)

You see, even Jesus prayed to change God's mind. Hebrews tells us that He was heard in this prayer (Hebrews 5:7), and we know that He not only survived the agonizing experience in the Garden, He was strengthened by it. After He finished praying, Jesus' words to His disciples were almost triumphant: "Rise, let us go! Here comes my betrayer!" (Matthew 26:46).

Jesus' prayer in the Garden, then, was hardly the fatalistic "Thy will be done" prayer most Christians believe it was. Certainly we cannot use that prayer as justification for our own apathetic or passive prayers. When Jesus ended His prayers in the Garden by saying, "Not as I will, but as you will" (Matthew 26:39), He was saying, "I am going to obey You, Father, even if My will is different from Yours." It was an affirmation of absolute commitment to the Father's purposes and will.

We must have that kind of commitment as well. We may disagree with what we perceive to be the mind of God in certain matters, and He may invite us to change His mind about those matters, but we must be willing to obey Him even if He doesn't change His mind.

Number 4: Make the salvation of others a primary prayer concern.

This is one sure way to apply God's expressed will in our prayer lives. In the third chapter of Ephesians Paul first describes the will of God for his life, which is

> to preach to the Gentiles the unsearchable riches of
> Christ, and to make plain to everyone the adminis-
> tration of this mystery [that through the Gospel the
> Gentiles are heirs together with Israel, members of
> one body and sharers in the promise in Christ Jesus],
> which for ages past was kept hidden in God, who
> created all things.   Ephesians 3:8–9

After this, Paul makes one of the most profound state-
ments in the Scriptures about God's purpose and will
for His creation:

> [God's] intent was that now, through the church, the
> manifold wisdom of God should be made known to
> the rulers and authorities in the heavenly realms, ac-
> cording to his eternal purpose which he accomplished
> in Christ Jesus our Lord. In him and through faith in
> him we may approach God *with freedom and confidence*.
>   Ephesians 3:10–12

Do you understand? God's expressed will and intention is that we, the Body of Christ, should demonstrate
to "rulers and authorities in the heavenly realms" the
depth and breadth of His wisdom *by our prayers*. That is
our role, individually and as a Church, and every angel,
every demon, every principality or power in the realm
of God is watching our performance. (If you have always felt like a nobody in this world, you can stop right
now!) It's time we all realized who we are as people
redeemed by Jesus Christ. The "eternal purpose" of
God is being accomplished in us through His Son.

And what *is* that eternal purpose? Here is what Jesus said:

> "I have come down from heaven not to do my will but to do the will of him who sent me. And *this is the will of him who sent me, that I shall lose none of all that he has given me, but raise them up at the last day.* For my Father's will is that everyone who looks to the Son and believes in him shall have eternal life."
>
> John 6:38–40

We must not neglect prayers for the salvation of others. Paul applied this to the prayer lives of all believers when he instructed Timothy:

> I urge. . . that requests, prayers, intercession and thanksgiving be made for everyone. . . . This is good, and pleases God our Savior, who wants all men to be saved and to come to a knowledge of the truth. For there is one God and one mediator between God and men, the man Christ Jesus, who gave himself as a ransom for all. . . . I want men everywhere to lift up holy hands in prayer.　　1 Timothy 2:1, 3–6, 8

So we see here that there's one thing we can pray that will always be in the center of God's will: Whenever we pray for someone's salvation, we are asking according to His will. We can say, conversely, that it is never God's will that anyone should be lost. People can freely choose not to accept Jesus Christ, but *it is never God's will that this should happen.*

This should give us tremendous freedom and confidence in our prayers. You can pray, "God, I *know* it's Your will that my children [or parents or friend] be saved, so I'm going to ask You and keep on asking until You do it!" You *never* have to say, "God, save my children *if it is Your will.*"

I can never forget an experience I had at the Worldwide Evangelization Crusade in London. That evening I preached about radical faith, saying I believe in being an "extremist" where love is concerned. (If I'm going to be rebuked in heaven, I told them, I'd rather be rebuked for loving too much than for loving too little during my time on this earth. It has always seemed to me that we tend to be overly careful about loving wholeheartedly. Perhaps we're afraid of getting hurt by letting other people into our hearts.)

I even managed to say that if C. T. Studd, the great pioneer missionary and founder of that particular mission, were to apply for membership today, he would probably be turned down as being "too fanatical." After all, what sort of missionary would write a booklet with the provocative title D.C.D.? C. T. Studd did! He even claimed that Jesus became a D.C.D. when He hung on the cross to take our sin. He became a curse because He "Did not Care a Damn."

Anyway, at the close of that service a couple, fine young Scottish friends, stopped to talk for a few minutes, and the husband, Alistair, told me with a big grin, "Andrew, we soon expect our first baby, D.V."

"D.V.," as Alistair used that expression, meant *Deo*

volento, a Latin phrase that translates "God willing." It's an expression that's become popular among Christians in recent years. But when Alistair said that, I immediately responded, "Alistair, God *wants* you to have this baby! Don't deviate from His plan. Never say 'D.V.'— after all, you *know* His will!" And in due time, yes, Alistair and his wife had a wonderful baby.

Knowing this principle, we can also intercede for the whole world. "Father," I can say, "I know it is Your will that *all* men should be saved; therefore, I ask You to save the man I met last week in Beirut. I ask You to save the leaders of my country. I ask You to save the terrorists who are doing such terrible things out of misguided zeal for their false religion." I can pray for everyone I know, for people I have never met, for beggars on the streets of Bogota, for people in the headlines of my newspaper, for world leaders and authorities in my nation. I can, as the poet James Montgomery said, "move the arm that moves the world, and bring salvation down!"

And I can take it still further: I can pray, "Father, show me what I can do to introduce these people to You." Then I must do what He shows me. I can use my resources to go—or to send others if I cannot go—to the people who need Christ desperately. I can take Bibles to those hungry for God's Word. I can go to the suffering Church and minister the love and encouragement of Jesus wherever He is needed—in my own nation or in Eastern Europe, America, the Far East, Russia, the Middle East, Central and South America, Africa.

There are no closed doors for me. I can go because God's will is that everyone be saved, and I have a responsibility to do everything in my power to work and to pray that His will may be done. I can go with the assurance that God goes with me, because it is the expressed will of Jesus:

> "All authority in heaven and on earth has been given to me. Therefore go and make disciples of all nations . . . teaching them to obey everything I have commanded you. And surely I will be with you always, to the very end of the age."
>
> Matthew 28:18–20

The promise of Jesus is that He will be with me *as I do what He has commanded*, thus fulfilling the will of God. I cannot take "I will be with you always" as my promise, and ignore "Go." That isn't how it works. I must take the whole counsel of God, not the bits and pieces that make me feel warm and comfortable. I must meet God's conditions, and then He will fulfill His promises.

This, you see, is how we should be living. In the matters where we know God's will—as we do in most things—we should be praying for it to be done, and—to the extent that we are able—we should be doing it. The Scriptures are the foundation for all guidance and we can act upon them without doubt. God is working within us "to will and to act according to his good purpose" (Philippians 2:13). As we go about our lives we can ask, "Am I doing the will of God as He has revealed it in the Scriptures?" The answer will tell us whether or not we are on the right track.

Number 5: Look to the Holy Spirit to serve as your Guide on matters that are difficult to discern.

He speaks in a "still, small voice" within us when we open ourselves to His direction. God's Spirit is available 24 hours a day to "guide [us] into all truth" (John 16:13) whenever we seek Him. We'll talk more about this kind of guidance in just a moment.

Number 6: Obey the Ten Commandments.

This may seem obvious, but you would be surprised how many times I have heard confusion expressed concerning them.

God gave us many specific declarations of His will that we can apply to almost every situation in our lives, but the Ten Commandments God handed down to Moses on Mount Sinai leave little room for questions about God's will in vital areas: Don't murder, steal, lie or commit adultery; don't covet what belongs to others; don't use His name profanely or frivolously; keep the Sabbath holy; treat your parents honorably; and above all, don't worship anything or anyone but God. Even little children can understand such straightforward expressions of God's will.

In our prayer lives, these commandments can serve as a checklist to remove confusion we might have over whether something we're praying for is God's will or not. If you're praying for something that violates one of the commandments of God, it's safe to assume that your prayer won't be answered. I can't pray, for example, that God will protect me when I lie. When I carry Bibles across borders into nations where they are illegal, I pray beforehand that the border guards will not ask me if I have Bibles hidden in my vehicle. If they ask me, I must tell them the truth. I cannot lie to them and then say, "God, please keep me out of trouble by making them believe my lie!" God would not hear that prayer, even though His will is I should take my Bibles into that country. The will of God is also for me to tell the truth. So I pray, before I reach the border, "God, please keep the guards from asking me about Bibles." And so far, I have never been asked! God honors our prayers when we honor His will by doing it, even when it may be dangerous.

Number 7: Let love be your motivation for changing God's mind.

This is revealed in the words of Jesus. He said, for example,

> "My command is this: Love each other as I have loved you. Greater love has no one than this, that one lay down his life for his friends. You are my friends if you do what I command. . . . I chose you to go and bear fruit—fruit that will last. Then the Father will give you whatever you ask in my name."
>
> John 15:12–14, 16

Earlier in the same chapter Jesus said, "This is to my Father's glory, that you bear much fruit, showing your-selves to be my disciples" (John 15:8).

These passages tell us several important things about God's will as it relates to the kind of prayer life we are trying to develop. First, we see that the will of God is for us to love others "above and beyond the call of duty"— even to the point of laying down our lives for them. We also see that we can prove we are His friends by obeying Him and bearing fruit for the Father's glory.

That is, we show our love for Jesus by loving as He loves, through the power of His abiding presence in us. Our oneness with Him will make our lives fruitful. The Father will be honored, and our prayers will be attuned to His purposes so perfectly that whatever we ask of the Father will be given us (John 15:16).

Jesus was talking in this passage not only about the will of the Father for us and our world, but also the will of the Father for Him. Jesus never commanded us to do anything on our own. "Without Me," He said, "you can do nothing." He was sent so that all men might be reconciled to the Father, and as we become a part of His family, our love for Jesus should impel us to help Him complete this unfinished task. We are His Body, and all that He is becomes ours to the extent that we allow Him to dwell in us. This is why Paul said, "We have the mind of Christ" (1 Corinthians 2:16). Our carnal minds cannot understand anything about God, but the mind of Christ *in us,* as revealed by the Holy Spirit, guides us into all Truth.

So when we pray with the mind of Christ, we can ask God for anything, and it will be ours. When we are in that position, you see, we will be asking *only* for those things that are the perfect will of God. And if our carnal minds sometimes refuse to allow the mind of Christ to rule in our lives, the Holy Spirit will immediately remind us and draw us back to the will of the Father. As we become more and more sensitive to His leading, our actions will more perfectly reflect His will.

And when we feel gripped to pray that He will change His mind about an issue, He will hear us.

We have talked a lot about knowing God and the reasons that is so important. It is only as we know Him that we understand the unchanging and eternal purposes that govern His will for our lives. And it is within this framework that we can live boldly, as God intends.

We can act with the maturity and confidence that come from understanding what pleases God and what doesn't. We can have the security of knowing, every moment of our lives, that we are in the center of His will and that our actions fulfill His purposes. This security removes the immobilizing fears and doubts—and the excuses as well—that keep so many of us from realizing our potential as Christians.

4
Come Boldly Before the Throne

Often someone will say to me as we talk about changing God's mind, "But how do I know what God has decided to do in the first place? After all, He doesn't speak to me from a burning bush the way He did to Moses. And even if He did, how would I know when His plans are subject to change? I just don't see how I can make that kind of judgment."

Sometimes the most elementary questions can be the most thought-provoking. Indeed, how *can* you know what God has made up His mind to do? I will be the first one to admit there is no way I can know for sure when He has made a decision in a specific situation unless He expressly says so. Without a direct revelation—like the one Jonah received when God announced His plans to destroy Ninevah in forty days (Jonah 3:1–4)—it would seem highly presumptuous even to talk about influencing those plans, much less, as we will learn, go about doing it.

But can I expect God to reveal Himself to me the same way He did to the Old Testament prophets? There may be circumstances in which this happens today. Indeed, I have heard some remarkable stories—from countries in the Middle and Far East, particularly—where Jesus reportedly walked right into people's houses and spoke with them. In some of these appearances, witnesses described miraculous healings and even the raising of the dead.

Most of the time, however, even Christians who know God intimately don't hear from Him so directly or dramatically. I believe this is because in most situations we simply don't need that kind of experience. When I must go from Holland to America I don't need to be able to walk across the Atlantic; I can take a plane. So the Lord doesn't miraculously bid me to walk on water the way He did Peter. And I wouldn't think of asking Him for it.

But people do seem to long for dramatic supernatural experiences—not because they need them, necessarily, but often simply because they are looking for something to shore up their faith. When they get their miracles, however, they are rarely changed by them. Why? Because dramatic and unusual experiences do not constitute a relationship. One miracle, or even several, does not keep anyone in the faith. The Israelites of Moses' and Abraham's time witnessed miracle after miracle, but they became idolaters anyway.

Back in the early 1950s in my own village of St. Pancras, when our little band of believers went around telling everyone we could find about Jesus, we encountered a lot of people who said to us, "Well, if God heals that poor sick girl in your group, *then* we'll believe." Everyone knew this girl. She was terribly ill with tuberculosis. So we prayed for her and she was instantly, miraculously healed—just like that! A tremendous miracle, like something out of the New Testament. But nobody believed!

That hardly ever works, you see. And there are countless Christians who have themselves been healed, or have witnessed other spectacular miracles, but who later have fallen into unbelief. We look at that and think, "How can this be? If I experienced a miracle I could never doubt the Lord again!"

But experiences wear off. You have only to ask a wife of fifty years whether she is still married to her husband because of how charming and attentive he was on their wedding day. If their relationship has not grown since then, and if their first heady experience of high romance has not matured through years of commitment, thoughtful communication, and mutual respect and affection, then even the most ecstatic memories of her perfect bridegroom and glorious honeymoon could not keep the marriage intact.

We simply cannot survive on experiences, no matter how thrilling they may seem at the time. They're like last week's dinner—lovely at the moment, but quickly used up. If I were depending on last Wednesday's delicious chicken stew to give me energy today, I'd be in real trouble!

It is the same with God. It's not the dazzling mountaintop experiences that reveal Him to us; it is His continuous daily presence in the ordinary and extraordinary events of our lives.

One of the most intriguing titles of Oswald Chambers' many books is *Can You Come Down?* His point was that we cannot remain forever on the mountaintop the way Peter hoped to do after the transfiguration of Jesus and the appearance of Moses and Elijah (Matthew 17: 1–4). We must inevitably come down again into the valley, where the conflict of real life surrounds us. It is there that the presence of Jesus is more real than on the mountain, where we may not be able to do or say anything sensible.

As we walk with Him, we learn to know and trust His love. Over time He builds in us slowly, steadily the faith and wisdom we need to pray with all the insight, power and authority Jesus talked about.

It is incredible, really, to realize that because of what Jesus accomplished on the cross, we can relate to God on a level that the prophets who witnessed His greatest miracles could not have imagined in their wildest dreams. It is impossible to overemphasize the cosmic significance of the cross.

As a result of the sacrifice Jesus made for us, we have been restored to even more of the position Adam and Eve enjoyed before they sinned.

The devil's statement, "You will be like God, knowing good and evil" (Genesis 3:5) was deliberately deceptive, of course. He did not tell Adam and Eve that they would not have the power to do good nor would they have the power not to do evil. We, however, through the Holy Spirit, have the power to do good, which is to keep the commandments of God, and we have the power not to do evil.

We can walk and talk with the Father 24 hours a day. Nothing stands in our way. The bloody altars of sacrifice have been demolished, the Law has been fulfilled once and for all, and the "iron curtain" separating mankind from the holiest of holy places where God met only with a chosen few has been torn away forever.

When Jesus stretched out His arms and died, those were the open arms of our God welcoming us back into unhindered fellowship with Him. I like to believe it was at that moment that the angel of God was dispatched to earth with the stunning invitation that still echoes across time:

> The Spirit and the bride say, "Come!" And let him who hears say, "Come!" Whoever is thirsty, let him come; and whoever wishes, let him take the free gift of the water of life.   Revelation 22:17

Yes, because of Jesus we no longer have to guess what God is like or wonder what He wants from us. We know the Father because we have seen and known His Son. We no longer have to speculate about God's purposes or will, because Jesus has told us what they are. He has also given us His Word—the perfect mirror of His character, the master blueprint of His plans for our world. And He hasn't left us on our own to apply and interpret this vast amount of information; He has sent His Spirit to live in us, guiding us into all truth. As if this were not enough, He has also made every believer a member of the Body of Christ—the Church—and our membership in that Body adds tremendously to our understanding of God's ways with man. As we have seen, it is "together with all the saints" that we glorify Him and carry out His purposes and will in the world.

Through these means, then, God has graciously provided everything we normally need to comprehend His plans and to participate in the execution of His will through our prayers. Our intimacy with the Father through Christ, our knowledge of the Scriptures, the constant guiding presence and enlightenment of the Holy Spirit and the operation of the Spirit's gifts through the Church form an unshakable foundation for our understanding of what God is doing today.

Until we understand this, it is easy to forget that God wants to communicate with us infinitely more than we do with Him. There is no reason we should look upon His ways as "past finding out," as most Old Testament believers did. He isn't hiding or playing games. He has gone to tremendous lengths to open His mind and heart to us, and to draw us so close that we can participate in all He is doing in our world—now and throughout eternity.

The only problem (if you could call it that) is that God's accessibility has made life somewhat more complicated for those among us who still don't grasp what is involved in this kind of New Covenant relationship. Some Christians would like it a lot better, in fact, if God still spoke to us the way He did in the days of the prophets. But can they possibly imagine what our lives would be like today if He did? We would still be living under the elaborate Old Testament system of laws and ordinances, struggling to obey the commands relayed to us by God's messengers without ever knowing God personally.

Not that God ever wanted it that way. His plan was for all of us to know Him as Adam and Eve originally did. And His New Covenant with mankind through Jesus not only *restores* the possibility of that kind of intimacy; it *requires* it. Without that kind of relationship, we find ourselves in a far worse position than the Israelites of Moses' time because we can no longer rely upon prophets to act as our intermediaries. Nor can we blame them when they lead us astray. God holds us personally responsible because He has made Himself personally accessible to everyone through Jesus.

So, while it is true that life might be simpler if God still related to us as He did in Abraham's and Moses' time, He always had greater things in mind for us. Jesus told us that God has elevated us to a new position in His Kingdom. We are no longer called *servants*, because servants don't know what their master is doing. We are called *friends*, because Jesus has shared with us His full knowledge of the Father (John 15:15). God has invited us to participate in the planning and execution of His will on earth by drawing so close to Him that not only do we understand what He is doing, but we actually get involved in His decision-making processes. In other words, we become part of His plan. When this happens, we know automatically when and in which ways God is open to change.

We have been given an absolute right to this kind of guidance. If this were not so, then we would have to conclude that the Advent of Christ and His Church, the writing of the Scriptures and the arrival of the Holy Spirit in the world constituted a giant step backward for mankind. If we don't understand far *more* about God's ways than Old Testament believers did, we have missed the boat completely!

You would probably never have the nerve to call the President of the United States or of the Soviet Union (if you could reach him) to ask about some specific action he has taken: "Why did you do that? Will you listen to some of my ideas before you go any further?" But you would not hesitate to ask the same questions of a spouse or parent. Intimacy makes all the difference.

Even as we begin to develop this kind of intimacy with God, however, some of us have a problem understanding how to reach the point at which we can say, "I know God has decided to do *this*, and I'm going to ask Him to change His mind." Precisely how do we learn what God is going to do next, say, in Eastern Europe or South Africa or China or, for that matter, in our own families? And how do we know when it is appropriate to ask Him to change His plans? Perhaps it will be easier to explain if I speak from my own experience. Not that my experience is universal, but it may help illustrate the ways in which the Lord most often reveals Himself today.

Many times in my life, God has chosen to communicate with me quite directly—not what I would call miraculously, but still directly, through His Spirit. It happened once when I was smuggling a carload of several hundred Bibles into Moscow. My companion and I had parked our specially built station wagon on the street, and we were starting to unload the Bibles from their hidden compartments so we could carry them to a church. A very dangerous situation, but not an uncommon one for me.

I looked up at one point and noticed a perfectly ordinary-looking man who had stopped to watch what we were doing. This was not especially remarkable; people often watched us while we were unloading our vehicles, and we paid little attention because they were only curious. But in my heart I knew this man was different. How? I can explain it only by saying that God's Spirit disturbed something within my own spirit. It was a subtle thing.

My reaction to that inner warning was not unlike it might have been if an old friend had whispered in my ear, "Andrew, watch out!" I recognized the Holy Spirit's subtle "voice" as a result of many years of friendship with Him. This ability to "hear" the Spirit grows over time, of course. Listening is one of the most important parts of our relationship with God.

I responded almost instinctively to the warning. First, I simply prayed silently as we continued to unload the Bibles. Almost in the same moment I began to pray, the man turned and walked away quickly.

In other circumstances, I would have breathed a sigh of relief at his departure. This time, however, I said to my colleague, "That man is on his way to report us at the KGB office." There was no mistaking the urgency I felt in my spirit, and there was no doubt in my mind about what was about to happen. So we stopped unloading and prayed together, asking God to divert the man—by whatever means necessary—to give us time to unload and deliver our precious cargo. We prayed against the evil powers that threatened to keep God's Word from the people who had been waiting years to receive it. When we finished praying, we went back to our task with full assurance that God had done what we asked. The Bibles were delivered without incident.

To this day I don't know exactly what God did to keep us safe in that situation, but I am certain that unless He had revealed to me the danger we were in and unless we had prayed, we would have ended up being questioned by the KGB that day. And if we had, we might have ended up in prison.

Some Christians would argue, no doubt, that prison might have been where God wanted us, and on other occasions I would agree to that possibility. Sometimes God needs a witness in prison, so He allows Christians to be incarcerated. But that day He did not want my friend or me in prison. He wanted us to deliver our Bibles, and that is what we did. How do I know? Because He warned me of the danger. That was God's way of offering us the chance to participate in the execution of His will by asking Him to change the outcome of the situation.

We could have ignored God's warning, of course. And if we had landed in prison as a result, we could still have executed His eternal will by ministering to our fellow prisoners or to our captors. But we could not have delivered those Bibles, which in my view was God's highest and best will in that specific situation. So He warned us, expecting us to heed that warning and carry out His plans. God's will would not have been thwarted if we had failed to heed it; indeed, He would have caused all things to work together for good. But I am convinced that in this case, we were able to do that which God *most* wanted us to do—deliver our Bibles—because we understood what He was telling us and acted upon that information by praying. This kind of revelation gives us extraordinary opportunities to work hand in hand with God.

But this is by no means the only way God reveals Himself to me. It is not even the way He usually does. Ninety-five percent of the time God reveals what I need to know through far less direct means, usually through a combination of spiritual insight gained over many years of friendship with Him and what I call "circumstantial evidence." Let me give you an example of how this works.

One day in Beirut as a businessman and I walked through the bombed-out rubble where hundreds of men, women and children had died, he said to me, "Andrew, God is fed up with us! He is no more in this place. He has gone away. He has forsaken us. All you have to do is look around and you can see it."

Now someone else might have said to that man, "God has not left; He's still here!" But I didn't say that. I looked around and thought, *I must admit, I've never seen a place that looks more God-forsaken*. We were standing in a place that had once been a beautiful, thriving city. Now it was a devastated war zone. Shots rang out on the streets around us. Mutilated bodies were being carted away. Looking at all this, I understood that in this man's perception—and probably in that of most people in Beirut—God had simply decided to wash His hands of this city. And with what I have learned in the many years I have visited Lebanon, I could see how they would draw that conclusion.

So I didn't dispute my friend's remarks. Instead I said, "Yes, it sure looks that way. Maybe God *has* made up His mind to abandon Beirut. But if enough people like you repented and invited God back again, I'm sure He would change His mind!"

Now how could I make such a statement? Did God appear in my bedroom that morning and announce, "Andrew, I'm going to abandon Beirut unless they turn to Me"? Of course not. But the circumstantial evidence, combined with an understanding of that part of the world and of God's Word, character and purposes, convinced me that Beirut was probably going to be reduced to a heap of ruins very soon unless some serious repentance took place. I also knew that the Lord's will was for Beirut's inhabitants to be saved. So I could draw a conclusion: "Yes, it looks like God has made up His mind, but His mind can be changed!"

I can hear someone protesting, "But Andrew, weren't you a bit presumptuous to talk that way? Wouldn't it have been safer and more accurate to say, 'We can't be one hundred percent certain what God has decided in Beirut'?"

I don't accept that. If we had to wait until we were one hundred percent certain about *anything*, we would be paralyzed. We would never draw any conclusions and we would never know when or how to pray. For that matter, we wouldn't even be able to decide when or how to make breakfast!

And, in fact, even if God had spoken to me the way He did with Abraham before He was going to destroy Sodom and Gomorrah (Genesis 18), I still would be in the same position Abraham was in—which was a very human position, and a rather uncertain position at that. Was Abraham one hundred percent sure God would spare those wretched cities if He could find fifty (or even ten) righteous people living there? No. But he took a chance—based on his own limited human perception of what God had told him—and prayed anyway. It might have been presumptuous by some people's standards, but Abraham wasn't concerned so much about the safety of his own position as he was about the people God was about to destroy.

And God honored him because of that. He didn't say, "Abraham, where did you get the crazy idea that I would change My mind for the sake of ten righteous people? I never told you that. Shame on you!"

No, God did something else: He said yes to everything Abraham asked—not for Sodom and Gomorrah's sake, but for Abraham's. You see, the accuracy of Abraham's perception was not the issue, nor was presumption. His friendship with God was. And in this case, I am convinced Abraham didn't go far enough in "presuming" upon that friendship. Why? Because the final outcome for Sodom and Gomorrah was the same as if Abraham had not prayed at all.

The cities would have self-destructed eventually, of course, because they were rotten from the inside. But Abraham, with his limited human understanding, could not bring himself to presume that God might change His own plans of destruction for the sake of fewer than ten righteous people, and ten could not be found. Like many of us, Abraham stopped too soon in his prayers.

There is an important lesson in this. It seems to me that too many Christians today think they are in danger of offending God by presuming too much. We hear it all the time: "I can't pray for healing; that's presumptuous!" The danger in most cases is not that we might presume too much, but rather that we presume far too little; the person might die before we decide it's O.K. to pray for him! When God takes the initiative and we accept the responsibility, when our prayers stay within the boundaries of God's expressed will as we understand it, we are not being presumptuous.

While there are always ways to offend God if we set our minds to it, I think too many of us use that possibility as an excuse for not praying. It's another case in which false piety turns us into fatalists. We should make every effort to know what we are doing when we pray, naturally, but if I were sick this morning I would much rather have someone pray for me presumptuously than not pray at all! I would always prefer to be found guilty of asking too much from God than to have to admit I asked too little. And I think God would prefer it, too.

The truth is, God never told us we should not try to influence His plans until we are one hundred percent sure about what those plans are. And it's a good thing! Otherwise, places like Beirut would be wiped off the face of the earth before we could ask God to give its people one more chance to turn things around by turning to Him.

Before I visited Lebanon in July 1990, God spoke to me through the Scriptures not only about Lebanon, but also about the Middle East crisis and the return of our Lord Jesus.

> Look, their brave men cry aloud in the streets; the envoys of peace weep bitterly. The highways are deserted, no travelers are on the roads. The treaty is broken, its witnesses are despised, no one is respected. The land mourns and wastes away, Lebanon is ashamed and withers. . . . "Now I will arise," says the Lord.　　　　　　　　　　　　　　　　　NIV

I felt compelled to pass on this message to the two rival warlords in Beirut who have brought so much destruction to their nation, so I immediately began to arrange a trip to Lebanon. Not surprisingly, I encountered tremendous problems in getting a visa. Delay after delay prevented my departure until finally I appealed to the Lebanese ambassador in The Hague, who intervened personally to issue a visa without his government's formal approval.

On the night I sailed from Cyprus to Beirut, I had a terrible dream about a great calamity coming upon Lebanon: The mountains exploded, the building in which I stood trembled, the walls cracked, but personally I had deep peace. Then a voice said, "The worst for Lebanon is yet to come."

To me this was clearly the voice of God. It made me feel even more urgent about seeing the two leaders in Beirut.

When I arrived I was permitted to speak with both of these leaders. I introduced myself as a servant of God and gave both of them exactly the same message. They listened very intently. I told them, "God says: It will get much worse in Lebanon, but if *you* and your *people* will repent, then it does not have to happen. God will change His mind, because your country is so very strategic in relation to Israel, to Jerusalem, to the whole conflict in the Middle East. The whole world will watch how this conflict—which generally is perceived as a Muslim-Christian conflict—will develop in Lebanon. It is not yet too late."

Since I gave my message to those two leaders, we have seen dramatic events unfold in the Middle East.

Iraq has attacked Kuwait and has threatened to attack all countries that surround Israel. Their ultimate aim is to destroy Israel. Our hearts have been filled with anxiety as we consider the immediate future of Israel and the nations surrounding her. It certainly underlines the urgent and very practical injunction in the Scriptures to pray for the peace of Jerusalem.

If there is peace in Jerusalem, there will be peace in Baghdad, in Egypt, in Saudi Arabia, in all the border countries and ultimately in all the world. Those who have seen the utter failure of military confrontations in that part of the world know that there is no alternative but to pray—more fervently than ever—for the peace of Jerusalem. I ask you to join me as a partner in this great spiritual battle.

One of the biggest mistakes we can make is to be afraid of going too far with God. I believe it is a satanic lie that we can get away from God's will by "running ahead of the Lord" in our prayers (as I have heard well-meaning Christian teachers describe it). Naturally we should seek guidance constantly and we must do our best to move in obedience, but I believe it is actually more pleasing to God when we blunder ahead and make mistakes than when we do nothing because we are afraid.

When I still had my garden and my children were small, they would sometimes go out and pull weeds for me. I might walk into the garden an hour later and find they had pulled up most of my flowers in their efforts to do a good job! But I never scolded them. They were blameless, you see. They were learning, and as their father I knew part of the learning process was making mistakes. I didn't get angry with them because they did imperfect things out of ignorance or impetuousness. No, I loved them for wanting to please me.

God is like that with us when we pray. He understands that we are going to make mistakes, but even when we do the wrong things, He doesn't blame us.

You might argue that honest mistakes are one thing, that the Lord won't frown on us for trying, but what about when we sin deliberately, when our desires are not to please Him but to follow our own sinful or lustful or evil ways? Won't God cast us aside then?

No, and do you know why not? Because there is really no difference between small, "honest" mistakes and big, selfish ones. In the sight of God's purity they are all blunders one way or another and need forgiveness. And the person whose heart is tender toward God will find His mercy equally available.

Look at David. We know he did many wrong things, but how did God describe him? He called him "David, who kept my commands and followed me with all his heart, doing only what was right in my eyes" (1 Kings 14:8). David sinned, both innocently and deliberately, but at the base of his character was a desire to love and honor God. His relationship with God was so intimate that the moment he sinned he had to say he was sorry. Relationship is the important thing.

Or look at good old Abraham, who stumbled, lied, cheated—but when God wrote Abraham's biography in

Romans He said, "Abraham believed God" (Romans 4:3). We might say, "But he lied, he cheated!" God didn't see him that way. He said, "Abraham believed God"—period. Everything else was incidental to that. He was blameless, not perfect. There's a big difference.

We are like that when we stand before God in prayer—blameless, not perfect—and it's a wonderful position to be in. We don't have to be afraid of going too far with God. Even if we do, He won't hold it against us. His grace is bigger than our foolish mistakes.

So God doesn't expect us to wait until we have all the facts before we pray, because we can never know everything about His plans. What we *can* do is seek earnestly to know Him, study the circumstantial evidence, listen to the Holy Spirit's guidance, take our knowledge of His character into account, draw reasonable conclusions and pray accordingly. As we do that, God will teach us to make fewer mistakes and our prayers will become more and more effective. We may often hear and understand Him imperfectly, but He will continue His promised work of perfecting us as we draw closer to Him.

All of this may be more complex for us than the miraculous revelations of Old Testament times, but it's also far more instructive. God is teaching us in practical ways, often through trial and error, how to apply the knowledge He has given us.

There can be no sin, then, in asking the Lord for whatever we believe will accomplish His will and purposes, regardless of our insecurity about our own limitations. We don't have to know the full scope of His plans to conclude that they are subject to change. God is always happy to hear our requests, even when our understanding is extremely limited, as Abraham's was when he interceded for Sodom and Gomorrah.

"You may ask me for anything in my name," Jesus said, "and I will do it" (John 14:14). I think those words are the ultimate answer to all our questions about when and how we can ask God to change His mind. Not that we should ask foolishly or recklessly or out of ignorance. But if we do, God will forgive us and use our mistakes to make us wiser the next time. The only people who don't make mistakes are the ones who never do anything for God or ask anything from Him—and if we should worry about anything, that's it!

5
How, Then, Shall We Pray?

Now that we have a clearer picture of what it takes to come before God's throne and ask Him to change His plans, it is time to look more specifically at how we can go about doing it. We have already uncovered, in the stories of Moses, Elijah and other prophets mentioned in previous chapters, some vital clues about how these legendary characters communicated with God and succeeded in changing His mind. We have learned some of the principles that guided their relationships with Him, principles that caused history to be rewritten as a result of their prayers.

The most important principle, as we have seen, is a recurring theme for this book. Let me say it one more time: It is only to the extent that we know God and understand His conditions for change that we are given opportunities to influence His plans. In other words, God changes His mind only for His friends—not for strangers or casual acquaintances. As we begin to look at how to pray—and in the final chapter, what we should be praying for—it's vital to remember this.

As soon as I begin to speak about how to pray in order to change God's mind, someone will usually shake his head at me and say, in the same tone of voice he would use with a naughty child, "Now, Brother Andrew, I know you don't mean to give people the impression that Christians can tell God what to do. After all, I'm sure that's not the way you pray. . . ."

This is a back door way of telling me that unless I take a fatalistic, *laissez-faire* approach to prayer, I'm a blasphemer. Such people hope that I will reply with a look of embarrassed horror, "No, no, of *course* I don't tell God what to do!" But I would never say that, because it's not true. I tell God what to do almost every time I pray!

Before you get too upset with me, let me give you an example of what I mean. Some of my most precious memories of Corrie ten Boom are of the many times we prayed together. Corrie was a passionate intercessor, and her urgency and excitement were quite infectious. You couldn't pray with her without being changed by the experience.

"Lord," she would say—except she always pro-

nounced it "Lort," like a good Dutchwoman—"Lort,
You must *do* something! There's no time to waste!" And
then she would tell the Lord very specifically and very
straightforwardly what she wanted Him to do. She
spoke just the way she spoke to me, her old friend.
Sometimes she would weep or laugh, sometimes she
would argue her points quite fiercely, but always she
was herself—and always she was totally honest. She
held nothing back from God, and He seemed to hold
nothing back from her.

Many times, in the midst of these lively prayer sessions of ours, she would quote God's own Word back to
Him to remind Him of His promises. She would have
made a great lawyer. When she grew especially impassioned, she would grab her Bible and thumb through
the pages rapidly until she found the exact passage she
could use to prove her case. Then she would lift her
Bible into the air, point to the verse and say trium-
phantly, "Here, Lort—read it Yourself!"

I always loved that. And I'm sure God did, too. He
loves it when we know Him well enough to talk to Him
that way. I don't know of anybody's prayers that had
more influence with God than Corrie's. She was not
deterred by false piety or legalism or a need to be anyone but herself. And after all, as she would often remind Him, she was not asking God for anything He had
not already promised. So she never hesitated to tell Him
what to do and to thank Him when He did it. "I *knew*
You would do it!" she would say with a jubilant smile.
"I just *knew* it!"

And she did, you see. She knew what God would do for her because she knew God. She understood His will and expected Him to keep His Word. It never crossed her mind that He wouldn't. What faith! If only the Lord had a few more friends like Corrie, our poor old world would not be in the mess it's in today.

Now you tell me: Were Corrie's prayers blasphemous? Presumptuous? Some might say so, but I would not, because her approach was totally scriptural. Jesus said, "Ask Me for anything," and Corrie took Him up on it, always basing her prayers on her deep understanding of God's will. And God answered her prayers. How could He do otherwise?

So as we look at the question "How do we pray to change God's mind?" I begin with the little reminder that we don't pray out of a desire to change His mind or to "tell Him what to do"; our desire is to know Him better as our Friend and Father. Opportunities to change God's mind are only one result of that relationship.

With that in mind, let's talk about how we can most effectively pray when we have decided it's time to ask the Lord to change His mind about a specific situation. I would like to keep things simple, and offer just two lessons God has taught me over the years as I have tried to learn how to intercede more effectively. I have chosen to concentrate on these lessons in particular because they solve for me the problems that seem most common to Christians wherever I travel.

The Power of Focused Prayer

The first of these lessons, which I learned early in my Christian experience, taught me why some prayers are more powerful than others.

We were in a prayer meeting—it was in 1950—in our little village of St. Pancras in Holland. We were a very dedicated and energetic bunch of intercessors, and we had spent quite a long time that night praying for missions and missionaries around the world. We interceded for the millions living in every nation from China to the Congo, prayed for governments and rulers, prayed for God to do tremendous things. We believed, as I still do, that we should be praying for big things—for the souls of men and the destiny of nations—not for a better refrigerator or a nicer car. We had great faith, so we were praying boldly that night about matters of vast consequence.

Now there were in our group some relatives of a little girl named Reina, whose Christian parents had died from a tragic domestic accident only a short time before. When her parents died, Reina had gone to live with her unbelieving grandmother. Her relatives were deeply concerned about her, so when we finished praying for world missions, we agreed to pray for little Reina. Almost as soon as we began to pray for her, the most amazing thing happened: Everyone began to cry. All of us were suddenly on our knees beseeching the Lord from the depths of our souls to intervene in that little girl's life. As we prayed, we were stirred in a way we had not been all night, and our faith multiplied as we prayed.

When we finally finished, while we were still wiping away our tears, I stood up and said to the group, "Wait a minute! What's happened here? Now we're praying for one little girl and we cry, but when we prayed for a million lost souls, we didn't cry. Why?" There was silence for a while, then someone answered, *"Because we cannot identify with the millions, but we can identify with that one."*

We went away from that meeting feeling that God had put a key into our hands. We understood something then that we had never really thought about before: We can pray for the world, for the hungry, for the oppressed, for the missionaries out on the field, for the poor, but until we can identify with and focus our prayers on one person we know about, our prayers will probably not be passionate.

After that night I understood why "God, protect the missionaries" and "God, help the people of Russia" aren't powerful prayers even though they might be big prayers and full of faith. Unless I can focus on that one missionary in prison in China, that one being persecuted in Lebanon, that one being held hostage in Colombia, unless I identify with him and understand his plight, I cannot really pray for him as I want to. But when I have taken the time to find out what he is facing, when I have experienced his discouragement over working for years without seeing a single soul won over to Christ, when I know the conditions he is living under—the torture he has suffered in captivity, the poverty and isolation and sickness he has endured, the opposition from every side—then I can pray! Then I can intercede passionately on behalf of that one missionary, or any believer.

In the years since that prayer meeting in St. Pancras, I have also made a commitment to go, wherever and whenever I can, to be with those who are the focus of my prayers, people who are cut off and struggling to survive in the most restricted and dangerous nations on earth. That's what God has called me to do. It is where I am really needed, and where I have told God I will be, because there is nobody to take my place if I don't go. I have often said to the Lord, "I don't know why it has to be me. I'm the least qualified guy You could find!" I know there are thousands of people who could be doing what I do, and probably doing it much better. But the fact is, most of them aren't doing it. So there is a tremendous void and God has to settle for me. I do all I can, but I'm only one man, and Open Doors is only one organization. Needs are not being met. The suffering Church continues to suffer.

You see, God doesn't have stand-ins. We're not replaceable. My heart breaks when I see the staggering needs in countries where nobody is taking the Word of God, or even a simple word of encouragement. I ask, "Lord, where are the people You've called to be here?"

That is one reason I preach, even though I am not

much of a preacher, and that is why I write, even though I am not a writer. I do it because I want desperately to shake you out of your lethargy if you are one of those God has called to *go*, and you have said, "No, I can't go. I have other priorities. I have my business to run, I have my responsibilities at home. God can find somebody else." He can't. You are free to choose your priorities, but if you don't do the job God has called you to do, it will go undone because nobody is waiting in the wings to do it.

It is exactly the same with our prayers: If we don't learn to focus our prayers and ask God to save our kids, our neighbors, our bosses and co-workers, our nation and the world, if we don't intercede for that poor widow we know about in some forgotten village in a remote part of the globe—then *there's nobody else to do it*. Jesus won't do it. He is not praying for the world; He's praying for *us*, so that *we* will do what He has commanded (John 17:9). It's *our* job to pray for and go into all the world (Mark 16:15).

So when you decide you are going to ask God for big things—as I hope you will—don't be satisfied to pray, "Lord, bless those nations and save those people." Pray for them specifically. Then go to them if you can. Ask God to help you make personal contacts with a few key individuals there. Get to know them. Listen to the cries of their hearts. Give them God's Word, encourage and pray with them. Do something practical to help them. If it is impossible for you to go, then study their culture, their history, their political structure, their leaders, and learn something about the forces that affect their lives, so you can pray with more insight and intelligence. I guarantee it will make all the difference in your prayers.

And you had better watch out when you begin to pray this way! The moment you say, "Lord, be with the suffering Christians in that city; give them Bibles, give them encouragement, show them that You care," God may very well reply, "Ah, that's what I've been trying to tell *you* all along!"

I heard a story recently about an American mother who learned this lesson only after several years of discouraging, unfocused prayer for the Far East. Her prayers—and her life—were transformed one day in the early 1970s when a friend handed her a news magazine that carried a photograph of an unidentified young Vietnamese mother, sobbing as she clutched a tiny mutilated body to her bosom. Her baby had been killed by bombs that had destroyed her whole village. The photograph was heart-wrenching to this American woman because as a mother, she could identify with that other young mother's agony and loss.

She was so moved by the photograph that she tore it out and taped it to the inside cover of her Bible. Starting that day, instead of praying vaguely for "the Far East" as she usually did, she looked into the face of that weeping mother and prayed for her and her whole family as well as the other suffering mothers and children in her village. After a few days of this she went to the library and came home with books and maps that gave her vivid mental images of that part of Vietnam. She began to ask the Holy Spirit to guide her prayers, and the focus of her prayers became clearer and clearer. She joined with other mothers to pray for an end to the conflict.

When the war finally ended, she came across a newspaper article about Vietnamese refugees living in a nearby community, and she made contact with one family through a social service agency. Within a year she was helping refugees in her area find employment and housing. Many of them became Christians.

In the years since then, I am told, this woman has expanded her "prayer war" for Vietnam. Today she has been joined by a large and committed circle of Christian friends who have caught her vision and are working to minister the love of Jesus to these beleaguered people. She and other members of her church adopted a number of unwanted orphans and found homes for many others who are illegitimate offspring of American servicemen. They have also helped found several new churches in Vietnam and in the U.S.

I don't know this woman's name, but that's not really important. She could be any one of us. In the moment she first identified herself with one young Vietnamese mother—instead of the whole Far East—she became a true intercessor whose prayers had a global impact. *She prayed for big things in a focused, specific way*, and eventually changed the lives of a substantial number of people who were once without hope.

Your prayers—and your obedience to the Holy Spirit's direction—can do the same. Or perhaps even more! There are no limits with God.

When God Is Silent

The second lesson is one that taught me several important things about those times when we pray with great faith and power, and we are sure we are praying according to God's will and meeting His conditions, but He doesn't seem to be answering. We have done everything "right," but He is either saying no, or is "giving us the silent treatment," as one of my friends likes to call it.

We have all experienced this problem. We pray for the healing of a devout brother or sister who is dying of some painful disease. We anoint them, we hold prayer meetings with the church, we know God is going to heal this person, but he or she doesn't get better. Or we pray for the conversion of a rebellious teenager, one who was dedicated to the Lord as a baby and has been raised by loving Christian parents, but who has become a drug addict who steals from his parents and lives a life of gross immorality. We pray and pray, but things seem to be going from bad to worse.

What do we do? How do we handle this? Amazingly enough, many Christians don't do anything. They don't respond at all! Or worse, they consign the whole experience to the convenient catch-all file labeled "Tests of Faith." They seem to take the attitude of Ali Khamenei, the leader of Iran's Muslims, who told the grief-stricken families of some 40,000 people who died in the great earthquake in June 1990 to accept the disaster as a "divine test" they must pass "through patience and cooperation." Incredible!

But the sad truth is, Christians talk like this all the time. Why? It's partly, of course, because fatalism has permeated much of our thinking, but I think there's another problem as well. We simply don't know how to respond to God's silence, so we do what seems safest and easiest: We gloss over the problem, tell ourselves that things aren't what they seem, that God has His mysterious reasons and that "someday we'll understand"—meaning someday in heaven, not in this lifetime.

We are a lot like the people in the old fable about the emperor's new clothes. They all knew something was wrong, that the emperor was parading around stark naked, but nobody was willing to be the one to point it out for fear of being thrown into the dungeon. So they all said how beautiful the emperor's new clothes were—and in pretending they eventually began to believe it themselves.

When we do this with God it isn't funny. It's tragic, because by ignoring God's silence or pretending nothing is wrong, we miss a tremendous opportunity to become more intimate with Him and find out some extremely important things about His character. We are so intent on avoiding the obvious that we miss the chance to find out the truth.

Or is it that we don't really believe God will give us our answers? Or are we afraid—afraid to take off our masks and be honest and authentic with each other and with God, and afraid of what we might discover if we do? We must not settle for that kind of "pretend" relationship with God—or with our fellow believers, for that matter. Or with a world that is looking to us for answers.

So what *should* we do when God is silent? First, I think we must go to God and *ask Him why*. That's the obvious question, isn't it? "Why did this happen? What's wrong here? Father, why aren't You healing this person? Why aren't You bringing that teenager to repentance? Why aren't You answering?" David asked the same question: "My God, my God, why have you forsaken me? Why are you so far from saving me?" (Psalm 22:1). Should I say here that even Jesus asked this question?

It's perfectly normal to ask why when we don't understand what's happening. What would you do if you called your best friend and said, "I'm sick in bed, I need you to bring me medicine," and she said, "I'll be right there," but ten hours later she still hadn't arrived? I hope you wouldn't lie there in bed saying, "This must be a test. I'm not going to ask her why she didn't come, I'm just going to grin and bear it. And anyway, she probably knows better than I do whether or not I need medicine."

Is that what you would do? Or would you call her

again and say, "Why haven't you come? You promised! What happened?" Friends don't think twice about asking each other such questions. So why shouldn't we ask God—especially when the issues and needs are vastly more important?

We have to find out the reasons. We are His friends, His children, His Body, the people for whom He died! We can't afford to make pious excuses or pretend everything is all right when it isn't. The Lord expects us to ask. "Call to me," He says, "and I will answer you and tell you great and unsearchable things you do not know" (Jeremiah 33:3).

If I have a pain in my back that is preventing me from doing work for God, and my wife and I have been praying for my healing for six weeks, it does me no good if she says, "Andrew, in God's timing you will surely be healed." That wouldn't satisfy me. That could mean six years from now! I wouldn't accept it, because I know God. I know I can go to Him directly and say, "Lord, why don't You heal me?" He's my Friend and my Father, and He knows the answer, so it would be crazy not to ask Him! What could be more logical or natural?

And I am sure, I am absolutely, positively *sure* God would find a way to give me an explanation. Maybe I wouldn't be healed—that's possible for any one of several reasons I could list—but I would have my explanation. The Holy Spirit would help me see my situation from His perspective, which would be even better than being healed; I would have gotten closer to God's heart in the process of finding out why I wasn't healed. And I would rather get closer to God than be healed any day, so I'd have nothing to lose. In any event, there has never been a case where God has failed to explain His silence when I have asked Him. There have been questions I have had to leave open for a while, but God always answers eventually if we really want to know.

Just recently He gave me the answer to a question I left open many years ago. A number of our teams were caught in East Germany over the years with the Russian Bibles they were trying to take over the borders. We lost many Bibles that way, and this troubled me. I asked God, "Are we doing something wrong? Why did You allow this? It's such a waste—all those Bibles that nobody will ever read! This cannot be Your will!" I asked and asked and never got a clear answer. So I left it open. I said, "O.K., Lord, but I expect an answer. I'll wait, but I'm not closing the file." (I never close a file without an answer!)

Then, only a few months after the Berlin Wall fell in 1989, I opened my Dutch newspaper one morning to read that the Stasi—the East German secret police—had been storing all the Russian Bibles they had taken from us, and had just shipped them off to the Church in Russia. There were *twenty thousand Bibles!* Not one was wasted, you see. I could finally close that file because I had my answer, right there in black and white: Those

Bibles were not lost; they were just "delayed in transit," and they are finally where they belong.

There is a second thing I believe we must do when God seems silent. It applies to intercession generally as well. Winston Churchill said it perfectly in his famous eight-word speech at a graduation ceremony during World War II: "Never, never, never, never, never . . . *never* give up!"

More and more these days I hear Christians say things like, "I don't pray for things more than once; I believe God heard me the first time." Some preacher made the statement—perhaps about justification—"God said it, I believe it, that settles it!" and Christians have taken that out of context and twisted it to mean something that preacher probably never intended. They say, "God said He would save my kids, I have asked Him, that settles it. Period." They convince themselves that asking again is evidence of a lack of faith—not "great faith," as Jesus said—and on that basis they stop praying.

But I believe we cannot call ourselves intercessors unless we are willing to persist in our prayers. We must keep on praying until God moves. If my kids were not saved I would nag God night and day; I would make His life miserable until I saw every last one of them saved and walking with Him! I wouldn't take any chances. I wouldn't sit back and say, "O.K., God, I've asked, that's it!" When I am asking God for something that important—and everything I pray for is important to me—I don't quit until I know He has done it.

Sometimes I don't have to see it to know it—as, for

example, I didn't have to see it to be sure God had stopped that man in Moscow who was going to report us to the KGB. But as a general rule, I pray until I am sure.

There is a tremendous amount of Scripture to support this idea of persistence. You can start with Abraham again and his prayers for Sodom and Gomorrah. We have already recalled how he went back again and again and again, until he was finally afraid to go back and ask God one more time, and as a result he lost what he had gained (Genesis 18:23–32). This is a perfect example of what happens when we stop praying too soon!

Then there was Jacob, who wrestled with God (Genesis 32:24–29). Where are the people who will wrestle with God today, men and women who will say, "God, I won't let You go until You give me what I ask"?

The psalmist cried to the Lord "day and night" (Psalm 88:1), and so did most of the prophets of the Old Testament. God always interpreted their "much asking" as evidence of faith. And in the Gospels we have many wonderful illustrations. Those familiar to most of us are the story of the Gentile woman whose daughter was demon-possessed (Matthew 15:22–28 and Mark 7:25–30); Jesus' parable about the unjust judge (Luke 18:1–8); the incident involving the two blind men of Jericho (Matthew 20:30–34); and Jesus' story about the friend asking for bread (Luke 11:5–10).

This last illustration is a particular favorite of mine because it is the Lord's direct response to His disciples' request "Teach us to pray." Jesus first gave them the pattern of the Lord's Prayer, and immediately followed that with His parable:

> "Suppose one of you has a friend, and he goes to him at midnight and says, 'Friend, lend me three loaves of bread, because a friend of mine on a journey has come to me, and I have nothing to set before him.'
>
> "Then the one inside answers, 'Don't bother me. The door is already locked, and my children are with me in bed. I can't get up and give you anything.' I tell you, though he will not get up and give him the bread because he is his friend, yet because of the man's persistence he will get up and give him as much as he needs.
>
> "So I say to you: Ask and it will be given to you; seek and you will find; knock and the door will be opened to you. For everyone who asks receives; he who seeks finds; and to him who knocks, the door will be opened." Luke 11:5–10

I like the Williams translation of this last verse, which is true to the spirit of the original text: "Keep on asking. . . keep on seeking. . . keep on knocking."

What a tremendous passage of Scripture! It is the same teaching as in the other passages I just mentioned and, taken together, they all convey the same message: If you really want to change God's mind, don't give up! Keep asking!

Now there are a couple of other points I would like to mention briefly in connection with what to do when God is silent. We could call them the two Fs.

Fasting and Fleeces

Whenever I finish a message on intercession, someone will stop me afterward and ask, "But Andrew, what about fasting?" They ask this because I don't usually talk about fasting at all.

First of all, let me make it clear that I am not against fasting. I have fasted a lot in my life, but I don't do it as much as I used to. Most of us eat too much anyway and the Bible says plenty against gluttony, so fasting can be wholesome from that standpoint alone. Some people fast one or two days a month and give the money they save to the poor or to the suffering Church, and I applaud that.

But I don't think Christians should use fasting as a means of getting God's ear when He seems silent. This is a personal opinion, you understand; it is a matter open to argument because the Scriptures don't give us a lot of instruction about fasting. But I personally feel that when we come up with the idea of fasting in order to get God's attention, it's a little like a child who holds his breath until he turns blue—and it usually accomplishes just about as much. It becomes another legalistic exercise, another way to earn merit badges to prove how spiritual and self-disciplined we are. Carried to an extreme, it can even become a way of trying to replicate or add to the sacrifice of Christ.

God will not respond to that. He hears us on the basis of what Jesus accomplished on the cross, not on the basis of our sacrifices. I always shudder when someone tells me, "I've decided to fast forty days the way Jesus did." What's the next step, I wonder? Are they going to have someone nail them to a cross? We must be careful when we start thinking our actions give us the "right" to approach God. We can come before Him on no basis other than the sacrifice of Jesus.

But don't misunderstand me. I believe there *are* times when fasting is appropriate. Jesus said something I have adopted as my own guideline about fasting. When people asked Him why His disciples didn't fast as the Pharisees and John's disciples did, Jesus said, "How can the guests of the bridegroom fast while he is with them? They cannot, so long as they have him with them. But the time will come when the bridegroom will be taken from them, and on that day they will fast" (Mark 2:19–20).

I take from that Scripture a general principle that goes something like this: "When you are close to God and everything is going fine, you don't fast—you feast! But when you are away from God, you fast." I don't mean when you are away from God through sin, because then you wouldn't even think of it. I mean when you are away from God in the sense that you have a problem, a burden, a vision, a project, a goal, something you must master, some area in which you cannot discern the will of God or cannot understand what it is He is trying to tell you, or something you must do that you feel too far from God to accomplish. *Then* you can fast on a meaningful level.

I have fasted in those sorts of situations, and many times it has been very helpful. But again, we are talking about fasting within our intimate relationship with God through Christ. We don't *have* to fast, ever, as a way of "paying the price" for what we want. Jesus has already paid the price in full. So our fasts are for our benefit, to bring us in line with God's thinking and help us clear away the debris in our own lives. In that sense, they can have a place in any Christian's life.

There is also a place for fasting in spiritual warfare, as we'll see in the next chapter.

Now as to the matter of fleeces. The concept of fleeces comes, of course, from the story of Gideon (Judges 6:12–40). I love this story because it not only illustrates an important point about how to pray, but underlines the concepts we dealt with earlier in this chapter about asking God why.

You will probably recall that God visited Gideon to announce that He was going to use him to rescue Israel after they had been oppressed and impoverished by the Midianites and the Amalekites for seven long years. The Lord began His dialogue with Gideon by saying, "The Lord is with you, mighty warrior." What a statement! You might expect Gideon to reply, "Wow, You have a pretty high opinion of me!" But Gideon answered instead, "If the Lord is with us, why has all this happened to us? Where are all the wonders that our fathers told us about?"

Those were good questions! Gideon didn't easily accept what the Lord was telling him, because he had good reason to be skeptical. He had been through seven terrible years, and he was not about to listen to any prophecy unless he could be absolutely sure it was God speaking to him. And as his conversation with the Lord continued, his skepticism did not diminish, even when God told him, "I will be with you, and you will strike down the Midianites as if they were but one man." Gideon replied, "If I have found favor in Your eyes, give me a sign that it is really You talking to me." Then he brought an offering before the Lord, and God gave Gideon his sign by causing fire to come out of a rock and consume it.

But this wasn't enough for Gideon. Even though he realized by now that it was God he was dealing with, he wanted another sign, just to be sure he had heard right about the way God was going to use him. So he said, "If You will save Israel by my hand as You have promised— look, I will place a wool fleece on the threshing floor. If there is dew only on the fleece and all the ground is dry, then I will know that You will save Israel by my hand." A tough test, but God did what he asked.

That still wasn't enough for Gideon. He went back to the Lord and said this time he wanted the fleece dry and the ground wet. And God did that, too. After this Gideon believed what God told him and went on to defeat the enemy as God had promised.

So here we are faced with the question that is debated so hotly in many Christian circles: Was Gideon wrong to "test" God? Many Christians have condemned his attitude. "God had spoken," they say. "Gideon was wrong to question Him, and even more wrong to test Him by demanding three signs. He should have believed God the first time He spoke!"

I don't agree. I think God understood Gideon's need for confirmation and loved his attitude. There is certainly not a single indication in the Scriptures that God was offended by it. When Gideon said, "If You're with us, why has all this happened?" God's reaction was, in essence, "Gideon, you are My man!" I believe God expected Gideon to be skeptical, because he had every reason to be. And He was fully prepared to meet that skepticism with whatever confirmations Gideon wanted.

There is no end to God's patience when we ask Him to confirm His Word in our lives. That's not unbelief, that's faith! As Christians we can ask for big things, but we are usually afraid to ask even for small things. Gideon was not. He had boldness and guts. He was a true warrior! And God gave him what he needed to accomplish His will.

So I think there are times when we can put out a fleece—not on an everyday basis, nor out of a desire for dramatic experiences, but in situations like the one Gideon faced, in which God seems to be saying something quite unbelievable to us and we need a definite confirmation. There are a number of instances like this in Scripture, including God's sign to Abraham (Genesis 15:7–17) when he needed reassurance that God would give him the inheritance He promised, and to Moses (Exodus 4:1–9) when he needed proof that he had spoken with God.

These were exceptional situations, yes. But God is open to our needs, and in exceptional situations He is always doing exceptional things. So we can't let fear or false piety paralyze or deter us from doing what He has told us to do. We know how to pray: with focused, persistent prayers. We can afford to be bold. God is bigger than we can possibly imagine!

6
When It's Satan's Will, Not God's

My English stepfather, Uncle Hoppy, never asked me, "Andrew, what's the time?" Instead he asked, "Andrew, how's the enemy?"

Uncle Hoppy was always fighting the devil, always looking for new ways to outwit him or foil his plans. He understood a lot about spiritual warfare and he knew the value of constant vigilance. I admired his fighting spirit and I've tried to develop more of it myself.

Now what does spiritual warfare have to do with a book on changing God's mind? Everything. In the first place, many Christians mistake the tragedy or evil they see around them as having arisen from a loving, permissive God, when it is really the work of the enemy.

In the second place, until you try to change God's mind you will never understand spiritual warfare. The devil will oppose you on this as on nothing else because he wants evil to exist in the world.

Look at it this way: If something exists, God has not decided to abolish it. And if we ask God to change His mind about letting an evil situation or circumstance exist, Satan will do everything he can to hinder us. He wants people to live in darkness and sin and is a dedicated enemy of prayer.

So it's odd to me that many Christians today still seem almost unaware of the enemy's presence in our world, much less the fact that he doesn't want us tampering with his schemes. Even with the tremendous popularity of recent bestselling books that talk in vivid terms about battle between the forces of God and Satan, in many churches I visit there is a startling lack of knowledge about spiritual warfare. Oddly enough, this is particularly true in nations where the Gospel is preached without restriction. As I visit churches in the free world I often hear remarks like, "I don't believe in talking about the devil; I'd much rather talk about God," as if somehow we're thinking negatively when we mention Satan, and the best thing we can do is ignore him the way we might ignore a snarling dog in the hope that he'll lose interest and go away.

The suffering Church worldwide doesn't have this attitude. They've experienced firsthand what happens when you ignore the devil and expect him to extend the same courtesy. It's always possible, of course, to focus to an unhealthy degree on Satan—and he probably gets blamed for too much in some circles—but most Christians I meet don't make that mistake. They choose, for one reason or another, not to pay any attention to him at all. As a result, they are unprepared for the kind of warfare the enemy is waging today.

Some believers miss the opportunity to change God's mind because they don't believe it ever needs changing. They don't see the importance of our prayers in battling evil. They are ignorant of Satan's activities because they have misinterpreted Scriptures or taken one or two verses out of context to support their head-in-the-sand attitude. "Jesus defeated the devil on behalf of everyone who believes," they'll say, "so Satan can't touch me. I belong to God, and He controls *everything* that happens to me—including the things that may *seem* evil from a human viewpoint. I'm not going to fight those, because I'll only be fighting God's will."

This attitude shocks and dismays me for three important reasons.

First of all, it's based on a lie: that Satan is not really a threat to Christians. The Bible teaches just the opposite. Jesus warned His followers about the satanic opposition they would encounter as they preached the Gospel, portraying the devil as a murderer and "the father of lies" (John 8:44). When Satan bragged that he controlled "all the kingdoms of the world and their splendor" and had the power to give them to whomever he chose, Jesus did not dispute his claim (Matthew 4:8). He even called him "the prince of this world" (John 14:30).

New Testament writers identify Satan as a relentless accuser of Christians (Revelation 12:10), a tempter (1 Thessalonians 3:5), a hinderer (1 Thessalonians 2:18), "the god of this age" (2 Corinthians 4:4), "the ruler of the kingdom of the air, the spirit who is now at work in those who are disobedient" (Ephesians 2:2), the evil one (Matthew 13:19) and the enemy (Matthew 13:39). Paul warns that Satan "masquerades as an angel of light" and his servants "as servants of righteousness" (2 Corinthians 11:14–15). Peter characterizes him as "a roaring lion" hunting for a good meal and instructs us to be alert because our adversary is constantly afflicting us and our brothers and sisters all over the world (1 Peter 5:8–9).

In the face of all this, how could any Christian believe Satan is not a threat to us today?

The second thing I object to in this attitude is that it is extremely callous. Taken to its logical conclusion it says, "I'm safe and my loved ones are protected, so who cares what happens to everyone else?" Do you see what happens when you believe a lie? You start with a false premise—that Satan cannot hurt Christians—and then you are drawn into sin. In this case, the sin is one of selfishness and hardheartedness toward the rest of the world. We cannot know and love God and then turn our backs on the perishing people He has commanded us to love and rescue. Unless, of course, we believe Satan's lie. Then—as Satan well knows—anything is possible!

The third reason I'm upset about this attitude is that

it says we should not actively resist evil because it may be good in disguise. This is simply a modern rendition of the so-called "wise counsel of Gamaliel," which was about as fatalistic and *un*wise as counsel can get.

You'll recall that Gamaliel, a leader of the Pharisees, argued that the Sanhedrin should not oppose the preaching of Peter and the other apostles because "if their purpose or activity is of human origin, it will fail. But if it is from God, you will not be able to stop these men; you will only find yourselves fighting against God" (Acts 5:38–39).

As Christians we should know better than embrace that kind of faulty reasoning. We who know God have been promised all the wisdom necessary to discern the difference between what is of human origin (the flesh) and what is from God (James 1:5; 1 John 4:1–6). We don't have to resort to pious-sounding excuses for ignorance of God's purposes by saying that "cream will rise to the top"—which, in essence, is what Gamaliel did with the Sanhedrin. It was the fatalism inherent in his argument, of course, that appealed to the hypocritical Pharisees, so in that case the devil shrewdly orchestrated his own defeat. The apostles survived to preach again!

But we cannot count on that in every case. We must understand that Satan will always attempt to inject some form of anesthetic to render the Body of Christ unconscious of his presence before he attacks. Apathetic fatalism is only one of the anesthetics or devices he likes to use. We'll talk about others later in this chapter.

I'm convinced that Uncle Hoppy's question—"How is the enemy?"—is a good one for all of us to ask, because we must stay alert to what our adversary is doing. But there are two larger questions we must also answer if we're going to become the powerful intercessors God wants us to be: Who is the enemy and how can we beat him? Let's look in this chapter at exactly who Satan is, and what some of his most successful tactics are. Then, in the next chapter, we'll talk about the specific weapons and strategies we can use to defeat him.

When you see his name—Satan, the devil, Beelzebub, Lucifer—what picture comes into your mind? The cartoon character with the mischievous grin, funny horns and long, pointy tail who dresses in red underwear and carries a pitchfork? Satan loves that image, I'm sure! After all, who could take such a ridiculous figure seriously? No doubt he smirks when people buy T-shirts for their children like the ones described to me recently, which feature creative caricatures of horned scamps beneath the logos *Little Devil* and *Cute As the Devil* and—most amazing of all—*Daddy's Little Demon*.

Many Christians have trouble thinking of the devil even in these cute comic-strip terms. They can identify him only as a "negative force" or an "evil influence"—not as a real being. The devil does everything he can to foster that kind of vagueness about his identity, because he knows that the moment we see exactly who he is, we become a real threat to him. Once we see him as someone who operates in predictable ways within specific boundaries, we can anticipate his strategies, see through his disguise and combat him successfully using the powerful weapons God has provided. So the devil spends a lot of time and energy trying to keep us blind to his actual identity.

There are several descriptions of Satan in the Scriptures that can help us get a realistic picture of his character and personality. We know that Satan was originally named Lucifer, and that he belonged to an elite corps of God's angels who were given the same privilege we have been given: They could choose freely to obey or disobey God. Lucifer, for reasons we may never be able to fathom, took such pride in his beauty, brilliance and exalted position that eventually he decided he deserved to occupy God's throne as sole ruler of the universe (Isaiah 14:12–15; Ezekiel 28:12–19). It was the first and only attempted *coup d'etat* in heaven. It failed. Lucifer was thrown out of heaven and one-third of God's angels (who had joined in his rebellion) were banished with him.

Where did they go? Look around! Satan is now "prince of this world." Our planet is under his control. It operates according to his rules. It is, in a very real sense, Satan's own personal kingdom, and his plan is that every human being will worship and obey him instead of God. His script hasn't changed, you see; only the cast and location have.

Who gave the devil so much power in our world? Not God! God created the world and turned it over to *us*, the people He made in His own image, the people He endowed with free wills so we could freely choose to love and obey Him. He entrusted the world to our care, and we gave it to Satan. Year after year, century after century, we have believed the devil's lies, allowed him to take more and more prisoners, more and more territory, and even attributed at times the work of his hands to God, since God is sovereign and His ways past searching out!

Now even those of us who refuse to give Satan an inch are forced to live in a world he dominates. The planet God lovingly created to be His own peaceable kingdom has been overrun by the enemy, and all of us are paying the devil's price. Christians, in particular.

That's because from the devil's point of view, we are the flies in the ointment. The way he sees it, we Christians are the only real threat to his power. Perhaps worse, we are a continual reminder of his failure. Every time the devil sees a Christian, he remembers that he will never occupy God's throne. This world is the only kingdom he will ever get the chance to control. Imagine his outrage when he finds that some of us are actually willing to lay down our lives to take this kingdom away from him and make it God's instead! How *dare* we?

We are, to be sure, a small and often disorganized army, but Satan still has good reason to be afraid of us. We have access to all the authority and power of God, and we have—as the devil well knows—a mighty angelic host on our side that vastly outnumbers his own. As you'll recall, Satan took only one-third of the angels with him when he fell, and he cannot create any more. Two-thirds of the angels, therefore, are still on God's side—and ours. You can be sure Satan never forgets that sobering fact. Neither should we.

Naturally, the devil finds this whole situation more than intolerable. It infuriates him. We Christians are the only thing standing between him and total domination of his planetary kingdom. If it were not for us, he would have the pleasure of saying to God at the Last Judgment, "You see? All the people You created have chosen me instead of You!"

But there's one thing even worse from Satan's standpoint—one thing that makes him tremble not only with rage, but with fear: the knowledge that we as the Body of Christ can join together with the unbreakable bond of love and take up arms against him, challenging his power with all the authority God has placed in our hands. We can do to him and his lackeys what the Rumanian people did in 1989 to the evil regime that had oppressed them for years: We can rise up as one and pull him off his throne. We can, by the authority of God, smash him and his evil army.

Satan's goal, then, is to prevent that at all costs from happening. He must keep the world and its inhabitants in darkness so they have no opportunity to know and experience God's love. If he can do that, Christians will never know God has given them the authority and means to take back the world and rescue those Satan holds captive—and his evil reign will continue.

In this way Satan still holds out hope that he can ruin God's plan for the new heaven and new earth reserved for those who freely choose to love and worship Him.

Satan is well aware that very few people will choose to follow him if they know who he is and understand their alternative. So he puts all his energy into keeping the light of the truth from shining in the darkness. And he is frantic to stop Christians from using our authority against him.

Satan's Strategies

What are some of the strategies Satan uses to accomplish this goal? There are six I would like to look at that have proved most successful. Only after we have examined these strategies will we look (in the next chapter) at some strategies of God's design for us to defeat him. Clearly we *can* win—if we know what we're up against and understand how to use the weapons God has provided. Greater is He that is in us than he that is in the world! (See 1 John 4:1–4.)

Number 1: The devil tries to block Christians' power against him by keeping us from our power source, keeping us from praying.

This is one of Satan's most important strategies. He will stop at nothing to disrupt our ability to communicate with God, to get to know Him and His will. It is through prayer that we join forces with our Commander-in-Chief and attack the enemy's strongholds. (One way we can gauge the effectiveness of our prayers, in fact, is to observe how hard the devil tries to stop them!)

How does he keep us from praying? By isolating us—

both from God and from one another. Isolation is a tried-and-true military strategy. If he can isolate us from God, he effectively cuts off our supply line (the power of the Holy Spirit), weakens our defenses and keeps us from getting our orders from headquarters.

Isolation from our fellow Christians is also critical for demonic forces because "where two or more are gathered together" to pray in the name of Jesus Christ, all the power of heaven is focused and released against them. Thus, while Satan works overtime to keep us from praying *individually*, he works a hundred times harder to keep us from praying *together* with other believers. Our united prayers spell disaster for him. They constitute the greatest threat to his power.

The way Satan goes about isolating us from God and one another almost always involves tempting us to sin. Why? Because when we do sin, there is a chance we won't confess it. And nothing separates us from God more than unconfessed sin. I have found that Satan usually tempts us to sin in two areas that have proven most fruitful for him throughout history:

—*Power*. Satan is especially clever at placing us in positions that give us a taste of power, because he knows we will probably hunger for more. Once we taste power, Satan puffs up our pride. We become more and more like him—and less and less aware of our dependency upon God. The rise of the occult in our time is a good example of what this temptation is all about. Satan has been able to draw millions into occult practices— horoscopes, palm-reading, tarot cards, ouiji boards, seances, witchcraft, the New Age movement—by convincing us that through these means we can gain control over our own lives and those of others.

Occult practices are Satan's phony substitutes for the genuine relationship we were created to have with God through prayer and an understanding of His Word. They also appeal to our curiosity about the future. There is an overwhelming desire in many people to know what tomorrow will bring. I wonder how many stop to think how boring and pointless, how predictable their existence would be if they actually knew? Millions of people will complain on the one hand about the predictability of their daily lives, while on the other hand they open their newspapers to the horoscope looking for answers that ostensibly will remove all the mystery and excitement that remain!

But the appeal of the occult has never been logical. Its drawing power is similar, I suppose, to the fake gemstones that are so popular today. "Even a jeweler can't tell the difference!" the advertisements say. "Looks exactly like a real diamond!"—or emerald, or ruby. If it looks exactly the same, why is the fake so cheap while the real thing is so expensive? And why are many people still willing to sacrifice to own the real thing?

The truth is, people who don't understand the value of the real thing will buy what *looks* expensive primarily so they can fool others into believing they own the genuine article! Deception is at the bottom of it all. This is the appeal of the occult, regardless of the masks it wears. It lures people into accepting glittery substitutes for spirituality that look real, but in the end only keep us separated from God.

—*Pleasure.* This second area in which Satan tempts us to sin is powerful because God created us with a tremendous capacity for pleasure. When we are in right relationship with Him, we can experience pleasure of a kind unknown to anyone but God's friends (and infinitely more is promised to us in the next world!). But Satan finds he can often get us to settle instead for pathetic and perverted substitutes.

We are, as C. S. Lewis said, like children who keep making mudpies in the slums because we can't imagine what is meant by the offer of a holiday by the seashore. Pleasure is especially effective as a means to draw us into sin because we will do almost anything to get it. We will degrade and humiliate and even kill ourselves and others to obtain a fleeting moment of it. Research scientists have found that when laboratory animals are allowed to self-administer cocaine whenever they want, they increase their ingestion quickly to the point at which they receive nonstop injections of the drug—until finally their hearts simply burst. They kill themselves literally out of an insatiable desire for more and more pleasure.

Human beings do the same thing. Thousands die every year from drug overdoses because they are addicted to pleasure and will stop at nothing to get it. Incredibly, many pregnant women refuse to deny themselves the pleasure of drugs even when they know their babies will die as a result. Satan knows how easy it is to tempt us in this area.

Promiscuous and perverted sex, of course, falls under the same category—everything from pornography to rape to child molestation and a thousand variations in between. Sex can be overwhelmingly magnetic and addictive to people who don't understand how it can seduce us away from God.

Money and possessions also fall into this category. When John D. Rockefeller, one of the world's wealthiest men, was asked by a reporter, "How much money is enough?" he replied with a sad smile, "Just a little more."

Remember: Pleasure in itself is not evil, any more than power or sex or money or possessions are. It's when we love these things instead of God—or when we want them so much we are willing to disobey God to have them—that they become idols for us. Satan loves to tempt us with perverted substitutes for the pleasures God has promised to give us through our relationship with Him.

When Satan can't tempt us to sin with power or pleasure, he will use other, more subtle ploys, such as introducing doubt into our minds to disable our faith. If we lose our faith we are obviously more likely to sin. He is still whispering to us the same question he asked Eve: "Has God *really* said. . . ?"

If he does manage to isolate us through sin, he will try to make that isolation permanent by convincing us that we can never be forgiven. So, while we should always be alert to temptations to sin, we must never let Satan fool us into believing that sin has placed us in a hopeless position, because that will *truly* defeat us. God is always ready to restore us when we seek His forgiveness.

If he cannot get us to stop using our authority against him by keeping us from praying, the devil often takes a more cunning approach.

Number 2: He tries to convince us that we can believe God but not obey Him.

This is something I have experienced myself. As an example, Satan will suggest—either directly or through other people (perhaps even Christians)—that God doesn't really expect me to go to dangerous places like Beirut, even though I know God has called me to go there, and even though He has confirmed that my usefulness to Him lies in ministering in such places.

Sometimes I find thoughts running through my mind that go something like this: "Andrew, you're too valuable to the cause of Christ to place yourself in such a risky position. After all, you're no good to the Body of Christ if you die! It would be much wiser to stay home and use the knowledge you have gained to teach others who are younger and stronger. This way you can multiply your ministry. Haven't you done enough? God knows you believe Him, and even if He *has* told you to go to Lebanon and all these other terrible places, He'll understand if you decide to stay home now and put your talents to work in other, less dangerous ways."

Do you see how subtle this kind of tactic can be? I have no doubt that millions of potential missionaries and evangelists have been neutralized by this same approach.

"Sure," Satan whispers, "God might have said, 'Go into all the world and preach the Gospel,' but did He say *everyone* should go? That would be unreasonable! If everyone went, who would be left in church?" (A terrific question, by the way! If our churches were doing what they should, they would be empty except for new converts and trainees, because the others would be leaving to do what God commanded them to do! That would be the first day the neighborhood would take the church seriously. As a result I am sure the church would be filled again the next week with new converts.)

But Satan likes to take this strategy a step further: "You can believe God and obey Him just by 'letting your light shine'—by looking after your family and taking care of your job responsibilities and living a life that sets a good example. You don't have to tell people about Jesus. You don't have to intercede for others. You don't have to give to the Lord's work or involve yourself in fighting against drugs, abortion, the occult, political corruption or pornography. There's no need for you to sacrifice yourself that way." This leads to Satan's third ploy to stop Christians from using our authority against him.

Number 3: He tries to convince us that we have a right to be happy.

No, we are not entitled to be "happy"—at least not in human terms. We are not entitled to a happy family, a nice house, beauty, prosperity, popularity or fame. God has, in fact, told us that in this world we will find our only real happiness in knowing Him and becoming involved in His plans.

I'll never forget the time I was ministering in a private home in the capital city of an Eastern European country in the sixties. I was teaching from the Scriptures to a sizeable group of Christians who were desperately hungry for the Word of God. While I was talking, the door opened and to my surprise an old friend of mine walked in. His name was Karl. I had thought he was still in prison. I'd worked with Karl in another country where the churches were—and still are—being bulldozed, believers are being imprisoned and Bibles are being destroyed. Karl had been arrested for evangelizing and sentenced to prison for three years. Now here I was in another city, and Karl walked in the door!

I was overjoyed, as you can imagine. We jumped around and hugged and cried, as you always do on such an occasion.

Eventually we all settled down, but we became very quiet because I found I just couldn't talk anymore. I wanted to listen instead of talk; I knew Karl could teach all of us more than I could. Everyone there knew that one day they, too, would have to pay the price Karl had paid, so they hung on his every word. He talked about his experiences in prison for a while and then turned to me, the only foreigner in the group. "Andrew," he said, "are there any pastors in Holland in prison for their faith?"

No one had ever asked me such a strange question, but I didn't have to think about my answer because I knew that if any pastor was in prison in Holland, it was because he wasn't a good Christian pastor—not because he was. "No," I told him.

I could see that my answer was painful to Karl. In his country, only the good Christians were in prison. He thought about this for a minute and then asked me, "Why not?"

I was really getting nervous by this time. How could I explain this to my brothers and sisters who were living under persecution? I started talking about all the freedoms we have—all the Christian book shops we have, all the Bibles we can own, how we can preach in our churches every hour of the week if we want to, how we can shout it from the rooftops, go into the streets, preach on television and radio and in magazines. I told them that in Holland I use all those means to preach the Good News, and I said I can even go out and invite my neighbors to come to church with me. In Karl's country, you could go to prison for three years for doing that. I said, "We can talk to the people we work with about Jesus. We can give Bibles to anyone."

Then I looked around and saw that those people could not understand what I was saying. It was beyond their comprehension. Suddenly I felt ashamed. I was making a fool of myself talking to these persecuted believers about such things. So I stopped talking. But I felt Karl's strangely blue eyes and serious face focused on me. After several minutes of silence he opened his mouth and said, "If all this is true, then tell me, Andrew: What do you in Holland do with 2 Timothy 3:12?"

It was obviously one of his favorite verses, but I didn't know it from memory, so I had to look it up. I opened my Bible and read it out loud. I will never forget what

God said there: "Everyone who wants to live a godly life in Christ Jesus will be persecuted. . . ." In the preceding verse, I noticed, persecution was mentioned two more times.

I was speechless for several minutes. Then I reacted in a way probably typical of the way most of us in the free world would have reacted in that situation. I turned into an instant theologian and began to explain that this verse applied to the early Church because Paul spoke specifically about the places where he had been beaten and put in prison, so it really referred to that period two thousand years ago, not to today. I was getting more nervous by the minute.

After I looked around at the sad, incredulous faces that surrounded me, I sighed and said, "These verses probably do apply today to restricted countries like yours. And to countries where revolution and war cause this same kind of suffering. But in Holland and America, and in other free countries, we do not suffer persecution for our faith. Why should we?"

I was sweating by this time. I stopped talking, and nobody said anything for a long time. Karl just kept looking at me with those piercing blue eyes of his. I read the verse again and again. *Everyone*, it said. *Everyone who wants to live a godly life in Christ Jesus will be persecuted.*

It hit me right between the eyes. We who live in the "free" world are not exempt. If we are not being persecuted, we should be asking ourselves Karl's question: *Why not?* More than half the population of the world today cannot take the Word of God seriously and live a godly life in Christ Jesus without being persecuted or imprisoned or killed for it.

Finally I looked up at Karl, whose eyes were still riveted on me. "Forgive me, Karl," I said, "but we do nothing with that verse."

He shook his head sadly, and so did I.

That moment will remain with me forever. It was a powerful reminder of a fact Satan wants us to forget: We are living in enemy territory, all of us—not just those in the restricted nations of the world. And if we love God and are living as Jesus taught us, we will be persecuted, reviled, hated, laughed at, or perhaps even imprisoned or killed for our faith. We will not be the toast of the town, we will not be heroes—except perhaps in a limited way among those in the minority who are also living for God. We will certainly not be applauded or even tolerated by the enemies of God.

So we must keep a proper perspective, remembering that we have all eternity to be happy. Happiness should not even be a consideration for us here. Jesus warned every believer that "in this world you will have trouble" (John 16:33). This doesn't mean that our lives will necessarily be one long stretch of unrelenting agony—although for many Christians today, this is the case. But we cannot forget that our enemy will not leave us alone to live lives of quiet harmony with our God. He will attack us constantly if we threaten him in any way by trying to change God's mind about allowing his activity.

Number 4: Satan tries to stop Christians by engendering fear—either fear on an individual level (like fear of witnessing to your neighbor or co-worker) or fear on a national level.

Satan is a master intimidator. He creates the oppressive, cruel political systems like Communism and fascism that seek to destroy all knowledge of God and make people afraid even to pray. Hundreds of millions of people have been cut off from the preaching of the Gospel for most of the twentieth century through this means. We can't forget that even with the advent of *glasnost* and *perestroika* in the Soviet Union, millions around the world still cannot read the Bible or speak the name of Christ without fear of torture, imprisonment or death.

Satan also inspires false religious systems that control whole nations and bring terrible suffering to Christians living in those lands. Such systems often send the Church underground. Even in many Western nations today, the influence of false religious systems has started to make it difficult for Christians to preach the Gospel. When they insist that salvation is found in Christ alone, they are attacked as "narrowminded, intolerant bigots."

I see this happening more and more. Recently a man on a television talk show in America got a big round of applause from the audience when he chatted about his recent conversion to a mystical Eastern religion and said, "I'm convinced that there is only one real sin, and that's narrowmindedness." His implication was, of course, that Christians—who contend there is only one God and only one way to know Him—are the worst sinners of all. I wonder who put that idea into his head?

I have often told my Christian friends in the restricted nations that they had better prepare themselves for missionary work, because soon we will be looking to them to help us. Those of us in the Western world who have never really suffered for our faith are going to face the reality of 2 Timothy 3:12. We are going to find ourselves the objects of persecution and ridicule and scorn of a sort that we have not experienced before, because we are in a weakened, vulnerable condition. If we don't prepare ourselves for what we are going to face in the next decade, I shudder to think what could happen. The more I see of what Satan is doing today, the more convinced I am of this.

Number 5: Satan tries to neutralize Christians by sowing seeds of dissension, accusation, anger, mistrust or bitterness among the brethren. This breaks the bond of loving unity and keeps Christians distracted and unable to organize for a counterattack. In other words, if the enemy can get us fighting among ourselves, we won't be able to fight him.

Churches and Christian organizations are not, as a rule, destroyed by opposition from outside. In fact, attack from the outside usually cements relationships and draws believers together, mobilizing them for battle. Satan has learned that the best way to attack groups of believers is to work from the inside. He disguises himself as an angel of light or sends his messengers as "servants of righteousness" to create confusion and mistrust, often working on just one or two individuals to begin with. Then, slowly, he stirs up bitterness, anger, envy—all the nasty attitudes that isolate us and keep our eyes off the Lord.

I have heard countless stories of prayer groups and Bible studies that have been destroyed by these means—usually just when the group is on the brink of a tremendous breakthrough. How does this happen?

In one fairly typical case I heard about, a new couple came into a Bible study and prayer group that had been meeting together for several years. Ron and Carla (we'll call them) seemed somehow more "spiritually qualified" for leadership than any who were already involved—partly because of their vast knowledge of Scripture, partly because they seemed to have special insights and gifts to provide the kind of leadership and direction the group thought they needed, and partly because of the sheer force of their personalities.

So they quickly became the unofficial leaders. Ron and Carla flashed lots of "spiritual credit cards"—stories of miraculously answered prayers, prophetic dreams, visions and direct "words from the Lord" that suggested to the group that soon they were going to have a powerful impact on their community for the Lord.

Very soon, however, members of the group began to get calls and visits from Carla and Ron. The purpose of these visits was always the same: to hint—very gently at first—that certain other members were hindering the progress of the group. These members, Ron and Carla suggested, were not on the same high spiritual plane as the rest of the group because they did not accept the agenda God had clearly given the group through the couple. The group would be better off, therefore, without these members.

After a long and agonizing struggle, several members began to discern what was happening. They met together, prayed and confronted Carla and Ron with what they had been doing. Naturally, the couple counterattacked, accusing those who confronted them of being un-Christian and out of tune with the Holy Spirit. Over a period of several weeks the group struggled to continue, but eventually—sadly—they decided simply to disband. Too much distrust had been sown and too many members hurt too badly to continue. Ron and Carla went off (presumably to join another prayer group) claiming that they had been the victims of demonic attack.

Tragically, they didn't know how right they were. Satan's "messengers" are also his victims. He hates them as much as he hates us—and they suffer in their own ways even more than we do.

Number 6: When these strategies fail, Satan may resort to direct attack to keep us from using our authority against him.

This can take many forms, but physical or emotional attacks on us or our families are among the most common. I have witnessed and experienced these kinds of battles so often that they have become almost routine.

I remember a story told to me by a preacher's widow about her husband, who was a pastor-evangelist in Eastern Europe many years ago while she remained back

home. Everywhere he preached they experienced tremendous revival. Then one night, just before he got up
to preach, a telegram was handed to the pastor: "Come
home. Your wife is dying." The preacher, an experienced spiritual warrior, recognized what was happening. After praying about it for a few moments he
announced, "That's not God. He will not let my wife die
when He's called me here to preach. I'm not going
home. She will not die." He asked for prayer on his
wife's behalf, and went on to complete his scheduled
meetings. By the time he returned home, his wife had
recovered.

After recounting this story to me, the widow smiled
at me and said, "You see, he knew God, and he knew
what God would and would not do. When you know
Him that way, you have the liberty to say yes or no
without fear. My husband was certain that only Satan
would attempt to keep him from preaching the Gospel
to people who might have no other chance to hear. So
he had to stay. He couldn't give the devil that kind of
victory. And he was able to trust God completely in
spite of the devil's attack."

In a sense, attacks like these should encourage us.
They are a sign that the enemy has run out of more
subtle options and has become desperate to stop us. But
physical and emotional attacks can be frustrating, de-
bilitating, painful and—if we don't identify them for
what they are—they can cause us to lose heart. So we
must be on guard against them.

Most of the time, I have found, the sickness and injuries Satan throws at us can be categorized as harassment more than anything else. Remember, he wants us to suffer because he thinks that will cause us to turn our backs on God or give up our efforts for Him. When he sees that he can't achieve his objectives that way, however, he usually gives up. Thus, it's important that we persevere through this kind of suffering and refuse to submit to his threats and harassment.

It's also wise to understand, when we are under this kind of attack and in emotional or physical pain, that we usually cannot pray effectively for ourselves. Effective prayer, as I have said, requires focus, and focus is the first thing to go when we are in pain. Most of the time we can think of nothing but our own suffering, and that's perfectly normal. When this happens, we must count on other Christians to pray for us. The first thing I do in such a situation is to call my favorite prayer partners and ask them to take up my cause. It gives me great comfort to imagine how this must frustrate the enemy!

There's much more we could say about the devil's strategies, but I think we have covered enough to give us a clear picture of the spiritual warfare in which we are engaged. Let's move on now and look at the final exciting question of how we can defeat our enemy!

7
How We Can Defeat the Enemy

A couple of years ago at an Open Doors prayer conference, an old friend was talking to me over dinner about how hard it is to present the Gospel in a world controlled by evil powers. "I know we must become more confrontational and aggressive," he said. "But how can we manage to battle the enemy in a hostile world and still represent nothing but the love of Christ?"

I answered him by telling a story about the time Corrie ten Boom and I were in a meeting in Holland in which the group was discussing the same problem. Somehow we had gotten off on a tangent into a conversation about thermostats for heating and cooling systems. It was not such a strange tangent, really, when you consider that Corrie was fascinated by everything technical. She was, as you remember, a watchmaker by trade, and she loved anything that moved—from watches to people and everything in between.

As it happened, everyone in the room that day seemed to know something about thermostats, and Corrie was bent on understanding how they worked. Once we satisfied her curiosity, Corrie said, "Tell me, what's the difference between a thermostat and a thermometer?"

Several more minutes of explanation followed, until Corrie's eyes lit up with understanding and she began to nod. "Yes, I see," she said. "A thermometer only indicates what the temperature is. But a thermostat changes the temperature." Then she practically jumped out of her chair. "Andrew!" she exclaimed. "That's the answer to our problem! We've got to be thermostats—not thermometers!"

As usual, Corrie hit the bull's-eye. In a world like ours it's always much easier—even for a Christian—to be a thermometer instead of a thermostat. All of us read the newspapers or watch television and observe the international and local events—war, revolution, hostage-taking, crime, government corruption, ethical bankruptcy. We see the decline in moral and spiritual values reflected everywhere. We can even observe the positive things—the open doors in Russia and Eastern Europe and other parts of the world that have been closed to the Gospel for decades, the release of those who have been imprisoned in Communist gulags and mental hospitals for their faith.

But if we only observe these conditions from day to day, if we only make note of them and say, "It's terrible" or "It's wonderful," we're nothing more than thermometers. And Corrie was right: If we're going to win the war against Satan, if we're going to beseech God to change His mind about what He allows the devil to do in this world, we must be more than thermometers. We must be thermostats.

Thermostats exist to change the situation. They don't merely register that it's too cold or too hot; they respond to our touch and actually alter the environment. In my office in the wintertime I can hear a little *click* in the thermostat when it goes on, and if I'm watching for it I can even see a little spark fly to make the connection. Then the central boiler swings into action and—boom!— something changes. The whole mechanism of my heating system will fight the cold because I made a decision: I decided how warm it should be in my office, and the thermostat responded by changing the temperature.

This is exactly what we must do as Christians. We must understand that we were not created to be mere thermometers for the world, shaking our heads or clucking our tongues over how hot or cold it's getting. We were created to respond to the Holy Spirit's touch by clicking on, firing up our boilers and causing change! God has placed in our hands the power and authority to do that.

Jesus spent a lot of time teaching His disciples how to defeat Satan. He also set the example for all of us who follow Him, because He managed to defeat Satan on his own battleground, and at the same time to love the world's inhabitants as no one ever had. Jesus was—to use Corrie's analogy—the perfect thermostat. Wherever He went, He responded to His Father's touch by causing drastic changes.

The story of Jesus' temptation in the wilderness (Matthew 4:1–11; Mark 1:13; Luke 4:1–13) teaches one of the most important of all principles regarding spiritual warfare. Let's look briefly at the Gospel of Luke to see the strategy Jesus used to defeat the devil.

When the devil first approached Jesus after His forty-day fast he said, "If you are the Son of God, tell this stone to become bread." Satan knew perfectly well, of course, that there were no ifs about it. He was there because of who Jesus was! Jesus had nothing to prove to the devil, so His counterattack was both simple and direct: "It is written: 'Man does not live on bread alone.' "

When Satan next approached Him, offering the largest bribe in history, Jesus didn't change His strategy. He struck back using His most potent weapon: "It is written: 'Worship the Lord your God and serve him only.' "

By now Satan saw that he wasn't getting anywhere with his standard approaches. He decided to fight fire with fire. In his third attack he quoted Scripture to Jesus, twisting it to serve his own nasty purpose (one of his favorite tactics throughout the ages, by the way, and one he still employs with great success). This time he took Jesus to the top of the Temple in Jerusalem. "If you are the Son of God," he said, "throw yourself down from here. For it is written: 'He will command his angels concerning you to guard you carefully; they will lift you up in their hands, so that you will not strike your foot against a stone.' "

Can you imagine? Satan had the gall to attack the Word of God by quoting the Word *to* the Word! Notice, however, that the devil did *not* quote the Scripture correctly. He omitted "to guard you in all your ways" (see Psalm 91:11), thus falsifying God's Word. Had Jesus succumbed to this temptation He would have walked away from the center of God's will—and from God's protection, as well.

A stunning example of Satan's arrogance. But Jesus was ready for him again. He replied, in essence, "The Scripture also says, 'Do not tempt the Lord your God.' " It was a duel between Jesus and Satan, and their swords, in this case, were the Scriptures! But Satan realized quickly that he was out of his depth, and he departed to lick his wounds.

Do you see how Jesus fought Satan in this hour of temptation by using the Scriptures as His weapon? The Bible doesn't list all of the specific temptations Jesus was subjected to during His face-off with the devil, but it does say in another place that He was tempted "in every way, just as we are—yet . . . without sin" (Hebrews 4:15). And from the three examples given, it is clear that Jesus' primary weapon was Scripture.

In each of these examples in the Gospel record, we should also note that Satan hoped to tempt Jesus to sin by using His power selfishly—to feed Himself after a forty-day fast, to prove Himself God's Son and to gain power in the world. But Satan vastly underestimated God's wisdom and selfless love, and even more vastly overestimated his own cleverness. (This has always been the devil's downfall.)

Satan is still using this same ploy today. As we saw in the last chapter, he likes to tempt us with power because he understands its appeal better than anyone. The moment we become Christians and gain access to God's power through our relationship with Him, Satan will jump in immediately and try to corrupt us by tempting us to use that power selfishly. If he can get us to spend our time praying for selfish things instead of interceding to "change the world's temperature" and defeat his strategies, he will have neutralized us.

It is written: That was the weapon Jesus chose to use in His confrontation with evil, and it was powerful enough to repel every temptation Satan brought His way. Jesus knew that the Word of God was His single best defense against all of Satan's temptations. It is ours as well.

I have always been a big advocate of Scripture memorization for this and many other reasons. I realize that memorization is out of fashion in many churches these days, especially in the free world where Bibles are available to everyone. "Why should we put the time and energy into memorizing," people say, "when we can open our Bibles and find whatever verses we want anytime we like?" Such people don't know how fortunate they are, and I'm afraid they don't understand how quickly such privileges can be taken away.

Nor do they realize *why* memorized Scriptures can give anyone a tremendous advantage in spiritual warfare. If enemy soldiers had kicked in your front door a few moments ago and lined up your family to be shot, would it help to shout at them, "I have a gun out in the garage"? No, if a weapon is going to be effective, it must be available where and when you need it.

Our best weapon against Satan is Scripture, and if it's going to be useful we can't keep it in the garage. When you memorize a Scripture you place it in the arsenal of weapons you carry with you. It's always right there in an emergency. In a surprise attack, you have at your command the potent, living Word that carries all the authority and power of God to repel the devil's soldiers and give you strength for combat.

I have known many people who have survived oppressive situations for years simply by recalling a few memorized verses from childhood. Others have had nothing more than bits and pieces passed on from believers who had memorized Scripture. In some places I've visited, underground Christians have pages torn from a Bible somebody was able to obtain, and everyone commits his page to memory before exchanging it with someone else. Sometimes the pages are never passed on or exchanged because believers can't bring themselves to give up the only Scripture they've ever had in their hands. It becomes their most precious treasure. When I walk into a group of believers like that, I find that as I open my own Bible, every eye in the room will be glued to the Book, as if it were a banquet table laid out before starving people.

In one Eastern European city a pastor told me of a young member of his underground church who, after receiving his single page of Scripture, stopped him on the street and said, "Pastor, now that I have my Scripture, I have hope!" The pastor asked which book of the Bible was represented on the young man's page, and he answered, "Jeremiah." The pastor replied, "But Jeremiah is not a very hopeful book—it's pretty depressing! How can a page from Jeremiah give you such hope?" The young man replied with great excitement, "Pastor, it says on that page that the word of the Lord came to Jeremiah. If the word of the Lord could come to Jeremiah, it can come to me, too!"

It is often among believers like this that I find the most profound, earth-shaking faith I've ever encountered. They may know only one page—or one verse—of Scripture, but it's enough to carry them to triumph in the midst of the worst sufferings Satan can invent! Those of us who have all the Bibles we want seldom seem to appreciate the dynamite we hold in our hands.

Many years ago—in 1966, I believe it was—I attended the first World Congress on Evangelism, a gathering of several thousand dedicated missionaries and evangelists who met in Berlin to share modern strategies for reaching mankind with the Gospel. My most vivid memory of that Congress was the moment when Rachel Saint, the South American missionary, stood at the podium with three primitive Auca Indians dressed in the colorful garb of their people. They were some of the first Christians in their tribe, which had been struggling to survive in its isolated jungle habitat and for most of the century had been considered one of the most unreachable tribes in Ecuador.

Someone asked these Indian Christians if they would tell the audience their favorite verses of Scripture. Everyone expected them to recite John 3:16 or some other basic verse relating to salvation, since most of the Bible had not yet been translated into their language. But the Indians had a surprise for us. They looked at each other, conferred briefly, and then one of them stepped forward, declaring with a broad smile, "Devil get out, and never come back!" It brought down the house.

I remember thinking as I watched this how until that moment most of the more "sophisticated" Christians gathered for that Congress had failed to take into account one crucial aspect of the Gospel we had been called to preach. It was this aspect that turned out to be the most powerful and life-changing one as far as these struggling Indian people were concerned: Jesus came into the world not only to express God's love and reconcile us to the Father. He also came to say, "Devil get out, and never come back!" It took three "primitive" Christians to cut through to the heart of the matter for the rest of us. Since then, I have often used their free translation of that verse (Mark 9:25) in my own battles with the devil!

I'm always encouraged when I remember that the apostle Paul said, "We wanted to come to you . . . but Satan stopped us" (1 Thessalonians 2:18). There are casualties on both sides in any war, and even though we know we're on the winning side in this war, we must be honest and mature enough to recognize that we will occasionally lose a battle. We have become so success- and victory-oriented that we think we shame our Lord if we admit a defeat.

Nothing is further from the truth. After all, the life of the Church on earth will end as did Jesus' life on earth: on a cross. There will not be a victorious Christian sweep of all the dirt from the floor of our world. But the seeming defeat of Jesus on the cross was His greatest victory, and it is ours as well. We must come to grips with God's point of view.

God is able to transform our defeats into victories as we learn from our mistakes with the wisdom and in- sight He provides. As someone has said, "That which does not destroy me makes me stronger." God takes the long view, and so must we. Although Satan inevitably wins a few battles in each of our lives, if we are mature we can go back to the place where we lost touch with God's will, or where Satan caught us unprepared, and ask God to help us make a new start. There's nothing wrong with that. God doesn't expect us to be perfect; "he knows how we are formed, he remembers that we are dust" (Psalm 103:14). Our setbacks and losses can ultimately teach us—and those who follow us—how to win bigger and even more important battles in the fu- ture.

There are five simple principles I believe we should keep in mind as we involve ourselves in combat with the enemy through prayer. In my own experience, these five principles can bring victory in all spiritual warfare. Remember: We will win the fight, even though we may sometimes lose a round to the devil. Setbacks and losses should not discourage or deter us, because the ultimate victory belongs to Christ and, through Him, to us.

Number 1: We must arm ourselves for battle.

This is a very basic and practical principle. Most of us have read (or even memorized!) Paul's instructions to the church at Ephesus regarding spiritual warfare:

> Be strong in the Lord and in his mighty power. Put on the full armor of God so that you can take your stand against the devil's schemes. For our struggle is not against flesh and blood, but against the . . . powers of this dark world and against the spiritual forces of evil in the heavenly realms. Therefore put on the full armor of God, so that when the day of evil comes, you may be able to stand your ground, and after you have done everything, to stand. Stand firm then, with the belt of truth buckled around your waist, with the breastplate of righteousness in place, and with your feet fitted with the readiness that comes from the gospel of peace. In addition to all this, take up the shield of faith, with which you can extinguish all the flaming arrows of the evil one. Take the helmet of salvation and the sword of the Spirit, which is the word of God. And pray in the Spirit on all occasions with all kinds of prayers and requests. With this in mind, be alert and always keep on praying for all the saints. Ephesians 6:10–18

Nothing could be more straightforward than this. If I must go to an important meeting and I know there's a storm in progress outside, I first dress to protect myself from the elements, and then I go. It's only common sense. Paul is telling us here to do exactly that: There's a storm outside, so dress for it before you walk into it. If you don't, you'll get soaked!

The application of Paul's instructions in this passage involves a spiritual leap from the theoretical to the practical. The armor must be worn consistently and deliberately if it's going to be effective:

—We must live the truth. That means we must speak the truth, defend the truth and, if necessary, be willing to die for the truth—as so many heroes of faith before us have done. Lies can have no place in our lives, because Satan is the father of lies—the deceiver.

—We must live righteously. Our God is righteous, and as He dwells in us we will reflect His character more and more. We are, of course, made righteous through Christ's sacrifice on the cross, but as members of His Body we must also strive to live according to His commands. This means that we must choose to live righteous lives whatever the cost, allowing God to reign in all that we do. Even if the whole world seems to embrace evil, we must be committed to standing as beacons of righteousness, supporting all who do right and speaking up for what is good. As the saying goes, "I'm the only Jesus some people will ever see." We must, therefore, allow Him to live His life in and through us in an uncompromising way.

—We must equip ourselves as well to proclaim the Gospel of peace. We must be messengers always ready to tell others about Christ. It is through the sharing of the Gospel that Satan's hold on mankind is broken and God's Kingdom is strengthened and enlarged.

—We must shield ourselves with faith. Faith, as the writer of Hebrews says, is "being sure of what we hope for and certain of what we do not see" (Hebrews 11:1). Through faith we see what others cannot, both in God's Kingdom and in Satan's. This enables us, among many other things, to protect ourselves and others from the invisible rulers, authorities and powers that control this dark world.

—We must wear the helmet salvation provides. The knowledge that we are saved and will spend eternity with Jesus can protect our minds from despair and help build our resilience.

—We must carry the sword of the Lord—His Word. Again, the Word was Jesus' most potent weapon, and it must be ours as well.

—We must pray continually (see also 1 Thessalonians 5:17). Is this really possible or practical? Probably not in a literal sense, but I believe the apostle is saying that our attitude can be one of constant attentiveness to God's Spirit. "Always keep on praying for all the saints," he says, much the way our mothers used to tell us, "Always take your umbrella." We must not only carry an umbrella to cover ourselves, but to cover our brothers and sisters as well. We are in this storm together.

We can pray and listen to God, just as we can worship

Him anywhere at all—while we're putting diapers on the baby or fighting traffic on the freeway, while we're typing letters in our offices or walking on the beach. There is nowhere we cannot pray if we commit ourselves to it.

A good friend of mine, Geoffrey Bull, who along with George Patterson was the last remaining missionary in Tibet when the Communists took over, was imprisoned for three years in a horrible prison. He was so tortured and shattered mentally by his captors that finally he could not think anymore. He told me that when his mind at last grew so paralyzed that he could not even pray coherent prayers, he said to God, "Lord, if I can somehow stand up in the center of my cell, will You accept that as an act of worship?" Each day thereafter until he was released, Geoff managed to pull himself to his feet in the center of his cell, silent and yielded before God. That was his prayer and his worship.

If Geoffrey Bull could find a way to pray even when he couldn't *think*, I believe it's safe to say that prayer is possible in any situation.

I am convinced, in fact, that we can pray even when we sleep. Many times I've awakened with a keen awareness of having just interceded for someone. I think it is not only possible but likely that the Holy Spirit can move us to pray in our spirits while our minds are asleep. Who knows? These may even be our best prayers!

Number 2: We must resist the devil and he will flee from us (James 4:7).

This second principle is so obvious it is easy to forget.

Exactly what does it mean? Various references offer words like these as synonyms for *resist:* combat, challenge, dispute, duel, oppose, repel, assail, assault, attack, contradict, impugn, baffle, frustrate, thwart, hinder, obstruct.

Get the picture? Resisting the devil means much more than just saying no to temptation, although that's part of it. It means more than asking God to rebuke him, although that, too, is often involved. Know and understand that since Calvary we have *more* authority than the archangel Michael. (See Jude 9.) Resisting also encompasses far more than saying, "Devil get out, and never come back!"

It means we act like thermostats: We cause changes in the situation by refusing to take the devil's attacks lying down. We go on the offensive against the devil in every possible way—through our prayers and through our Spirit-inspired actions. Using the Word of God as our sword and wearing the whole armor of God, we contend forcefully for the faith. We say, "I am against this!" when we encounter evil, and we take action to oppose wickedness in every form. We say, "I am for this!" as we uphold righteousness and justice. In other words, *we refuse to give the devil an inch of ground in our world without a fight*—always remembering that people are not our enemies.

An interviewer on Christian television once asked me, "Andrew, do you think the Communists are our biggest enemies or the Arabs? Or the terrorists and revolutionaries and drug traffickers?" I replied, "They are not our enemies." The interviewer looked shocked. She said, "But then who *is* our enemy?" I said, "The devil." She seemed more shocked! Even those of us who are on the front lines can forget this important truth. This leads us to our next principle.

Number 3: We must learn how to pray for and how to pray against.

By this I mean we can break down the powers of evil and build up the righteous through our prayers. Let me give you a couple of examples from my own experience.

I have been teaching many pastors in Eastern Europe in recent years. One of the things I do is take them up on hills or mountains that overlook their cities and we pray *for* the city, for all the inhabitants, for those who love God and live righteously. We bless them. We name those we know who are aiding the suffering Church, and we bless those we don't know who are quietly serving God's purposes. Then we pray *against* the evil powers that hold the city in bondage.

I took an old friend named Stefanoff with me above the city of Plovdiv, Bulgaria, a city that had no church. We looked out on the city from that vantage point and prayed against the oppression that was keeping the city in bondage, against the powers of darkness, atheism, persecution and tyranny. We "bound the strong man," as Jesus said we should in Matthew 12:29, commanding evil spirits and demons to depart. Then we prayed for the souls of all the people and for the establishment of a church.

Our seven years of prayer for the U.S.S.R. was another example of praying for and praying against. Open Doors alone had at least three prayer chains going around the clock, day and night. Over a thousand people in each prayer chain were each praying at least ten minutes a day specifically *for* the release of new leadership in the U.S.S.R., *for* the opening of doors for prisoners, *for* opportunities to take Bibles to the people, *for* believers to be strengthened in specific ways and much more. We also prayed *against* the atheistic, oppressive powers and asked God to remove from power those who were enemies of the Church. And God answered!

I believe this kind of "for/against" prayer can be a highly effective strategy in spiritual warfare. I don't reserve it for special situations; I use it every day. When I'm driving or walking down the street and I see someone stopped at a traffic light or waiting at the curb next to me, I bless him or her. We should bless everyone who keeps the law. Even if I don't have any personal contact with others, I can still bless them. When I'm in an airplane I like to take the window seat because I can look out upon cities and farms and freeways and bless those people who are keeping the law. I do it in almost every imaginable circumstance. And when I bless anyone, he is blessed! I believe that. It's scriptural.

At the same time, there are certain circumstances—and this is a very tricky area—when praying against may involve a kind of prayer most of us have never even considered. I'm referring to the rare situations in which we can actually pray for the deaths of people who have sold their souls to Satan.

This is extreme—even frightening. And in light of what I said about people not being our enemies, it may even look as though I'm being inconsistent, not to say unloving. But I don't believe this is true. We should hope that people who are committed to the devil's active service will have every opportunity for repentance. But if they are too hardened to change, I believe we can ask God to change His mind about letting them continue to live.

There are exceptions to most rules—including God's. God's rule is love, but here is the exception: He does not love Satan or his demonic servants, nor does He love the evil that Satan perpetrates through those who are his slaves—and neither should we (Psalm 97:10; Amos 5:15; Romans 12:9). We certainly must not pray for anyone's demise without being sure of God's will in the matter, but there are occasions when I believe this kind of prayer is warranted.

We must recognize there are people in our world who are controlled completely by Satan. As long as they live, such people will do nothing but evil. As examples, I would cite both Hitler and Stalin. I've studied their lives in great detail. (My hobby is reading biographies, and I have hundreds of them in my library.) I can say without the slightest hesitation that both men sold themselves one hundred percent to the devil. I will go even further and say that anyone who prayed for either of them was wasting his breath.

I know this sounds shocking, because we are talking about drastic situations, about life-and-death prayers and about souls that cannot be redeemed. I am convinced there is nothing in the Scriptures that gives the slightest hint that men like Stalin or Hitler are redeemable. The Scriptures make it clear, in fact, that men like these should die, because they pollute and defile the earth with their violence and bloodshed, causing nothing but anguish and suffering to humanity (Numbers 35:31–33).

So, while I caution you again that we have to be *very* careful in this matter because we don't want to try to manipulate God for selfish purposes, I believe there are times when we can properly ask God to do more than remove certain people from positions of power. We can pray for the deaths of those who are remorseless and irredeemable murderers and persecutors of the innocent. I would include in this group the murderers of our children—leaders of drug cartels and child pornography rings, for example—as well as murderers who blatantly acknowledge that they worship Satan and do his bidding. Such people live only to destroy, and it is not God's will that they should do so.

You may remember the old story about the church members who prayed for God to show them how to get rid of the spiderwebs that covered the highest windows of the sanctuary. The church was forced regularly to hire a cleaning crew with special equipment to clear away the webs—an expense the church could not afford. After several weeks of intermittent prayer for guidance, one of the elders finally went to the heart of the problem by praying, "Lord, kill the spiders!" There are moments when we have a right and a responsibility to do the same.

We can also pray against systems. These are the organized evil empires we must learn to break down through prayer, because in tolerating them, we allow them to corrupt us. We must fight against them in every way we can. I would include in this category such diverse satanic systems as Communism, Islam and all the other evil, perverse cults and occultic religions that wreak havoc and destruction and terrorism wherever they gain a foothold.

How do we pray against such systems? We can express our opposition in a variety of ways. We can, as I suggested in the section on resisting the devil, say, "I am against this!" every time we find an opportunity—not only in prayer, but in public. This will help stir us up to holy indignation. We can have the courage to stand up and say, "This is not right! I won't accept it!" And then we can go out and do something about it.

We can also bind those systems by the authority of Jesus Christ. Remember Matthew 18:18: "Whatever you bind on earth will be bound in heaven, and whatever you loose on earth will be loosed in heaven." How do we bind an evil system? We can speak to it: "I bind this evil system [or demonic power] in Jesus' name." You will find this declaration in most circumstances to be highly effective. (Again, there may be exceptions: Jesus said there are some evil spirits so powerful that they can be bound or driven out only by combining fasting with prayer. This is one of those situations we talked about earlier where fasting may be God-ordained. We can ask the Holy Spirit to help us discern such situations, and He will do so.)

One way or another, we have the responsibility as Christians to express our opposition to Satan *somehow*. If we do not, we condone his evil deeds and enable his power to grow. I believe it was an American patriot who said, "All that is necessary for evil to triumph is for good men to do nothing." We must do *something* to fight these oppressive and destructive systems; God holds us accountable. His Spirit will reveal to us specific ways to pray against them in each situation if we seek His counsel.

How effective we are in praying for and against depends on how well we know God and His desires in our lives. I would never recommend that Christians jump into this kind of prayer without plenty of preparation and study of God's Word. It is dangerous territory—territory that is also tremendously challenging and exciting. For it is on such battlefields that we can watch God lift the world off its hinges in response to our prayers. If there is a greater thrill in this world, I don't know what it is.

Number 4: The fourth principle that will help us defeat the enemy is that we must give ourselves completely to Christ and be willing to live His life.

We must, as Paul said, "consider everything a loss compared to the surpassing greatness of knowing Christ Jesus . . . and the power of his resurrection and the fellowship of sharing his sufferings, becoming like him in his death" (Philippians 3:8, 10).

This verse of Scripture is so profound that I almost hesitate to use it in a chapter like this where we don't have the space to discuss it fully. But I cannot fail to mention it because it is vital, as we conclude our discussion of spiritual warfare, that we think and pray about whether we are prepared to live the kind of fully committed life that Jesus said we must, and that Paul in this passage challenges us to do.

It is easy to read such words and be moved by them emotionally. But do we comprehend what this kind of total commitment to God may cost us in terms of our daily existence? Too often, I'm afraid, we confuse aspiration with achievement. We think we've made the ultimate commitment when we say tearfully, "I'm Yours, Lord, heart and soul." Then, when He takes us up on it and asks us to get out of our easy chairs and do something that interferes with our own plans, we murmur and complain. "Well!" we say indignantly. "I didn't think He would ask so much! Why can't someone else do it?"

Just how far *are* we willing to go? How much of our comfort and pleasure and "security" are we willing to sacrifice, if necessary, so that others may live? How much opposition are we willing to face? We may sing that we have laid "our all on the altar"—but are we ready to lay down our possessions? our careers? our plans for a quiet, comfortable retirement? our lives? Are we willing to go where God tells us to go—even places where we might be imprisoned, tortured or killed for sharing the Gospel?

Are we, in fact, prepared to face the disapproval or ridicule of neighbors, colleagues, families or other Christians as we take a bold stand for God? When was the last time we faced the kind of persecution my friend Karl talked about—the persecution that "all who would live godly" lives must face? And if we have never faced it, are we asking ourselves why? Or are we willing to give ourselves to God only to the extent that He grants all our selfish wishes and asks nothing too hard in return?

We have to face these questions, I am convinced, if we are going to fight Satan with any real effectiveness and ask God to change His mind about what He allows Satan to do. The devil knows our strengths and weaknesses. He knows our cherished little hypocrisies. He hears our pious boasts that "we're ready to give one hundred percent to the Lord," but he also watches with glee as we grumble over the pittance we are scarcely willing to part with. He sees how little of our time we are willing to spend interceding faithfully for others and obeying Christ in taking the Gospel to our dying world. He gloats when we close our ears to the cries of the suffering Church and chortles as he notes how easily we rationalize our favorite sins by worshiping before modern Christendom's sacred idols: prosperity, success, fame and power.

Now don't misunderstand me: We don't have to be corrupted by these things. We can use wealth to promote God's work. Fame and power can be used for good instead of selfish purposes. But the sad truth is, 99 percent of the time Christians do not use the success or power God gives them in any but the most self-serving ways. They're simply not able to cope with the responsibility.

I've seen it dozens of times: A Christian will pray for "prosperity or power or fame so I can have a real impact for the Lord" (conveniently ignoring 1 Corinthians 1:27, which says that God chooses the weak and foolish things of the earth to confound the mighty). After he (or she) has poured all his time and energy into building his empire—often losing everything else in the process—he cannot bring himself to give away what he has gained. "God's portion" becomes smaller and smaller, until at last God gets little or nothing. And a potentially fruitful life ends up utterly wasted. What a sad and unnecessary victory for the devil!

The truth is, we Christians can be as reluctant as the heathen to give up any of our idols. We even imagine that God will indulge us like spoiled children, that He will perhaps let us keep our favorite idols if we clean them up a bit—that He may, in fact, even bless them if we spiritualize them enough. So we dress our idols in nice Christian costumes and invite God to give them His seal of approval. We may even pretend, as Aaron did to Moses, that they were miraculously created by God in the first place! There is apparently no limit to our self-deception.

But this is not God's will for us. He asks us to turn our backs on our idols, our halfheartedness and our selfishness so that we can finally discover what living is. The Lord has exciting plans, and He wants nothing more than to involve us in those plans. He has battles for us to fight, mountains for us to climb, exploits for us to perform, and He waits for us to do what He asks: "Follow me" (Matthew 4:19, 8:22, 9:9; Mark 2:14, 10:21; Luke 5:27, 9:23, 9:59; John 1:43, 21:19, 21:22). This brings us to our fifth and final principle for successful combat with the enemy.

Number 5: We must oppose Satan's power with the authority and love of God (Luke 10:19).

Remembering that we fight not against flesh and blood, but against Satan and his forces of evil, we must remind ourselves and each other constantly that every person on this planet is an object of God's love. Those who act the nastiest are that way because they have not known the love of God. Our task is the same one we talked about at the beginning of this chapter: to share the love of God with people who are hostages of Satan in a world under his control.

This is, to be sure, a task we cannot hope to carry out by our own power or with our own authority. God must authorize and empower us every step of the way. That is why we must be true thermostats, sensitive and responsive to the Holy Spirit's loving touch. Unless we have this kind of sensitivity, the weapons of our warfare may do more harm than good for the cause of Christ. When we blast away at the devil blindly, on our own initiative, we may find that the bullets we're using are shotgun shells that wound innocent bystanders instead of destroying our target. There are no lone rangers in God's army! We need Him—and the other members of His Body as well—to help us fight effectively.

The writer of Hebrews says it beautifully:

> Therefore, since we are surrounded by such a great cloud of witnesses, let us throw off everything that hinders and the sin that so easily entangles, and let us run with perseverance the race marked out for us. Let us fix our eyes on Jesus, the author and perfecter of our faith, who for the joy set before him endured the cross, scorning its shame, and sat down at the right hand of the throne of God.   Hebrews 12:1–3

That, of course, is the final and most powerful secret of how we can manage to battle the enemy and still represent nothing but the love of Christ. As we fix our eyes upon Jesus and rid our lives of everything that weighs us down, we discover that all things *are* possible through Him. As Corrie would say if she were here right now, this is how we become God's thermostats—His agents of change—in a world in which the temperature is approaching the boiling point.

8
What Should We Be Asking God to Do Today?

Some years ago a woman interviewer asked me a familiar and provocative hypothetical question: If you knew you had only 24 hours to live, how would you spend your last day on earth? The question made me smile because it reminded me of the fellow who said, "If you live every day as if it were your last, someday you will be right!"

But it was a serious question and a good one—one I think we Christians should ask ourselves regularly. How would we arrange—or rearrange—our priorities if we had to squeeze everything important into just one day's time? What would we do? Where would we go? With whom would we want to spend those last precious hours?

More to the point, how would we pray? What would we ask God to do—not only for us, but for our loved ones and for the world that would go on without us? What kinds of things would we ask Him to change His mind about?

I think questions like these are a good starting point for deciding how we ought to be praying in these last days before the return of Christ. Not that we should live entirely for the moment, because that would limit our vision *and* our prayers. But there's a great deal of truth in the adage that says, "The only time we really have to spend is *now*." As the Scripture says, "Now is the day of salvation" (2 Corinthians 6:2).

But one of the beautiful things about prayer is the way it transcends the boundaries of time and distance. We may pray *now*, but the ripples caused by this day's petitions can go on and on. In a way we can barely imagine, our prayers can be immortal, reaching beyond the grave to change lives and events far into the future.

Most of us, whether we know it or not, are the beneficiaries of the prayers of people who departed this earth long before we were born. And it's safe to say that history is being changed every day, in every part of the world, as a direct result of faithful intercession by those who died without seeing their prayers answered. Like the heroes of faith in the book of Hebrews, "none of them received what had been promised. God had planned something better for us so that only together with us would they be made perfect" (Hebrews 11:39–40).

An American friend who grew up in a family of ag-
nostics told me about his Christian grandmother, whom
he never knew because she died a few months after he
was born. My friend came to Christ as a young man
without ever hearing the Gospel preached or knowing a
single Christian, simply by reading a Bible he found at
school. Some years later, after he got involved in public
ministry, he received a letter from a woman who had
known and prayed with his grandmother for many
years before her death. "When your grandmother realized she would not live to see you," the woman wrote,
"she asked me to help her pray for your salvation."
Some fifteen years after the grandmother's death those
prayers were answered.

In the years since then, the ripple effect has continued
as other members of that family have come to know the
Lord. No doubt it will continue into future generations
as well, because long after my friend has left the world
behind, his own prayers will continue to influence lives
and events, just as his grandmother's still do and always shall.

It's a fabulous thing to consider, isn't it? There are no
limits to the effects or the effectiveness of our prayers. If
we want to leave our indelible mark upon the world,
there is no more powerful way to do it than by getting
involved in God's purposes through prayer. Our
prayers can go where we cannot (although they are not
a substitute for our going, if we can). There are no borders, no prison walls, no doors that are closed to us
when we pray. The political, economic, military and

spiritual leaders of the world may not know our names, but we can have more influence on their plans than all their closest advisers put together. While many things may be impossible from a human standpoint, in the realm of prayer there are no impossibilities. And, perhaps most exciting of all, through prayer we can reach into the future and with loving hands touch those beyond our reach, just as my friend's grandmother was able to do.

How would *you* pray if today were your last day on earth? It's a question worth answering, because it can help establish clear prayer priorities. In the process of sifting and categorizing, we can come to a better understanding of what matters most, to God as well as to us. We can then make deliberate, positive changes that will greatly improve the quality of our prayers.

So, what *should* we be asking God to do today? If I answered off the top of my head I might say, "We should ask the same kinds of things the apostles and prophets did." But that's not really a very good answer—or at least it's not a complete answer—because God loves to do new things. He is, after all, the God of creation, the God of the "new and living way" (Hebrews 10:20). Even when He chooses to do the same things again and again—like saving men's souls, healing them and calling them to ministry—He delights in finding ways to do the *same* things *differently* each time. Have you ever heard of two people who took exactly the same path to Christ? Just as no two snowflakes or sets of fingerprints are alike, no two acts of our creative God are precisely the same.

We all have our ideas about how we think God is going to work because we figure that's how He did it in Moses' time or Joshua's or Paul's or at Pentecost. But God is original. The minute we say, "We're going to give out handkerchiefs and people will be healed by touching them because that's what the apostles did," we've got a surprise coming: God will do something completely different! He doesn't want us to ritualize yesterday's experiences; He longs to reveal Himself by doing something for us *today* that He has never done before.

Often we can't accept that because we're afraid it means God can't be counted on to do *what* we want the *way* we want. We forget that while God's character and principles are unchanging, everything else about Him is "new every morning" (Lamentations 3:23) and His plan is to "make everything new" (Revelation 21:5).

This should give us a great sense of adventure about life. If we could predict everything God was going to do tomorrow, we wouldn't even need to get out of bed, would we? But the fact that He has surprises in store for us every day should be enough to make us awaken each morning with a fresh sense of wonder and an intense curiosity about what the day will hold. Where will God lead me? What will He ask me to do? For whom will He ask me to pray? And how will He answer?

You see, if we confine ourselves to asking *only* for

those things God has done in the past, or even for things we can imagine, we may actually be limiting God and losing out on some tremendous surprises and blessings. So I like to ask God to show me possibilities that have never occurred to me, things nobody has ever thought of asking Him before. I want to keep the doors open for God to do what "no eye has seen, no ear has heard, no mind has conceived" (1 Corinthians 2:9; see also Isaiah 64:4).

I suppose that's why almost all of my prayers are for *big* things, not small ones. Why should we think small? If the President of the United States invited you to the White House and promised to grant any request you made, would you use the opportunity to ask him for a new toaster—or would you begin to think in bigger terms?

We're all guilty of underestimating God. If we really knew Him as He wants us to, if we understood the potential of our prayers, we would be on our knees a hundred times a day asking Him for things that would turn the world upside-down. We would not waste our time pleading for new toasters when God says, "You may ask me for *anything* in my name, and I will do it" (John 14:14).

But we're like guests at a wedding who fight over the smallest piece of cake; we have fallen into the habit of thinking small because we think it's a sign of humility. In reality the opposite is true: If we are truly humble, we will see God's surpassing greatness and omnipotence and ask Him to raise us up to a level where His priorities become our own. Then we can begin to participate in executing His will by asking Him for things of *real* consequence.

What kinds of things am I talking about? There are a number of things I pray for—and against—in virtually all of my intercessory prayers. Part of spiritual warfare is active resistance against the hostile, so-called "natural" forces that Satan can use to destroy us or thwart God's plans for our world. Jesus often prayed against these forces. I'm thinking particularly of the time he calmed the storm on the Sea of Galilee (which I believe was another demonic attempt to kill Him) and the time He rebuked the fever from Peter's mother-in-law. (See Luke 8:24; Mark 1:31.)

I'm convinced that many events we call "natural disasters" are really satanic attacks. Storms, earthquakes, floods, forest fires—all of these could be (but are not always) the devil's attempts to kill a certain project or a person of value to God's Kingdom. We must be ready to pray against the evil forces when such disasters occur. In fact, I believe many of us have been engaged in this kind of spiritual warfare even when we haven't been conscious of what we're doing. I think, for example, of the countless mothers who pray at the bedsides of children who are burning with fever. They may not be aware of the warfare they're engaged in, but they know they are against what they see happening before their eyes, so they put up any kind of resistance they can. They pray against the fever without really understanding they are doing so, by praying for their child's recovery.

When we know about this kind of warfare, we can better choose the right weapons to fight all the so-called natural calamities Satan may utilize in his constant attempts to prevent us from doing God's will.

Once, for example, when I was preaching at a large rally in South Africa, a sudden storm arose. We were meeting in a huge tin-roofed building, so we were not insulated from the noise outside. It was the most terrible storm I'd ever experienced—trees outside were crashing to the ground, the roof was shaking, and the wind seemed to be approaching hurricane level. I realized that the roof was about to be torn off by the force of the wind. Nobody could hear anything I was saying, so I stopped and prayed, rebuking the storm. Within a few seconds the wind stopped and we went on with our meeting.

Incidents like this are commonplace for me, and they've taught me to use the weapons God has placed at our disposal. I have no hesitation about praying against the forces that might keep me from obeying God, and neither should you. The weapons of our warfare are not reserved for the giants of faith who are fighting for the nations of the earth. They have been given to all of us.

There will undoubtedly be special areas that the Holy Spirit will lead *you* to pray about, and naturally you'll want to put extra emphasis on these. God seems to give each Christian who becomes serious about intercession a few unique prayer "burdens"—a poor term for what is really a gift, but we'll use it anyway because most of us have heard it. A burden is something we become deeply motivated to pray about or act on, some part of history that God's Spirit invites us to influence through our prayers.

If we think of ourselves as thermostats, we could say that when God's touch moves us to change the temperature in a specific room, we have received a burden. It can be for an individual or a nation, a cause or a movement, a societal malaise like materialism or a localized problem like violent gang activity in our own neighborhood. We can ask God's Spirit to show us exactly what to pray for beyond the obvious big things that every Christian should be praying about today. He will *always* do it. God is delighted when we ask to become involved in what He is doing.

There is, of course, a difference between intercession and other kinds of prayer, like personal prayer about our own concerns, needs and growth, and "prayer telegrams," those urgent, instantaneous prayers in times of emergency that focus solely on an immediate threat or problem. (If I'm walking down a street in Beirut and bullets start flying past my head, I don't start praying for the people of Beijing!)

In intercession we become involved in the bigger issues of God's long-term purposes in our world, but we also focus on specific prayer for just *one* person, *one* event, *one* change that will make the difference in a situation. We join with the Body of Christ all over the world and pray in a united, dynamic way for those things that will advance God's Kingdom and defeat His enemies—and we ask Him to act in specific ways.

Using the Lord's Prayer

We can pray, in fact, as Jesus taught us in the Lord's Prayer. I believe all Christians could benefit from using the Lord's Prayer as a starting point and pattern, not just as something we memorize and recite. Jesus never intended that we do that. "Pray *like* this," He said, not, "Recite this prayer." In Ephesians 3 we can read Paul's version of the Lord's Prayer, made up of many of the same elements (Ephesians 3:14–21). I believe this is how Jesus intended His prayer to be taken. If we use His prayer as our guide for intercession (Matthew 6:9–13), we can move from the general to the specific in a very practical way.

So let's look at the Lord's Prayer as a way of organizing and focusing our prayers.

Beginning with "Our Father," we can pray for all the people we know who call Him *Father*. Sometimes I've started praying at "Our Father" and have gone on for two hours without ever getting beyond all the needs of people I know. I think of each person. I identify with him or her. I think of each church or denomination by remembering individuals within those churches and denominations, and as I pray for them we become part of each other, real family.

Then, as I pray for all those I know in the suffering Church, the world becomes smaller. I feel their pain, wrestle with their problems, and my prayers become fierce, protective, impassioned. The people of the suffering Church are my special burden, and it is on their behalf that most of my intercessions are made. I have learned of the gulags and prisons, visited clandestine churches, slept in bombed-out homes. I have seen the dead bodies, the mutilated babies, the starvation and anguish.

I can pray, "Father, You are their Father as well as mine. Show me how I can do more for these children of Yours who are suffering so terribly. Show me how to awaken the sleeping Church so *all* of us can obey Your command to care for our brothers and sisters who are so isolated, abused and tormented."

Once I begin to pray this way, my prayers become more and more specific and focused. And, I believe, more effective. All this is included when we begin to pray, "Our Father."

Then we can move on through the Lord's Prayer one phrase at a time. As we speak each phrase we can ask God, *What does this mean?* What does it mean when we pray to Him "in heaven" and say, "Hallowed be Your name"?

We say, "Your Kingdom come," and often don't understand what a profound statement and prayer that is. That includes prayer for change in everything that is imperfect, sick, maimed, sinful. We can pray on the basis that this person, this situation, this country, this tribe, this church, this government should be changed and brought into alignment with the principles of God's Kingdom—principles of justice, righteousness, soundness of mind and body and, above all, love.

It also includes prayer for such diverse Kingdom elements as Christian education, the protection of God-given liberties, the protection of the innocent, the opening of borders so Bibles and Christian missionaries can reach people in every dark corner of the world. And for the winds of change to blow in nations still controlled by Communism.

That was what our Open Doors prayer partners began to pray on December 14, 1989, just three days before the Rumanian uprising that toppled the Ceaucescu government. Our weekly prayer fax on that date read: "Pray for difficult situation of Christians in Rumania and also that in this country the winds of change may start to blow." On the same date, we asked our partners to pray "for the release of the last few prisoners being held" in the U.S.S.R.

God answered both prayers—which I'm sure were being prayed as well by countless thousands of Christians all over the world—almost overnight, and in ways that none of us could have envisioned. This should encourage us to pray with even more authority and boldness for the winds of change to blow across the whole world where people are being held hostage by evil and oppressive governments.

Then we come to "Your will be done on earth as it is in heaven." We are praying here that God's will be unopposed and unchallenged, the way it is in heaven. What a prayer and what a task! We are praying for a complete reversal of the direction this world is going. We ask, *What is Your will, Father?* and we remember what the Scriptures say—everything we talked about in chapter 3 on knowing God's will.

We know it is God's will, for example, that everyone be saved. So we can pray for all the unsaved, everyone we know. And we can pray that God will show us the best ways to reach those people so they can be saved. We can pray against the powers that would keep them from understanding the Gospel. Again, the Holy Spirit will show us how to pray as we seek His direction.

Then we remember that God's will is that we "go into all the world and preach the good news to all creation" (Mark 16:15). Thus, we can pray for every unreached tribe, every language, every city where people are not being reached with the good news of Christ. Perhaps even the people living next door!

God's will is *righteousness*. So we can remember all the *un*righteousness in the world and in ourselves. There is so much unrighteousness in all of us. What do we do about our own unrighteousness? We don't wrestle with it, we don't struggle with it, we get rid of it! We *put it to death*, as Paul said (Galatians 5:16–26), so that the Spirit of God can bring fruitfulness to our lives. We *put away* all the works of the flesh mentioned in that passage, everything from adultery to witchcraft to envy, and we *put on* the garments of the Spirit: goodness, faith, patience, moderation, joy, peace, gentleness, meekness and above all love, which binds everything together in perfect harmony.

Then, as we pray further about righteousness and unrighteousness, we can think about the unrighteousness of war, hatred, crime, violence, stealing, immorality, excesses of all kinds. It pours a stream of compassion into our hearts as we pray in these areas.

As you pray for God's will for the nations, your thinking enlarges as the world grows smaller. And perhaps not the first or the second time you pray, but the fifth and the tenth, you begin to see the nations as you have never seen them before. You may even read and study about specific places as God brings them to mind. Your interest and faith will increase as you begin to understand something about people you never knew existed. You may find out that Timbuktu is a real place—that it's the largest city in the nation of Mali, in Africa. Thousands of people there have never seen the Bible, never heard the Gospel. You begin to pray for them, and for the missionaries and churches reaching out to them.

This leads you to become interested in many other remote areas of the world, and you discover there are more than three thousand languages that do not have the Bible. How can they know or *do* the will of God—which is what you've been praying for in the Lord's Prayer—if they don't have the Bible? As you think about this you begin to pray for Bible translators. You discover who some of them are so you can pray for them as individuals and as organizations. You start giving your money to support them. Then maybe one day while you're praying, God puts the thought into your head that you're pretty good with languages. Why couldn't you join an organization like Wycliffe that translates the Bible into new languages?

You see what can happen as you pray, "Your will be done"!

As you pray for God's will, you'll also find that your prayers begin to become much more personal. Instead of praying vaguely and generally for "laborers for the harvest," pretty soon you'll find yourself praying, "God, use *me* to reach my family, my neighbors and my city."

Praying for God's will is a risky matter. If we are really seeking His will, we will end up committing ourselves to joining those on the firing line and making ourselves targets for the enemy. If we ask God to make us prophets we will become unpopular. We will be laughed at, reviled and persecuted for righteousness' sake, because not a single prophet in the Bible was ever popular or accepted by the people of his community. But all the prophets made history—not because they were great, but because they submitted their cause to an almighty God and His authority became theirs.

There will be times, of course, when you look at a situation and say, "Lord, that *cannot* be Your will! And if it is, then I want You to change Your mind about it." You toss the ball back to God. Your intercessions become desperate and intense. And God's Spirit enters into your prayers, prompting you to pray in ways you have never prayed before.

You may be praying for missionaries and suddenly think, "Why are there no missionaries going out from *my* church? Why hasn't God called anyone in our fellowship [or Bible study] to serve on the mission field?"

So you begin to pray, "Father, I want You to change Your mind about that. I want You to call *us*." That is praying for God's will to be done.

You know, in my fellowship in Holland, one hundred percent of the young people have gone onto the mission field. Not one has stayed home. I'm the worst missionary in the bunch from their point of view because, as they say, "Andrew always comes back!" (The others stay away from home five years or more at a stretch. They're *real* missionaries.) But we prayed that God would call *us*, and He has! The only people in our fellowship who have not gone onto the mission field are those too old or too sick to go. They have a big job to do, however: They pray, give, train others and do everything in their power to support those who are going and have already gone to the field.

As I suggested in chapter 6, that's what the local church is supposed to be: a recruiting station, a basic training camp, a support and supply conduit for those called to the front. It was *never* intended to become a center for entertainment, social activity, self-promotion or empire-building.

That, unfortunately, is what the church is in many places today. Some of our biggest Christian churches have absolutely zero impact on their communities and the world because they are nothing more than luxurious showcases for people who want to "feel good about themselves" and impress each other with the way God has "blessed" them, instead of doing what God has commanded them to do. They are places where Christians can devote themselves to the pursuit of happiness instead of to the pursuit of God's Kingdom. They import an endless succession of celebrities and entertainers who feed people's desire for distraction and drama, and in the process anesthetize them so they no longer feel the pain in the Body of Christ.

I have been in many of these churches. I have preached in them. And I am appalled and saddened by what I see: a herd of Christians so busy tapping their feet to the music, so entranced by the showcase of talent up on stage, and pastors so consumed with the task of counting new members (and building ever bigger and more elaborate edifices to house and entertain them on Sunday) that hardly anyone hears the cries of those who are suffering and dying all over the globe—or even in the few square miles surrounding their church building. And when someone like Brother Andrew tries to challenge them with the truth, they refuse to accept it because that would mean getting up and leaving the beautiful cocoon they have built to protect and comfort themselves. No wonder we are losing the battle for men's souls!

Now, are you beginning to see what happens when we get serious about praying, "Your will be done"? As we look at all the things we *know* to be God's will and we begin to pray for them to happen—as thermostats we click on and start doing what we were designed to do—we cause *change*.

Too many Christians say, "Oh, I want the Lord's will to be done. But what can one person's prayers really

179

accomplish in terms of the whole world?" Too many Christians use that as an excuse not to pray. But if only one person knows God, that person's light shines all the more brightly in the dark. If only one person in five billion really understands and communicates with God, the five billion can never say He doesn't exist, because one gram of experience weighs more than ten tons of argument.

Once we believers have finished praying for everything that comes under the heading of "Your will be done," we can begin to pray, "Give us today our daily bread"—which is a prayer not just for my own bread, but for that of the whole Body that needs nourishment and strengthening. We can pray for the practical and personal needs of our families, our friends, our co-workers—all who have spiritual and physical and emotional needs.

We can pray for those suffering from famines and epidemics or from disasters like floods and earthquakes in all parts of the world. We can pray for healing, deliverance, provision, *whatever is essential to enable people to do the work God has called them to do.*

"Give us this day" prayers are not "gimme" prayers or "bless me" prayers. We should never get into a selfish habit of asking God to "bless me"; we should be praying for *others* to be blessed, and as our lives begin to count for others, that will be *our* blessing. If I insist upon asking for selfish blessings, God may give them to me.

Sometimes the only way we'll learn our lesson is to experience the consequences of our own selfishness.

"O.K.," God may say, "you can have your bag of candy. If you want to get sick, get sick. Maybe you'll learn." Many of us never learn, unfortunately, and we get stuck in the habit of asking for candy because it tastes good and makes us happy for a little while, even though in the long run it only rots our teeth and makes us fat and lazy. God shakes His head and says, "If that's what you want, I won't say no, but you'll have to pay the price."

The price of selfish prayer is almost always a terrible one, for us and for the lives we should be influencing for God. We become unfruitful, purposeless, ineffective, and our lives cease to have any meaning at all in terms of God's plans and purposes.

And this leads us to pray, "Forgive us our debts, as we also have forgiven our debtors." We must forgive if we want to be forgiven. It's a two-way street. Most of us don't take these words of Christ seriously enough.

I was visiting with a good friend of mine, a woman in the Middle East who is both a Christian and with the P.L.O. A shocking combination in some people's eyes, but I find Christians sometimes in the strangest places! Even more surprising, in the middle of our visit this woman said to me, "Andrew, Christianity has become for me a daily commitment. My greatest struggle is to forgive my enemies. How can I forgive those who want to kill me and my brothers and sisters, and who would deny me my homeland? But I *must* forgive. I get on my face before God and I sweat over this. I want to say, '*God, I forgive my enemies.*' I picture them, I see what they are doing every day. I see the dead bodies, the suffering, the blood. I try to forgive, but I cannot. So I pray, *'God, You must help me forgive, because I cannot!'* ''

I tell you, I was deeply impressed with that woman, and I know God is much more impressed with her wrestling prayers than He is with all the silly, foolish ones that attempt to wipe the slate clean with one easy swipe: "God bless all our friends and enemies, Amen!" That woman is struggling with issues the magnitude of which most of us have never even imagined. She's serious about forgiveness, which I believe is a sign of great maturity.

We often seem to think we can brush aside the forgiveness part of the Lord's Prayer. "Well, sure, I forgive my enemies," we say, carefully adjusting our halos. But then we go on our way nursing our petty grudges and clinging to memories of insults and offenses that happened years ago. We don't struggle over our lack of forgiveness because we think we're *entitled*—and we don't see the harm in it. We don't fall on our faces and say, "God, I *will* forgive—help my unforgiveness!" We shrug it off by saying, "I'm perfectly willing to forgive those who have hurt me—when they come to me and beg me." Or we take the attitude of a fellow named Heinrich Heine, who said back in the early 1800s, "One should forgive one's enemies, but not before they are hanged."

Sure, we can laugh, because we're all in the same boat. We all have things to forgive that we don't want to forgive, just as we fail to ask forgiveness because we don't want to admit we've done anything wrong. We would rather rationalize our sin than admit it and have to change. But we want to see others punished, even if we have to do the punishing ourselves.

Until we begin to get serious about letting go of our bitterness and anger, however, the way that woman in the P.L.O. did, our prayer lives will be stuck in the mud of unforgiveness and we won't see God doing all that He wants to do in and through us.

Now we reach the part of the Lord's Prayer that says, "Lead us not into temptation, but deliver us from the evil one." This is where we ask God to equip us for battle and guard us and the whole Body of Christ against temptation. Again, we must make this more than a selfish prayer, because if we don't pray for one another in this regard, we leave our brothers and sisters open to attack.

I often wonder whether many of the prominent Christians whose lives and ministries have been destroyed by their moral and spiritual failure during the past few years might not have been kept from such failure if those in the Church had been praying for them as they should. Not that these prominent men and women are not personally responsible for their choices; we're all responsible, and we will be held accountable by God. It's just that we must recognize that when one member of the Body fails, we all fail, and we are responsible for each other. We must not point our fingers and say, "How *could* they?" We must examine ourselves and say, "How could *we*?" and, "What could I have done to prevent this?"

We are that intimately connected, you see. When I see my brother fall, I must remember that I *am* my brother's keeper. It is my responsibility to pray, to support, to do everything possible to keep him from falling. And if he *does* fall—regardless of how or why—it is also my responsibility to help restore him as a functioning member of the Body. We cannot afford to do otherwise.

This is also where we combat satanic schemes and systems, as we discussed in the last chapter. We pray against such evils as drug trafficking and addiction, rampant corruption and sin in every area from government to business to the arts, international terrorism, crime, the rise of false religions and the occult, and the tyranny of atheistic systems like Communism, fascism and a hundred other "isms" from which the world needs to be delivered. (In spite of the changes we've seen in Eastern Europe and the Soviet Union, Communism is still responsible for more suffering on a worldwide scale than any other system or entity, so I call upon all Christians to continue to attack one of Satan's primary strongholds by praying against Communism.)

It is in this area of intercession that we must also learn to pray that God will remove from our lives all that keeps us superficial in our relationship with Him. Superficiality is the greatest peril in the Christian life. Satan wants nothing more than to keep us superficial. I'm terribly serious about this, not only in my own life, but in that of the Church at large. Not a single prophet I know of has warned us adequately about this terrible danger.

In the last half of the twentieth century the Church has become more superficial than I ever imagined possible. We say we want to see God, we want to be used, we want to see the miracles the apostles saw, we want to have "the deeper life." But our lives and our personal relationships with God are so shallow that most Christians never get close to that kind of experience. We want to *look* and *sound* like the Christians we read about in the Bible, but because we are not prepared to pray, live and sacrifice as they did, we accept substitutes for a genuine Christian experience that satisfy our need for drama and excitement and leave us powerless, weak and ineffectual.

We shout *hallelujah* and raise our hands because that's what believers did at Pentecost, and we may exhibit "gifts of the Spirit" that we've manufactured ourselves because we have no idea what the *real* gifts of the Spirit are like.

We may even accept prophecies that do not come from God because we don't really know God's voice, and as a result we have no way of telling when a false prophet speaks in His place. In fact, I am convinced that in many churches today the devil himself could appear and shout, "Thus saith the Lord . . ." and we would not challenge him because many of us don't know the difference between his voice and God's. As a result the Church is easily led astray by false prophets and charlatans. What a tragedy!

We may little know what it's like when the power of the Holy Spirit *actually* comes down on His people the way He did at Pentecost, and as He has in all the great revivals in history. And we're not really prepared to have our lives turned upside-down as they would be if we *did* experience that kind of visitation. Most of us are not ready to have our comfortable, secure existences shattered forever.

When I preach in large churches in Europe and America I sometimes ask, as I begin my message, "If God had died yesterday, would anybody here have noticed?" It shocks everyone, and that's what I want. Then I go on to suggest that they have arranged their lives in such a way that they don't really *need* or *want* a living God who disturbs the status quo—a God intimately involved on a moment-to-moment basis in every decision and activity of their lives.

Everything is decided and planned in advance, so it would only be an inconvenience if they asked Him to get involved on Sunday morning. After all, they came to church already knowing with whom they were going to sit, how much they were going to put into the collection plate and where they would go as soon as the service ended (and it had better end on schedule, because they wouldn't want to arrive late!).

The pastor and his staff probably already decided the songs they would sing, the prayers they would pray, the Scriptures they would read, the sermon that would be preached and even the announcements they were going to make. It's all printed right there in the bulletin! If there's a time set aside for the congregation to request prayer or to offer thanksgiving, it is limited to a strict five- or ten-minute period.

Then I like to ask, "When was the last time you heard a pastor get into a pulpit and say, 'God hasn't given me a message today, so we're going to sing a song and pray together and go home'?" As pastors we are often more concerned with our reputations and the expectations of the congregation than we are about hearing from God. And we can always pull out one of our books of sermon topics and put together a nice sermon if God doesn't give us one. Or we can preach a message we've preached before. I have done it myself more times than I like to admit. It's too easy. And it's made easier by the fact that most congregations are so superficial in their walks with God that they won't know the difference between a message breathed by God and one that comes out of a book of stale sermons.

That is a great pity. We're in this fix together! We must expect more of each other and of God.

When I have finished saying all this to the congregation, I ask them again: "If God had died yesterday, would you have noticed?" It shakes them up—I hope. They may not like it, but that doesn't concern me. What concerns me is that believers wake up and rediscover who God is and what He is doing today. And we must not accept lukewarmness in our own hearts. We must get ourselves by the scruffs of our own necks and *do* something instead of sitting week after week in our churches waiting to be entertained! We must become thermostats instead of thermometers, causing *change* in response to the Holy Spirit's touch. But if we never get close enough to Him to experience His touch, and if we never hear His voice, how can we?

"Deliver us from the evil one" must therefore include our prayer that God will deliver us from shallow Christianity—the lifeless, superficial lifestyle that pays lip service to everything Jesus did for us on the cross, and leaves God outside the front door where we won't have to bother with Him unless we have an urgent problem. We need to be delivered from our desire to claim the blessings God has given to the Church through the ages without paying the price they paid.

I'm not talking about salvation here—for that, of course, there is no price to be paid, because Jesus paid it all. But there *is* a price to be paid for the privileges God gives only to those who know and love Him. We cannot have such privileges or blessings without cost. How much are we willing to pay? What are we willing to give up so God can use us?

Are we willing to become a proletarian people? Are we willing to give up our middle-class and upper-class lifestyles? We don't *have* to have a prestigious job, our kids don't *have* to go to the "best" colleges, we don't *have* to have a second car or a second home or a second television at the cost of everything that's important, including our relationship with God. Jesus said, "The man who loves his life will lose it, while the man who hates his life in this world will keep it for eternal life" (John 12:25). Do we believe Him? Are we willing to *live* it?

Jesus also said, as we quoted earlier,

> "As the Father has loved me, so have I loved you. Now remain in my love. If you obey my commands,

you will remain in my love, just as I have obeyed my
Father's commands and remain in his love. I have
told you this so that my joy may be in you and that
your joy may be complete. My command is this: Love
each other as I have loved you. Greater love has no
one than this, that one lay down his life for his
friends. You are my friends if you do what I command. . . . You did not choose me, but I chose you to
go and bear fruit—fruit that will last. Then the Father
will give you whatever you ask in my name. This is
my command: Love each other."

John 15:9–14, 16–17

When we fully comprehend what this means in terms
of the courageous decisions we must make every day of
our lives, we will be elevated to that level at which we
can become true intercessors—which is a level passive
or superficial Christians can never understand. They
may call us "out-of-touch," "super-spiritual" or "fanatical," not realizing we are the only ones who are in
touch with reality, because we're the only ones in a
position to tackle causes instead of having to deal with
symptoms like the rest of the world. We're the ones
who can *cause change* instead of merely *reacting* to it.

When we reach this level, our lives become really
exciting! We begin to live in the supernatural realm,
where God and His purposes are a reality greater than
any other and His desires have become our own. Our
minds and spirits unite with His, and we live, move and
have our beings in Him.

It is here that we come full-circle from the point where

we began to talk about changing God's mind. Here we pray the final words of Jesus' prayer, "For Yours is the Kingdom and the power and the glory forever." When we know His will for His Kingdom, we will be able to ask God to change His mind about allowing anything short of that to continue.

Paul's expanded prayer in Ephesians ends,

> Now to him who is able to do immeasurably more than all we ask or imagine, according to his power that is at work within us, to him be glory in the church and in Christ Jesus throughout all generations, for ever and ever! Amen. Ephesians 3:20-21

How do we begin to realize what it means to be children of the living God who is not only able but willing to do "immeasurably more than all we ask or imagine"? How do we respond when God says, "Ask of me, and I will make the nations your inheritance, the ends of the earth your possession" (Psalm 2:8)?

Yes, we must *ask* for the nations and for the ends of the earth. God will give them to us! The unsaved world is waiting for us to ask. Our oppressed brothers and sisters in the suffering Church are waiting for us to ask. Above all, God is waiting for us to ask. "This is a people plundered and looted," God reminds us, "all of them trapped in pits or hidden away in prisons . . . with no one to rescue them . . . no one to say, 'Send them back.' Which of you will listen to this or pay close attention in time to come?" (Isaiah 42:22-23).

PART OF HER LIFE

Anne buried her face in her hands. "I'm sorry I got you messed up in this," she said. "All you wanted to do this month was fish and think."

"I'm not sorry," David said.

He crossed the room quietly until he stood behind her. He lifted his hands to her shoulders and with deft, sure strength began kneading her knotted muscles.

She moaned a little and surrendered herself to his touch. No, she wasn't sorry, either. Not really. She didn't know if she would have had to face the problems in her upstairs room if he hadn't been there. She suspected she wouldn't. But he *was* here, and she *did* have the problems, and she didn't know how she could face them without his help.

And she didn't know how he had so quickly become a part of her life, or why his touch was so impossibly familiar. So blessedly welcome.

Too welcome.

Books by Modean Moon

The Covenant
A Little Peace and Quiet

Published by HarperPaperbacks

A LITTLE
PEACE AND
QUIET

Modean Moon

HarperPaperbacks
A Division of HarperCollinsPublishers

🔥 HarperPaperbacks
A Division of HarperCollinsPublishers
10 East 53rd Street, New York, N.Y. 10022-5299

This is a work of fiction. The characters, incidents, and
dialogues are products of the author's imagination and are not to
be construed as real. Any resemblance to actual events or
persons, living or dead, is entirely coincidental.

ISBN 0-06-108315-1

HarperCollins®, 🔥®, HarperPaperbacks™, and
HarperMonogram® are trademarks of HarperCollinsPublishers Inc.

Cover design by Jon Paul

First printing: September 1996

Printed in the United States of America

Visit HarperPaperbacks on the World Wide Web at
http://www.harpercollins.com/paperbacks

❖ 10 9 8 7 6 5 4 3 2 1

A LITTLE PEACE
AND QUIET

Prologue

The wind forced its way in from the north, drinking up moisture as it crossed the Great River and sounding its way through the leaves remaining on the trees. It hesitated at the ring of low-built earthen mounds, and the torches there flared as the wind shared its breath with its brother, fire, gently so as not to extinguish him or enrage him, then hurtled its way across the plaza.

Woman-From-The-West paused as she felt its chill embrace of her face and her bare legs. Her life would change this night. The two warriors who had been sent with her to bear the Warrior's burial gift to the Priest paused when she did, waiting silently.

Woman-From-The-West turned slowly, heavy with child. From where she stood, between the house of the Priest and the raised earthen platform of the temple, she could not see the mortuary on the burial mound, readied and waiting for the bones of the honored dead, but far to the east, across the smaller river which flowed from the south, from a raised earthen work much the same as the one on which the temple stood, a signal fire glowed.

She continued in her slow circling. To the south she saw the lights from the fires of those who had come bringing their dead; to the west and to the north, the fires of the villages, swollen now with still more arrivals.

So many had come. And from so far. But the Warrior had said, "It is time," and the word had gone out. Had he known the Priest would die? Or had it been only that the mortuary house was full? Woman-From-The-West could not know, and the Warrior would not say. Had he known that he, too, would die?

Woman-From-The-West felt the chill that was not caused by the wind. It prickled her arms, raised the fine hairs on her neck, and misted her eyes. She had not known these people two winters past, but now two lives connected her with them: the one that grew within her, and the one that ebbed from the man in the house where she had lived since the time of the green corn.

She heard a low growl, different from but carried by the wind, and with a pain she could never share, she knew what that meant. The Guardians were restless. The Warrior's time grew short. Drawing about her her soft cloak of colored fiber woven from the sturdy cane that grew near the Great River and from the hair of the rabbit, she turned to the two warriors who waited. They, too, had heard the growl. They, too, knew what it signified. They, unlike some others, had remained loyal to the man who lay dying.

Quickly, accompanied by them, protected by them and by the spirits of the Guardians, Woman-From-The-West returned to the man who had taken her from the caravan of slaves being shipped to the great water of the south and had chosen her to be his mate. For him, to accompany him, she would gladly give her life, but that was not to be allowed, even though at this moment the wives of the Priest readied themselves to join their mate in burial. For the Warrior, another service was required.

The smell of death was strong in the house. None of her healing arts had been able even to slow its relentless approach. The Warrior lay near the fire, his great length stretched out on a litter she had ordered brought close to the warmth. Although he did not raise his head, she knew he watched her. "You heard them?"

"I heard them," she said.

"Then it is to be tonight. You will prepare me?"

She heard no fear and no sorrow in his voice and vowed that he would hear none in hers. "I will prepare you."

She knelt beside him, testing the water that waited near the fire, and drew away the furs that covered him. He was silent as she touched the damp cloth to his chest, as though knowing she mourned his wasted strength. Silent. Leaving her in silence to bathe him as she had bathed him before, as once, he had bathed her. She had fought the women he sent to her that first day, her greater size and strength and fear easily overcoming their efforts to prepare her for this giant who had claimed her for his own. He had laughed and dismissed the women. "What a mate you will make for me," he said. "You will never cringe from me. You will bear me many fine sons. And you will stand by my side through this life and the hereafter."

She had never cringed from him; from that moment she realized there was no reason. She carried his child, the only child she would ever bear. And because of that child, she was preparing him to go into the hereafter without her.

He caught her hand in his. "I will miss you."

She looked up, seeing the pain that glazed his eyes. "And I will miss you."

"I must wear the armor," he told her. "There are those who would try to claim the position of Warrior. For their sakes, as well as the sake of our people, I cannot allow them to do so. And you —" He groped beneath the edge of the litter and brought forth a copper breastplate with his likeness engraved upon it. "You must wear this. No one will harm you while you do. The Guardians will see to that. As they will see that I am not disturbed. I cannot command them to leave me until a new Warrior arises. I have copied the designs. You will find them on a scroll hidden beneath our bedrobes. When our son is ready to assume his place as the Warrior, you will have new armor made for him. Then they will come to him. You will do this."

"I will do this," she promised. "And then *I* will come to you."

He dropped his hand on the rise of her belly where their child lay protected. "Woman-From-The-West," he said softly, and she knew he was remembering. It was he who had named her. With a gentle sigh, he left her.

1985

 Anne had returned to Allegro to heal, and
sometimes she almost felt that she had. Her body had,
of course. Even before she closed up her apartment and
practice and ran from Chicago, she knew there would
be no problem with that. It was the other, the emotional
and mental wounds, that seemed in no hurry to close or
scar over. But on that crisp, clear Saturday morning in
late November, with the forest and the hills of south-
eastern Oklahoma spread out around her, surrounding
her, enclosing her, protecting her, she felt almost whole
again.

 It was strange, but lying there in that hospital bed in
Chicago, something within her had said, *It's time to go
home,* and she had known she had to return to Allegro,
even though she had never truly considered this tired
little town as home, even though she had not been here
but a few times in her life, and those with her mother as
a child or as a very young adult, before medical school.

 The people of Allegro had needed a doctor for too
long not to accept her back into the fold, even if she

wasn't sure just how long she could stay in medicine. Besides, Great Uncle Ralph had once owned more than half the town, and she still had family, numerous though not close, living here. But she wasn't really welcomed back like the prodigal son, although some seemed to think she was a "prodigal." And, to quote Bobby Preston, an eight year old with a penchant for broken arms, split lips, and black eyes, she "talked funny."

She wasn't thinking of any of those things, though, when David Huerra came, literally, crashing into her life. She was sitting in Agnes, her brown Ford pickup, at the end of the lane leaving Johnson's sawmill, thinking about the vagaries of one-by-sixes, how all lumber is not created equal, or even the same size, and about the ongoing objections Willie Johnson kept voicing about her renovations to the house that had been a landmark in Allegro since before statehood.

She was mildly miffed that she had to have the trim lumber for her hundred-year-old house specially sawed because modern techniques had reduced what she'd always thought to be the actual measure. A one-by-six ought to be an inch wide, not three-quarters, not five-eighths. And she was more than mildly pleased that Willie Johnson was willing and able to custom-saw the lumber she needed even though he never failed to lecture her.

"Ah, Anne, my girl, you should have let your cousin Joe take the house," he'd said today, as he had already said a dozen times since she bought the house from Aunt Ellie and Uncle Ralph's estate. "He would have done good. He would have torn it down and built those apartment houses like he's been wanting to for years."

So that was what he had wanted with it, she thought, as a troubling puzzle piece tumbled into place.

"You wouldn't have been bothered with it," Willie said, drawing her attention back to him and the present.

"You wouldn't have been worried about hurting your fine hands."

Willie worried about her hands. Not because she needed them in the practice of medicine, but because he was one of the few people who had actually looked at the jewelry she used to make before she became consumed with medicine and success, had in fact bought a piece of it from her when she was just a fumbling adolescent who thought she knew where her life was going.

"Why'd you want to go and buy a big old place like that, anyway?" he'd asked her.

She'd had to laugh, and she'd had to be honest; that was the only thing you could be with Willie Johnson. Although she didn't tell him that buying the house hadn't truly been her decision. At least not at first.

"I don't know," she told him. "I just felt it was something I had to do."

"Well, you ought to hire somebody to do that work for you," he said, not willing to back off completely from his subject. "Just move out, turn it over to a contractor, and don't go back till the work is finished. You got better things to do than worry about power tools and hammers and lugging this lumber up and down the stairs."

She'd laughed again, thanked Willie for the week's worth of materials he'd loaded into Agnes, and left. In retrospect, though, she sometimes wondered if he had been right. Not about letting Joe have the house—that would only have made things worse—but about hiring someone. If she had been able to, and if after doing so she had been able to keep any of those she had hired working long enough to finish the job, if she hadn't personally been so involved in cutting and trimming and measuring, would she have noticed the discrepancies?

And there she was, sitting at the end of the lane, waiting for a log truck to turn into the narrow road from the highway when her life changed once again. She had fought back an irrational moment of urban impatience at the truck for taking so long to turn, and at herself for being too timid to turn onto the road when she'd probably had the chance, accepting that she wasn't in so much of a hurry that a few more minutes of her time were really going to be of any earth-shattering importance.

She had taken those moments to look again over the magnificent view spread out in front of her and was letting the beauty of that view calm her, as it always did when she surrendered to it. Fall had come late to this isolated area. There hadn't yet been a killing frost or even a harsh wind or heavy rain to complete the job of denuding the trees. Yellows, pale greens, oranges, and shades of red marched up the mountains before her in step with the dark greens of pine and cedar, crowned in the distance by a veil of rising fog from the meandering river.

Granted, surrendering to the calming influence of nature was a little difficult, because the log truck was groaning and creaking under its load of pines loudly enough, almost, to drown out the sound of its straining, belching diesel engine, and definitely loudly enough to disrupt her amateur attempts at meditation, but she was working on it.

That's when she saw the approaching car and abandoned all attempts at meditation. And that's when the driver of that car saw that the log truck was all but stopped in the middle of its turn in the road in front of him. He hit his brakes. There wasn't anything for him to do but try to stop; a hundred-foot sheer drop marked the other side of the road, and although Anne shoved Agnes in reverse gear and was frantically trying to back out of his one alternate path, there was no way she could do so fast enough to help him. He stopped, with a controlled skid and a more responsive car than she had seen in a long time, just inches from the back of the protruding logs. She saw him slump over the steering wheel in relief. And then she saw Hank Foresman's souped-up red one-ton truck come around the curve so fast he hadn't a prayer of stopping in time, even if his brakes had been in order. And the driver of the car saw him, too.

How long had the lights behind those mud-encrusted reflectors been glowing? David Huerra swore swiftly and violently when he realized that the heavily laden log truck on the grade below him was stopping and begin-ning a tortured left turn. He hit the brakes while scan-ning for an escape route. Not to the right; that meant at least a hundred-foot drop off the side of the mountain to the first rock outcropping, with nothing to break the fall but a few scrubby pines and winter-dead oak trees. And not to the left; the truck was already into its turn. Even if he could beat it to the side road he couldn't squeeze between it and the brown pickup truck waiting to turn onto the highway.

He heard the borrowed fishing tackle and gear he had stacked so carefully on the backseat crash to the floor as the car shuddered to a stop barely a foot from the end of the logs protruding from the back of the truck. He let out a long breath and slumped against the seat.

Swearing, he thought as he felt the effects of adrenaline racing through his system and remembered the oath that had spewed so naturally from him. He swallowed once and began taking deep, even breaths. That was something else he could work on this month. Swearing was becoming a matter of routine, a thought-less response to almost any situation. Like this one, he told himself, seeing the slight tremor in his hand when he released his death grip on the steering wheel. If he were going to swear over this, he ought to be swearing at himself for not paying more attention to the unfamiliar road, not at the truck driver for making a left turn.

Swearing. Yes, he definitely would work on that. Clean up his language while he cleaned up his life.

He glanced again at the drop to his right, then into the rearview mirror. His jaw clenched when he saw the oncoming truck, a bright red one, nose down as it approached, coming around the curve too fast to be able to stop in time.

All thoughts of cleaning up his language fled, chased out of his mind by a swift, certain knowledge: *that idiot is going to kill me!*

And then, as had happened to him too many times for comfort, as if he were considering it from the safety of his office or his living room or in some secluded spot well away from all danger, everything slowed down. Slow motion with occasional stop-action. With him completely unable to act in any way to prevent what was happening. The truck still came toward him, the knowledge of his impending death still danced around the edges of his consciousness. He felt a moment of sadness for his brother, for his niece, for those whose lives had touched his, for the words he had often spoken heedlessly, for the words he had left unsaid in spite of all his good intentions.

There was no time for fear. That had come earlier, when there had been a prayer of his saving himself. Now there was nothing to do but accept the inevitable. But his hands still gripped the wheel, twisting it in an effort to turn away from the protruding logs, his feet slammed onto the brake pedal, shoving down, without his knowledge but with all of his strength, in an effort to stop the unstoppable, and his body twisted sideways in an effort to avoid the unavoidable.

"Son of a bitch," David whispered in what only he would recognize as a convoluted prayer before the windshield shattered, his head slammed forward, then back, and the slow-motion action stopped. Silenced. Darkened.

The sickening sounds of metal on metal and green-pine log on metal and glass released Anne from the paralysis that had held her immobile through the slow-motion video. The driver of the log truck had stopped in the middle of the road. He slammed out of the cab of his truck, and she, even knowing what she must find, jumped from hers.

Hank Foresman wasn't hurt; he had the advantage of the weight of his truck and the slack-muscled responses of the slightly drunk. The driver of the brown Chevy was a different story. One of the protruding logs had gone through his windshield, missing his head by no more than a thickness of skin; he had a nasty knot already rising on his forehead; and he was out cold.

She slapped Hank's hands away as he tried to release the man's seat belt. "Get my bag out of my truck," she told him, knowing she'd have to distract him or he'd yank the man out of his car without respect for any possible injuries.

"What can I do, Doc?" the driver of the log truck asked from behind her. Anne hadn't recognized him, but she breathed a sigh of relief that he wasn't one of those locals who felt the need to take charge.

"Give me a minute," she told him.

Her examination was perfunctory at best but, given the decided smell of gasoline, as adequate as she could make it. Only when she had finished did she realize that her recently too-familiar sense of panic hadn't overwhelmed her. But then, there hadn't been any blood. Thank God.

"Help me get him out of here and across the road."

They stretched him out on the grassy slope beside her truck. Hank shoved her bag at her, and she quickly checked for vital signs. When assured that the man wasn't in imminent danger of dying on her, she began checking for other injuries. He was a slender man, a little under six feet tall, with muscle tone that spoke of a strength not evident from his size. His features were slightly Hispanic, his eyes a dark brown, she discovered, and showing no signs of a serious head injury. Altogether, he wasn't bad looking. And he was definitely a stranger to the area, with a smashed car and a whale of a headache coming on.

"Damn!" he muttered, thick tongued and groggy but quite succinctly. He raised a hand to his head and opened his eyes. Giving up the effort to focus, he closed one eye and peered at her with the other. Apparently deciding she was no threat to him, he relaxed again. "I'm going to quit swearing," he said experimentally, as though not sure his voice would work. "That's what I promised myself just before that— *Son of a bitch!*"

His open eye widened; his other popped open.

"Move away from him, Doc."

She twisted around at the menace in Hank's voice and came eyeball to gaping black barrel with the rifle he held one-handed and trained on her semiconscious patient.

"What?" she choked out as involuntary fear sank its claws into her. Yep. *There* was the panic. But she didn't have time for it now.

"Put the gun down, Hank," she ordered quietly.

"No, ma'am," he said. "You move away from him."

"Put the damned gun down, Hank, before you get into more trouble than you're already in."

"It's not me that's in trouble," Hank said. "And it's not my gun you ought to be worried about. It's his." He held up his left hand, brandishing a deadly looking blue revolver.

"Found it in the front floorboard of his car. No telling what all's in those bags in the back."

"Fishing tackle," she heard from behind her.

Hank snorted. "With Texas tags on your car? Likely story," he said, ignoring the fact that the entire area around Allegro and the man-made lake with which it shared its name derived most of its meager income from catering to fishermen.

"No." He took a shaky step closer. "With the way you look, you shouldn't have any trouble coming back and forth across from Mexico. I think maybe you're one of them drug runners. Or maybe one of them folks that brings in illegal aliens. I think old Hank's just caught him a wanted criminal."

Most of the people Anne dealt with were decent, hard working, and too concerned with their own survival to worry too much about who or what other people were. But occasionally prejudice reared its head. She didn't like it here any better than she had in Chicago. Less, because it seemed so out of character with the history of this area and the natural beauty that ought to have seeped into the pores of every living being.

"Hank Foresman," she said as indignation overcame the residue of her fear. He wasn't a threat to her, only to her patient, and perhaps, to himself. She could stop him. Yes. She could do this. "If you don't put that gun down, I'm going to stick you with a megadose of tranquilizers that will have you singing lullabies for three days."

"I can explain," her patient said, reaching for his pocket.

"Don't move."

The man sighed and looked over her shoulder. "You look sane," he said to the truck driver beside her. "Will you see if you can find a blue windbreaker in the back-seat of my car? My wallet is in the pocket."

They waited, with only the sounds of Hank's heavy breathing and distant fumbling noises from the car until the driver returned. "You caught yourself a bad one all right, Hank," he said, and she saw that he was trying not to laugh. "David Huerra, Dallas P.D. Detective."

"Oh, shit," Hank said, lowering the rifle just before his knees gave out and he sank into a loose-jointed pile on the road. The truck driver walked over and relieved him of both the rifle and the revolver.

She heard the squeal of brakes, followed by Willie Johnson's shout. "Sheriff's on his way. I've got him on the CB. Do we need an ambulance?"

"Yes," she shouted back, only to be overruled.

"No," David Huerra said quietly.

Anne could have insisted. Maybe she should have. Instead, she heard herself saying, "Tell him we'll let him know."

By that time quite a crowd had gathered. With Hank collapsed at her feet, her conscience prickled until she gave him a cursory examination to make sure that nothing other than alcohol contributed to his blackout. As she finished, she heard the scream of the sheriff's siren approaching.

The tableau in the highway made what happened obvious, and any answers that might be needed seemed to her to be supplied by Hank snoring, blissfully ignorant of the stories that were passing through the growing crowd of spectators from those who had witnessed his big arrest.

David Huerra, the Dallas cop, was trying to get to his

feet when she put a hand on his shoulder and pushed him back toward the ground. "Unless you want to pass out like your buddy Hank, maybe you'd better sit still for a minute or two," she told him quietly. He grimaced but apparently decided she might know what she was talking about, because he didn't struggle against her restraining hand.

Sheriff Blake Foresman pushed his way through the crowd toward them, and knelt beside his brother Hank, looking up at her with concern written in every weathered line of his face. When Hank snored and belched in his sleep, Blake backed away from him. "Oh, hell," he muttered and turned to survey the wreckage on the road. "I don't suppose that brown Chevy ran into the truck and then backed into my brother," he asked wryly.

The driver of the log truck chuckled. "Don't think so, Sheriff."

Blake looked at him, trying to place him. "Sam Wilson?"

"Yep," the driver said.

"You saw what happened?"

"Yep," the driver—Sam—said again. "Me and the doc, and of course Detective Huerra, here."

"Oh, hell," Blake said again, raking his hand across his forehead. He looked at her with weary resignation. "You want to draw me a blood sample?"

"I'm sorry, Blake," she told him, meaning she was sorry for him and for Hank's wife Ida. "He's really done it this time."

"I'm sorry, too," he said, looking at her patient. "Are you going to be okay?"

Huerra nodded, then winced. "It could have been worse. It could have been a car full of kids he ran into."

Anne cringed at still another unwanted reminder of something she had managed to put out of her mind for almost half a day.

Blake sighed. "I know. He promised he was dry. I told him I'd lock him up if I caught him driving drunk. I guess he didn't believe me. Detective?" he asked. "What jurisdiction?" And Anne knew she heard in his voice his almost futile hope that Sam had been wrong.

"Dallas P.D."

"Great. Just great," Blake muttered. "Thank God I just got reelected. The county paper's going to have a field day with this. Are you sure you're okay?"

"No, he isn't sure, Blake," Anne said, needing this diversion from the ugly track her thoughts had taken. Once again, she put her hand on his shoulder to push Huerra back down into a semblance of sitting. "And neither am I. A log came within less than an inch of taking his head off." She saw Huerra wince when she said that, and once again he stopped struggling to rise. "He's got a whale of a headache, assorted cuts and bruises, maybe a cracked rib or two, and possibly a concussion, not to mention a wiped-out car and a ruined fishing trip."

"Oh, hell," Blake said still again, dragging the word hell into more syllables than she had ever thought possible.

She softened toward him. Blake was a good man. And it was only moderately his fault that Hank was still driving around the country. "Get the consent form," she said gently. "Shake Hank awake enough to sign it, and I'll draw the blood sample for the blood alcohol analysis."

"Right," he said, but his heart wasn't in it. He looked toward the road, where a deputy was taking pictures and measurements of the accident. "I'll need a statement from you, Huerra."

David Huerra managed a wry grin of his own. "I don't think I'm going very far in the near future, and it looks like you've got plenty on your plate right now. Why don't I come by your office in the next day or so?"

Blake nodded. "Yeah. Sam? It looks like you can move that log truck now." He looked toward her. "Do you need an ambulance?"

Anne glanced at Huerra and shook her head. "No. But I'm going to take him into the clinic for a checkup. Would you ask someone to unload his luggage from the car and put it in the back of my truck?"

"That isn't necessary," Huerra said.

She shook her head. "It's either that or a thirty-mile code-three ride to the county hospital in Fairview with an ambulance driver who thinks he's training for the Indy 500."

He raised an eyebrow as though questioning her truthfulness.

"Trust me," she said, then smiled at him. "Do you have reservations for someplace around here?"

"Yeah. The Tompkins fish camp."

Anne nodded. She knew where the Tompkins place was. "That's not too far from town," she told him. "I'll take you there after I get a good look at your skull and ribs."

She took hold of his arm to help him rise, but he glared at her as though she had just insulted his manhood instead of merely offering the help she would have given anyone.

"I'm all right," he said. "My head's hard."

Somehow that didn't surprise her. But she didn't say anything. She just gestured toward her truck and forced herself not to offend his pride by insisting on helping him as he struggled to his feet.

The last of the crowd remained until after the wreckers carried off the car and the pickup truck, the sheriff's car left with Hank once again snoring, and David Huerra reluctantly allowed Sam Wilson to help him into Agnes's cab after he discovered he wasn't quite as steady on his feet as he'd thought he would be.

A couple of the hardier gawkers began following Anne's truck toward town, but she knew how to handle that. She slowed Agnes down to about three miles an hour and after less than a mile the two voyeurs pulled out and passed them.

"You handled that well," Huerra said in the tight voice that told more about his pain than he would want her to know.

She grinned at him, using that excuse to take a quick look at his face. He was pale, but not more so than he had been.

"I meant it," he said, apparently recognizing her surreptitious examination for what it was. "My head is hard. I've had worse bumps in the past. I'm fine. All I need is a shower and a change of clothes to get rid of all of this glass grit, a meal, and a bed. I don't want, I don't need, and I won't sit still for any x-rays."

While she pondered her response to that, he used the closeness of the truck cab for an examination of his own—a long, detailed examination of her face, her hands, and the rest of her five feet four inches visible in jeans, sneakers, and the heavy fisherman's knit sweater and knit cap she wore. Without speaking, he reached over and tugged the cap from her head. Most of the hairpins had either already slithered out of their moorings or were caught in the cap, and her hair tumbled in a willy-nilly disarray of unruly auburn curls over her shoulders.

His lips quirked in a grin. "Doc?" he asked. "Do you have another name?"

She snatched the cap from him but realized there was no way she could stuff the mass of hair back into it without pulling off the road. She dropped the cap onto the seat. "Anne. Anne Locke."

His lips twitched again. "Annie?"

"Not if you want to live to catch another fish," she said tightly.

"Annie," he said, smirking only a little. "I bet you keep that hair of yours whipped into submission and pinned to within an inch of its life when there's any chance anyone's going to see it." Apparently he just couldn't let it rest. "Doesn't anybody call you Annie?"

She acknowledged defeat. She really didn't mind. Her need for maintaining a perfect image had been blasted out of her life along with her need for success at any cost. "Only one person," she said, "but he's only ten years old and lives half a world away."

He leaned back against the seat, mouth drawn tight against pain for a moment, then took a deep breath and let it out slowly.

"I mean it," he said again. "All I need is a shower, a meal, and a bed."

"Yeah, right," she said. "But if you've had your hard head thumped before, you know there's no way I'm going to let you go to sleep until I'm sure you haven't cracked or scrambled something up there." However, his insistence that he needed food was a good sign. "Tell you what," she said, making a quick decision. "I'll feed you and lend you my shower. And if you're still doing okay after a couple of hours, I'll take you to Tompkins and let you out of the x-rays."

"Ah," he said. "A sensible woman."

And that was the last he said until they reached her house.

He opened his eyes as she pulled into the driveway and downshifted for the climb. She glanced at him for his reaction and wasn't disappointed. Few could fail to react to the Victorian monstrosity perched near the top of the hill overlooking the town of Allegro.

He swallowed once and then looked at her as if to see

if she had grown some additional appendage or sprouted some outward sign of instability. "Did I say sensible?" he asked. "My God woman, that house is purple."

She fought to keep from laughing. Purple was too kind a word for the colors her aunt had painted the house after Uncle Ralph's death. All shades of purple. As many shades of purple as there were in the hedge of crape myrtle, rose of Sharon, and weigela Great Aunt Ellie had planted along the back property line and which now tangled together in drooping, inseparable branches, effectively fencing her yard from the forest behind her.

"Yes," she said. "It is. At least in those places it still has paint.

"But it has running water," she reminded him. "And the kitchen is functional."

"Sorry," he muttered. "I have better manners than that. Maybe I did get thumped a little harder than I thought."

She let her laugh escape then.

"You're obviously working on it," he said. "That's why you've got a truck full of lumber, isn't it?"

She pulled to a stop in the back yard and turned to face him. "Your brain seems to be functioning again," she said. "We may not have to amputate after all. Sit still," she told him as he reached for the door handle. "I'll let you out."

"I can manage," he muttered.

"Right." she hopped out of the truck and walked around to the passenger side.

He hadn't managed—at least not to get the door open—as she had known he wouldn't.

"Agnes has character," she told him as she opened the door. "That means not all of her parts work, including the inside door handle on this side." She winked at him. "It comes in handy sometimes. Like today. Now, put your arm over my shoulder and lean on me until we get you into the house."

He hesitated, as she knew he would, and then leaned on her as he got out of the truck. She sensed his hesitation and looked up to see him studying the house.

She followed his glance, seeing it with the first shock as he must be—the turrets, the gingerbread, the outlandish clashing shades of purple in the walls, trim, and sash—and then with the familiarity she had grown into.

Her attention snagged then lingered at the second floor rear bedroom, at the solid wall of faded purple, a solid wall when all other walls were studded with windows—rectangular, square, round, arched, or diamond-shaped windows. This weekend, she had promised herself.

This weekend she was going to explore the reasons for that wall, the reasons why it, of all the walls, was not riddled with windows, when it was so perfectly positioned to overlook what must once have been a superb herb and perennial garden.

This weekend, she promised herself again, just as she felt David Huerra slump against her. "What's this," she asked. "Weakness, Detective? Do we need to go to the clinic after all?"

He grinned back. "Why, Annie, that was my best wounded warrior ploy. I'm disappointed in you for not succumbing."

"Fat chance," she told him, managing a lightness at odds with the dark emotions his innocent words triggered. "Warriors . . . Warriors aren't my style at all. Now come on." At last she felt herself back on steady ground and able to maintain an—almost—easy banter. "Let's get you into the house. I swear I've just about worn myself out lugging you all over the country."

He stiffened and started to withdraw his arm.

"I'm teasing," she said hurriedly. "My goodness, you are touchy, aren't you?"

"Not . . . usually," he answered tightly, and she didn't believe him for a minute. But after a quick, almost panicked look at the house, he relaxed his arm over her shoulder, and she took the first step up to the porch. A chill, as unexpected as it was unexplainable, shuddered through her, and she stopped there on the first step, for the moment unable to go any farther. He glanced at her with a wary question in his eyes.

"Uh—" she cleared her throat. What on earth was happening?

This was her house, for goodness sake. True, she'd heard the rumors that it was haunted, but only after she'd found herself committed to purchase it, and she suspected those rumors had been started by Joe to keep the place vacant, and to keep anyone other than him from even thinking about bidding on it. Hadn't she walked into it in the dark on countless occasions and not bothered to turn on a light? Hadn't she'd slept in it every night for almost six months and never even heard a board squeak after she got to sleep?

"You too, huh?" David asked.

"I don't know what you're talking about," she told him. Admittedly her words lacked conviction, but she tried.

"Sure," he said. "But if you don't know what I'm talking about, then why do you look as if someone just walked over your grave?"

2

1926

The man stood hesitantly beside the back of the farm truck. Dust covered him and the truck, and dried mud coated his boots and the legs of his overalls.

Ralph Hansom kept well back from the mud and the dust and the man, as if by doing so he could hold himself aloof from the poverty that had spawned his visitor. "What did you bring, Jackson? I've got better things to do than stand out here all morning playing guessing games."

Tom Jackson gestured toward the tarpaulin-covered bundle in the back of the truck, almost invisible among the spare tire and boxes of broken tools and debris.

"Haul it out. You know I have to examine it. Too many of you people have tried to pawn off bogus trash on me."

Grimacing, Jackson climbed into the back of the truck and wrestled two baskets from beneath the tarp and to the rear of the truck bed. Only then did Hansom step forward. The first, a peck basket, obviously the one Jackson thought the prize, was over half full of objects Hansom had long ago identified as fresh-water pearls. He plunged his hand into the basket, confirming that pearls actually filled it, and not a hidden layer of dirt or gravel or bone. Then he turned his attention to the other, larger, bushel basket.

A pile of thin leaves of copper, engraved but green and fused together, lay wedged near the top. He glanced at the copper but moved it out of his way. A half-dozen conch shells were next. And then—Hansom told himself to breathe, to betray no emotion—as one by one he lifted six engraved shell gorgets from the basket, finding only one of them chipped, and then pushed aside four bones, leg probably—why the hell did these people think he was interested in bones?

Something lay on its side in the bottom of the basket. Tentatively, not letting himself hope, he touched it, then lifted out a stone statuette almost a foot tall and in the shape of one of the recurring heathen images he had seen engraved on the shells.

A pipe. Without the stem, of course; the stem had probably long ago rotted away. But a pipe? *God!* He fought not to suck in his breath. He had heard of these pipes, but this was the first he'd seen.

"Well," Jackson asked. "It's good, isn't it?"

The little girl had come from behind the house, unnoticed. Barefooted and almost as dusty as Jackson, she stopped by the rear of the truck and reached for the pile of copper. "Pretty," she said, touching it reverently.

Ralph Hansom looked at his four-year-old daughter. The child's Choctaw blood showed in her dark hair, her bronze-gold coloring, in the fineness of her hands. Ralph's stomach revolted when he thought of this child springing from his loins. She had no class, and as she had just demonstrated by reaching for the junk copper, no taste and no knowledge. Just like her mother.

Her mother, however, had had the advantage of money and land.

"Ellie!" Ralph yelled. "Come and get your brat out of my way!"

A woman appeared on the long back porch. "Lucy," she called softly. "Come in the house. You know better than to bother your father."

Bitch, Ralph thought. She'd said that deliberately, goading him in front of this piece of white trash. But maybe he could make it work to his advantage.

Lucy clutched the copper. "Pretty," she said again. Ralph disengaged her fingers from her treasure. *"Pretty!"* she screamed.

"Ellie!"

Soundlessly the woman left the porch and walked to the truck. She reached down and gathered the child in her arms, crooning softly to her in her own language as she carried her to the house. For once Ralph bit back his habitual order for her to speak English. Jackson had seen and heard enough.

"How much?" Jackson asked.

Ralph sifted a few of the pearls through his fingers and waved dismissively toward the rest. "Ten dollars."

Jackson paled beneath the dust. "Ten dollars? God, man. I've snuck in there every night for two weeks, digging all night and hiding the hole the next day, lied to my brother-in-law to get this truck, drove down here—more'n a hundred miles before I get back home. I got a family to feed."

"Sorry," Ralph told him. "But this stuff is broken and rusted. I won't be able to get much more than ten for it myself. So if you know someone else who'll buy it, take it to them."

"Wait!" Jackson called out as Ralph turned to leave. "Twenty. And I'll get you more. Not broken. It's there, Hansom. And I know where it is."

Ralph looked at him. Slowly and carefully he reached

over and picked up the copper. "My kid liked this," he said. "I'll give you twelve fifty. You bring me more, not broken, and we'll work out a deal."

3

The porch door opened into Anne's kitchen, cavernous beneath the skeletal framework for a dropped ceiling. She pulled one of the mismatched oak chairs out from the round table, and with only a sharp glance at her, as though he wanted to argue the necessity for sitting but knew he'd lose, David Huerra sank onto it. She left him there while she went back out to the truck to retrieve her bag and his, but when she returned, he'd recovered enough to go exploring.

Just off the kitchen, also at the rear of the house, was a room that might have once been a sleeping porch or possibly a housekeeper's quarters. The double glass-paned doors argued for a more formal use, but the location denied it. She thought it would probably be perfect for her jewelry workshop if she ever got the courage to do what she already suspected was inevitable, but for now that same location made it just as perfect for her renovation tools and clutter.

She found him in that room, studying what had to be the oldest table saw in existence. He traced his hand along the homemade rip-fence and looked up, grinning. "This is vintage. It came with the house, I presume?"

She chuckled. "It's not quite that old. And it came with two cases of chicken pox and a broken ankle."

"And a pint of blackberry jelly?"

"I wish."

He reached for his bag, but she stepped back, holding it away from him and studying him. Thank God for safety glass. Without it, he'd have been a maze of cuts and slashes, but even safety glass had its limits when bashed by pine logs. "Come on. I'll show you to the downstairs bathroom and let you wash away some of that glass grit."

He nodded and followed her back into the kitchen and out the door she'd had knocked through the wall into the front hallway. The bathroom under the stairs would eventually be little more than a powder room, but because she was more or less confined to the ground floor until she did major work upstairs, she had finished this one with new fixtures and a small, tiled shower enclosure.

"Nice," he said, when she opened the door to the tiny room.

Yes, it was, Anne admitted to herself as she saw it for the first time through a stranger's eyes. "Thanks." She stepped back to let him enter and handed him his bag as she pointed out the obvious: fresh towels and washcloths on the wicker shelf, a basket holding soaps and even a package of disposable razors, the hair dryer in its tole-painted rack. "Call out if you need anything," she told him. "I'll be in the kitchen. Oh—and don't even think about putting those clothes in your bag. I'll run them through the washer and dryer with a load of my work clothes."

"Have you ever been told you're pushy, Doc?" Huerra asked her. But there wasn't any heat in his words. There wasn't much energy either, and she could tell he was far from the "all right" he had insisted he was.

"Yeah," she said. "Probably about as often as you've been told you're stubborn, Detective."

He absorbed that, gave her a weary smile, and closed the door against her.

She listened outside the door for a moment until she was sure he wasn't going to collapse on the floor and then went back into the kitchen.

And realized what she was doing.

She gripped the edge of the poor, beat-up old kitchen sink. She'd brought a complete stranger home with her, bossed and bullied him into stripping off and bathing in her private space, and was now preparing to cook for him and do his laundry?

Maybe the house was haunted, after all. *Something* had her acting like *she* was the one who had gotten thumped on the head.

Nonsense, she told herself. She was a doctor, for God's sake. She had chosen and had been trained to nurture her patients.

But she had also been trained not to take unnecessary risks with her safety, and that lesson was one she'd sworn she'd never again forget.

He was a cop, she reminded herself, not an ax murderer or a drug dealer, not a danger to her. Well, at least not to her physical safety. The last thing she needed in the wreck her life had become was a cop. She'd had enough of cops—and all the pain that they drew like magnets—to last her the rest of several lifetimes.

But he was injured. She reminded herself of that, too. "He's your patient," she whispered to herself. "Remember that."

And she did, at least until he walked into the kitchen several minutes later, all scrubbed from his shower and dressed in jeans and a shirt so fresh from the laundry that the creases fairly crackled. He held a small stack of his clothes carefully away from his body.

"I don't think you want to wash these with anything

of yours," he said. "If you'll give me a bag of some sort, I'll let a commercial machine take the risk." He grimaced. "Or maybe I'll just throw them away."

He didn't look like a cop, and except for an unnatural pallor, a few nicks now visible on his jaw and throat, and the burgeoning bruise near his left temple, he didn't look like a patient.

"Nonsense." She reached for the clothes, but he held them away from her. "Okay." She smiled and pointed to the washer and dryer across the room.

Huerra nodded. In only moments he had competently loaded his things into the washer, added soap, and started the cycle. Well, well, she thought. Maybe his clothes were commercially starched and pressed because he liked them that way, and not because he didn't know how to take care of them himself.

Which was none of her business. None at all.

"Any dizziness?" she asked, as he closed the lid and turned to study the wreck of the kitchen. "Blurred vision? Blood where it shouldn't be?"

He grinned and shook his head, then winced and leaned back against the washing machine. "You've got a he—heck of a bedside manner. Anybody ever tell you that?"

"Yeah." She pulled out a chair and pointed at him, then at it. "Sit."

"I'm only letting you get away with that because I see a coffeepot on the counter and I haven't had my quota of caffeine this morning," he told her as he eased himself onto the chair.

"And you're not getting any from me, either, until I'm sure it won't do you more harm."

"Come look in my eyes, Doc, and feel my pulse. No concussion. And, to answer your last, oblique question, no signs of internal bleeding. No lumps or bulges," he volunteered, "that don't appear superficial, manageable, or normal. Nothing requiring stitches, intensive care, or even taping up. So, please, Annie," he said, giving her what she suspected was his best good-little-boy grin—a grin that had probably gotten him just about anything he'd ever asked for. "Please, please, please can I have some coffee?"

She gave him a laugh as seemingly easy, and as false, as his grin and reached for the second of two canisters. He didn't have to know it was decaf. "Is that how you solve your cases?" she asked, determined to continue their light, meaningless patter. "Beg until the perpetrator confesses?"

His grin faded, and although he made a quick attempt at recovery, it wasn't quite successful. Ah hah, she thought. Secrets. And definitely a man who wasn't as superficial as he'd tried to make her think. Well, she understood secrets, and the necessity for keeping them private, quiet, and contained. "I suppose the next thing you're going to ask for is cholesterol. And carbohydrates."

"And calories?" The little boy was back, more naturally now, with just a touch of flirt. Not so much that she couldn't handle it. Not so much that for a little while she couldn't enjoy it.

"I've heard nasty rumors that those things are bad for you," she told him as she filled the coffeepot and turned it on.

"Yeah. Me too. Problem is, those same rumors would have you believing everything's bad for you. You do have sausage, don't you?" he asked, looking at her in feigned horror. "You do have . . . eggs?"

"Of course I have sausage and eggs."

He put his hand over his heart and grinned again, but as she turned her attention to the refrigerator she glanced at him and realized that he was fading fast. If she was going to feed him, it would have to be soon, or he'd be sleeping at her table. And feed him she would. He was displaying no signs of concussion or internal injury. Of course, if he lost his breakfast, she'd have to do some fast rethinking.

And it would be all right for him to sleep. She was confident of that now. In fact, it would be better for him if he did. The human body had miraculous powers of recovery, as long as it was given time and, in some cases, permission to recover.

In deference to his failing energy and her less than wonderful kitchen skills, she opted for toast instead of biscuits, but she did dig out a jar of blackberry jelly—purchased, not homemade—and for once everything else she cooked turned out better than just edible . . . pretty good, in fact. It was amazing what six months without a McDonald's had done for her kitchen chemistry.

Huerra was exhausted but trying to hide it when he finished off the last slice of toast. "That was great, Doc. Now if I could just trouble you for a ride out to the Tompkins place—"

She shook her head. "I said a couple of hours, and I meant a couple of hours." She picked up their plates and carried them to the sink. "If your breakfast doesn't come up—" He raised a hand as if to assure her. She ignored it. "—and if you don't start seeing four of me, I'll deliver you out there before noon."

He winced again, and turned in his chair in a surreptitious effort to get comfortable. Before he realized what she was doing, she returned to the table and captured his face in her hands, looking into his eyes.

"Are they crossed?" he asked.

She released him. "No. And they're not dilated, either." She nodded toward the front of the house. "Come with me. Your body's got to be screaming for some rest."

He rebelled at the bedroom door, looking in at her unashamedly romantic comforter and curtains. "That's your bed."

She nodded and pretended to write on a chart. "Very good. Abstract thinking and cognitive skills appear unimpaired."

"Come on, Annie," he said, "I can't take your bed."

He'd dropped all pretense of humor; so did she. "You can barely stand up," she told him. "You need to rest. Your choices are exactly two: my bed or a sofa with about as much support as a marshmallow."

"Or my own rented bed at a fishing camp just outside of town. I can rest there."

"Maybe," she admitted. "Probably. But I wouldn't feel good about abandoning you there, and since I can't leave until my weekend carpenters show up, the question is not debatable. Another hour," she said, relenting when she saw how uncomfortable her skewed impersonation of Marcus Welby must be making this big-city cop. "Humor me for an hour longer."

She gestured toward the bed. "There's a phone. Make any calls you think necessary, and then lie down before you fall down."

He looked at her, still dubious, she knew, but nodded. "An hour." he said, as though confirming a contract. When she nodded, too, it was as though all the argument went out of him. "All right," he told her, "I'll rest. But I won't sleep."

He slept for three hours.

She checked on him frequently, but after the first time she unplugged her bedside telephone so he wouldn't accidentally be awakened and fought her own battle with her conscience about awakening him deliberately to check on him. He'd shown no signs of concussion, and he slept the sleep of the exhausted, not the injured.

She amended that thought as she stood in the doorway and watched him sprawled in sleep across her bed. The exhausted *and* the injured. Because the collision he'd been through today would take its toll on his body—in bruises and sore muscles he didn't yet suspect. But something else, something more, had already taken a toll, as evidenced by the dark shadows under his eyes, of the way, in sleep and without his deliberate attempt to hide it with smiles and animation, his face seemed drawn and lined beyond his years.

Secrets.

She had enough of her own.

She didn't need his, too.

She shook her head. Food, a shower, and a couple of hours observation. That was all she had promised him. That was all she—owed him. And she did owe David Huerra in some strange, off-kilter way. If she hadn't been stopped at the end of the lane, he might have had an escape route.

After he woke up, after she delivered him out to Gene and Gretta Tompkins's place, she would have lived up to her obligations. He could have his fishing trip and then take his secrets and his big-city problems back where they belonged, to the city, and leave her in the peaceful small-town solitude she had sought out and was so carefully wrapping around herself.

Solitude or not, Anne was pretty close to cursing small-town living hours later when Huerra carefully walked his bruised and battered body back into her kitchen.

"You let me sleep longer than an hour."

He headed immediately for the coffeepot—now filled with the fresh, real coffee she'd decided she needed instead of decaf—helped himself to a cup as though he had every right in the world to do so, and leaned back against the counter frowning at the lumber she'd carried in from Agnes's bed and stashed mostly in the room with the power tools, with only a little over-flowing into the already cluttered kitchen.

He pointed to his left temple, to the bruise that promised to spread colorfully over most of that side of his face. "Did you see this?" She nodded, but he didn't seem to want an answer. "If your good buddy Hank could see me now, he'd really think I was one of the bad guys. How the hell did I get bruised on that side of my head?"

"And other places?" she asked.

"Yes," he admitted. "Oh, hell, yes." He glared at her. "You knew, didn't you?"

She suspected that if he had been shot, if he had been seriously injured, he would have borne it with stoic acceptance, but he hadn't been, and he didn't. "Didn't you ever work traffic detail?" she asked.

He slumped against the counter. After a moment, while they both considered the unexpected trauma even the mildest wreck could inflict on a person, he took a drink from his cup and looked across to where she sat with her feet propped up on a nearby chair. "Too long," he said. "Sorry."

"Apology accepted." She dropped her feet from the chair and gestured toward it with her coffee cup. "Maybe you'd like to sit for a while?"

He nodded. "Do you think I could have a couple of aspirin now?"

"On the counter beside the sink." She'd put them there earlier, knowing he was probably going to need them. She watched while he swallowed three with his coffee and then came over and eased himself onto the chair.

"So what's got you down in the dumps, Doc? And where's your help?"

"It's the same question," she said, saluting him with her cup. "And the same answer."

"Are they coming later?"

Her glower at her now empty coffee cup had to have answered him.

"Well," he said, "the economy here can't be so good that there's not a half-dozen other people waiting in line for a job."

She transferred her glower to him, knowing he didn't deserve it but needing to vent her frustration in some way. "That was my fourth crew. This one didn't even bother to tell me they weren't coming. When I called the lumberyard here in town to find out what the holdup was, the clerk there told me they hadn't even been in to pick up the drywall and other standard supplies I need. And that they'd started a different job."

"And left you with a half-finished kitchen ceiling, at least one unfinished doorway, and—and what else?"

She felt a grin trying to break through. She didn't have to waste her energy getting indignant. David Huerra, the big-city cop, was doing it for her. "An upstairs that is practically uninhabitable."

"And a fading purple paint job."

Inside the house she could and often did forget how bad it looked from the outside. Apparently Huerra's first impression was still too new for him to forget. "That, too," she told him. "But an outside paint job is way down on my list of must dos. First I'd like to make sure I'm warm and dry for the winter."

"You could import a crew or two and have this done in no time," he said.

Antsy, frustrated, and needing the release of movement, she got up from the chair and paced to the coffeepot. She filled her cup and carried the pot back to the table. "In case you haven't noticed, I practice family medicine in a small town, not a specialty in some affluent suburb. I'm not exactly rolling in money."

For the first time she saw a touch of cynicism in David Huerra's eyes, but it was gone almost before she saw it, replaced by—what? chagrin? "So what do you do now?" he asked.

Good question. What did she do? She poured him some coffee and sat back down. "I guess I do the things I can do around here, put out the word at the lumberyard and at Willie Johnson's sawmill and among my patients, and hope to find a couple more out-of-work carpenters."

He lifted his cup and tried to hide his body's reaction to his sore muscles. "Four crews?" he asked. "In how long?"

"Not quite six months." But for the first time since he'd entered the kitchen, she didn't want to talk about carpenters and repairs. She suddenly remembered what discomfort he had to be in.

"Isn't that stretching bad luck a little far, even in a place as small as Allegro?"

That echoed her own earlier thoughts too closely for comfort. "Or good luck," she told him. "Since it seems that everyone I manage to find winds up with a job that's both bigger and better than the one I offered."

The cynicism she now saw open and unmasked in David Huerra's expression was not new to her. It was one of the reasons she had fled Chicago. It was something she sometimes still saw in her own bathroom mirror. But she had never expected to face it across the oak table in her disaster area of a kitchen.

"Are you hungry?" she asked him.

He let her change the subject. "No."

But he was still tired, still sore, and still needing rest. "I called Gretta Tompkins while you were asleep. Gene is out on the lake with some fishermen, but she promised to hold your cabin and have it ready for you when we get there."

Why was she dismissing him? Maybe it was because he was far from recovered from the accident. But maybe, and the thought nagged at her like a toothache, maybe it was because for the first time in months she didn't want to cut herself off from anyone and everyone who knew what life away from Allegro was like. And maybe, just maybe, it was because she sensed more of a tie between the two of them than just that knowledge.

Gretta Tompkins had done more than keep the cabin for him. She had stocked the pantry and the small refrigerator, and turned up the heat and turned back the covers on the only moderately lumpy bed. Obviously she'd heard about the accident. Of course, David thought, remembering. Anne had probably told her when she telephoned earlier.

And Pete—her son and his captain—had undoubtedly called and warned her about the short fuse David had been traveling on for so long, maybe even told her he'd ordered David to vacation and all but ordered he do it with them.

"Well—" Anne turned in a circle, surveying the room, taking note of the roaring panel-ray heater and the empty spot on the nightstand where no telephone sat. "You'll be all right?" she asked, sounding anything but convinced that he would be. "It's pretty basic out here. You might need a telephone."

"I'll be all right," he said. He was no more convinced than she was at the moment, but he hoped his voice didn't give his doubts away. Damn. All he wanted right now was to crawl into that bed and sink into oblivion while his body healed. He must really have taken a battering if he could stand in a rented room with a woman who looked as tempting as Anne Locke and desire only—well, almost only—rest.

Anne smiled at him. Taking a package from a pocket

in the light windbreaker she wore, she placed it on the nightstand. "It isn't much," she said hesitantly. "Just something a little stronger than aspirin in case you need it. You'll call me if you have any problems?"

"Yeah." He nodded, too fast, and his head began pounding again. "But I won't have any problems."

"Right." Her face lit with a crooked grin before she gestured toward the minuscule kitchen. "You probably won't, but you should avoid caffeine for a while. And definitely no alcohol for a couple of days. Rest. Yes. That's—"

"Doc." And damned if she wasn't. A doctor that was. He was having trouble remembering that. "I told you. I've been thumped before. I know the drill."

"Right," she said again. "Then I'll— I'll see you if you— I'd like to check you over—I mean . . . "

He almost laughed. He would have if he hadn't known how much it would hurt. Slowly, he walked to the door, holding it half open while she backed out, embarrassed and tongue-tied. "Thanks for everything," he said.

"Go home, Annie," he told her when she continued to stand on the small porch, obviously reluctant to leave him in the primitive cabin. Finally though, she gave an abrupt nod, spun on her heel, and marched away toward her parked truck.

David watched until she climbed into the truck and drove away. Agnes. The woman had actually given her truck a name. He wondered for a moment if she'd named that purple monstrosity of a house.

Cautiously, he worked his arms out of the windbreaker and dropped it over the back of a chair. The aspirin he'd taken earlier hadn't begun to cut the bone-deep aches that had started sometime during his unexpected nap. He picked up the bag she'd left, took out one of the sample packages it contained, read the label, and shook out two of the capsules.

The water from the kitchen tap was icy cold and free of any chemical taste. He downed the capsules with a generous swallow, then finished the remainder of the glass. A well, he thought. Deep and clear and clean. It had been a long time, years, since he'd tasted water so pure.

Maybe that was something else he had to think about this month.

As if there wasn't enough already.

He managed to get his boots off and stretched out on the bed, fully clothed, giving in to the groan because there was no longer any reason to hide it.

A doctor for God's sake. He'd been rescued by a doctor.

He glanced at the wooden planks of the ceiling, and beyond. He'd been a scrawny little kid in west Texas, growing up poor and Hispanic and Catholic. He'd been a scrawny, scrappy adolescent, still poor, still Hispanic, still Catholic, when he fell in love with Marla Hamilton, the rich, Anglo Protestant daughter of the county's only private-practice doctor.

He hadn't been good enough for her. That was the lesson he'd learned the summer of his seventeenth year. That was the lesson her daddy had made sure he and all his family learned.

Lying through his teeth but smiling all the while, Dr. Hamilton had fired David's mother from her job as his housekeeper and accused his brother Patrick of stealing his medical bag. Of course, Dr. Hamilton's word had been taken over David's, his mother's, and his brother's. In that county, at that time, doctors were ranked right up there with God. His payment for dropping the false charges was David's leaving the county, leaving the doctor's precious daughter. David had left to save his brother from prison, but Marla hadn't been willing to leave her father, his money, or his prestige.

Yes, that had been a hard lesson, one David barely

survived and one he had stubbornly, angrily rejected. But he'd absorbed another one, not even realizing he had, until his prejudice against all doctors had come crashing into his professional life. He'd been a good cop. At least he thought he had been. Impartial, objective, even dispassionate in a job that exposed him to all human passions and emotions. Until he'd been blindsided by a hatred as irrational and as deeply ingrained in himself as the one that had spawned his own.

And apparently his childhood Catholicism was as deeply ingrained. "I don't need more lessons," he said to a spot somewhere beyond the ceiling. "I've already had those. Remember? We did that last month. What I'm here to do is—"

Is what?

Decide whether or not he had more blind spots ready to jump out in ambush.

Decide whether he had what it took to be a cop. No. To be a good cop. A decent cop.

And after fifteen years of living with the dark side of humanity, to learn whether he still had—if he'd ever had—the ability to be a decent human being.

And for that, he didn't need another lesson. He didn't need another doctor in his life, no matter how . . . human she seemed. No matter how appealing he found her. How attractive.

No matter how much he felt as though the God of his Catholic childhood had put her in his path.

No. What he needed was solitude, peace, and quiet for at least long enough to examine what was in his own heart and psyche, and then, if he still thought it necessary, the strength to say good-bye to a job he loved but was no longer competent to perform.

4

Sometime around midnight the Saturday
before Thanksgiving, winter found Allegro, Oklahoma.
Grateful for even the increasing cold that dragged her
from the dreams that continued to haunt her, Anne still
had to force herself out from under the electric blanket.
She knew that some folks swore electric blankets were
as bad for a person as sausage and eggs, but she happened to think terminal frostbite was worse.

She also knew that she couldn't just crawl back under
that blanket and ignore the drop in temperature. Shivering
in the chilled room, she struggled into fuzzy slippers and a
cotton terry-cloth robe. Then, still shivering, she worked
through the house lighting small gas heaters.

The idea of central heating was appealing more and
more as she made her way through the drafty hallways
and back to the warmth of her bed. Flick a thermostat
before retiring and never have to get up to protect
plumbing or plants? Heaven, maybe, but she still hadn't
made up her mind about the economy or practicality of
one huge gas burner in a house this size.

Surprisingly though, it wasn't thoughts of giant gas
bills or miles of snake-like ductwork that kept her awake

after she settled back into the cocoon of her bed and upped the thermostat on the blanket. Nor was it the all too frequent fear of falling back into her troubled dreams. It was that out-of-the way bedroom upstairs. The one with the lavatory. And the off-center light fixture. And the blank wall that should have been filled with windows looking out over the garden.

And a cop. A cop who had come crashing into her life and was spawning thoughts, emotions, and memories she couldn't afford, didn't want, and wouldn't tolerate.

By noon it appeared that winter had come for more than a brief visit. The bright, crisp blue sky of Saturday had settled into something between pewter and wet fireplace ash in color, and periodically spat little needles of cold rain against the equally cold expanses of windows in the kitchen.

Anne had begged and bartered for a delivery from the lumberyard yesterday, and now rolls of pink insulation and four-by-eight sheets of drywall spilled out from the overflowing tool room, but she hadn't been able to beg or barter anyone to install it, or even to help her do so.

She'd lit all the burners on the charming but antiquated gas range, and cranked the new, highly touted gas heater up to full roar, so the old kitchen wasn't too bad, except when the wind rattled the windows. Then she shivered and cursed the naïveté that had lulled her into thinking she was going to be forever warm in the winter just because she had moved back to the south. While she shivered, she huddled over a cup of coffee and continued toting up the cost of something that should have been so simple: making this monster of a house into a home.

Maybe Willie Johnson was right, she thought in disgust. Maybe she ought to have let Joe have the house. That would be one more way of simplifying her life. Maybe she ought to call him now and see if he was still interested. But she knew she wouldn't. This grand old relic deserved a better fate than demolition to make room for a pile of lookalike boxes like the ones Joe Hansom owned on the other side of town.

Between bouts of feeling sorry for herself, she spent a few minutes in silent sympathy for her unwilling houseguest of the day before. She had signed on for the long haul in this part of the country; he had come looking for rest and recreation. What a vacation he was having.

What the hell was he doing?

David shook his head, letting his attention wander from the rain-slick road and the lumbering shock-sprung Blazer he was driving long enough for the rattling relic to try to take a dive off the twisting road. Hell and damnation. He needed another wreck even less than he needed what he was inviting by what he intended to do.

He'd convinced himself last night that he could spend the next month in Allegro without seeing Anne Locke.

Yeah.

But that had been in a fit of self-righteous self-examination.

And before Blake Foresman had come by for him this morning and driven him to the Sheriff's Department to take his statement about the collision, before Blake, a basically decent man, had helped find him transportation, and before he'd just happened to mention Dr. Locke.

"She's a fine woman," Foresman had said. "And from all accounts a fine doctor. She doesn't need the grief that cousin of hers is trying to give her. Hell, everybody knew he thought that place would be his. It's not her fault that his grandmother didn't inherit it. Or that he didn't have enough sense to suspect someone besides himself might want it."

David didn't need this. He had enough on his plate as it was. He wouldn't get involved. Nope. Not him. Under orders from his captain, this was vacation time. This was reflection time. This was her problem.

"What kind of grief?" he heard himself ask.

"Oh, hell," Foresman said. He rubbed his hand across the back of his neck and shrugged. "It's gossip. Just gossip. I shouldn't have said anything. They'll work it out."

"What kind of grief?" David repeated, looking steadily into Foresman's eyes until the sheriff shifted, turned, sighed. "It's ancient history," he said finally. "Katherine—that's Anne's mama—moved away from here years ago, as soon as *her* mama died. To get away from family. To get away from gossip. Unfortunately, some folks have long memories. They remember the mistake Katherine made as a girl, never mind how much she turned her life around and raised that little girl into a fine woman. Never mind that Joe's side of the family never gave her a lick of help."

Foresman met his steady questioning inspection. What he hadn't said was where Anne's father had been during all this time. But then he didn't need to, did he? So old family gossip was again circulating. And Anne had lost four work crews in six months. Nice cousin. Welcome home, Annie.

She deserved better.

It wasn't any of his business, he'd told himself when he'd headed the Blazer out of Fairview. He didn't need to go riding to the rescue like some damned cowboy. It wasn't any of his business, he'd told himself when he reached the turnoff to the Tompkins place, and passed it. It wasn't any of his business, he told himself again, when he reached the bottom of Anne Locke's driveway and turned in, when he stopped beside that fading purple wall and felt the back of his neck prickle, when he crossed the yard and stepped up onto the back porch and felt a chill that had no relationship to any cold-weather chill he'd ever felt before shudder down his spine.

He didn't owe her anything. Except maybe payment for a medical bill and a genuine word of thanks.

None of his business.

Right.

He raised his fist and knocked at the door.

Anne almost kicked over the chair she had her feet propped on when she heard the knock on the kitchen door. On Sunday? In this weather?

She carried the cup of coffee to the door with her and cautiously moved the curtain to one side to peer out at the shadowed porch. David Huerra stood there, bareheaded, hunched into his blue windbreaker.

She fumbled the deadbolts open with one hand and stepped back in a wordless invitation which he didn't hesitate to accept. He entered, stamping his feet and blowing on his hands. She didn't bother to ask, she just parked her cup on the table, went to the counter, and poured him a cup of coffee. When she turned around, he'd already gravitated to the open heater and stood backed up to it. She handed him the cup, and he took it in both hands.

"Thanks."

She cocked her head, looking up at him but resisting her initial impulse to order him into a chair and begin an examination. Instead she went to the basket of folded, clean laundry beside the dryer and returned to his side with a towel.

"You look—"

"Like your buddy Hank's worst nightmare?" he finished for her. He smiled, but smiling did little to dispel the image of desperado his assorted bruises and cuts had hung on his already dark looks.

"I was going to say cold," she told him. She held the towel out for him. "And wet."

He traded her his cup for the towel and wiped still glistening drops of rain from his hair, then followed her to the table where she set his cup and retrieved her own. He grinned at the arrangement of chairs, probably realizing she'd had her feet propped up again, and looked around the room as he sat down. His grin faded when he saw the stacks of new supplies.

"What brings you to town?" she asked. "Figuratively and literally?"

He laughed softly. "Sheriff Foresman came to the cabin this morning. It seems he didn't want to wait to see how much trouble his brother was in, or if he could somehow mitigate it. He took me into his office in Fairview to make my statement, then tracked down Hank's insurance agent and the owner of the Chevy dealership." He shook his head. "I'd forgotten how different small towns could be."

She chuckled. She'd had that same slightly dazed feeling herself for the first several weeks, before she'd remembered there was a flip side to the good things a small town offered—such as long memories and a surprising lack of choices in the matter of craftsmen and carpenters. "So when is Blake coming back for you?" she asked. A sudden thought sobered her. "Are you in pain? Discomfort? Did I miss something—"

He waved his coffee cup in dismissal of her fears. "I

feel like hell," he admitted, "and I probably will for a few days, but no, you didn't miss anything. And Foresman's not coming back, because he didn't bring me here. Thanks to his influence with the Chevy dealer, I have the use of what is probably the oldest Chevy Blazer still on the road until my car is either repaired or replaced."

"Then what—"

"Annie, Annie," he said on a long sigh. "I came to say thanks and to take you out for Sunday dinner to repay you for yesterday's meal, provided of course you don't mind being seen with someone who looks as bad as I do right now."

Oh.

Oh, my.

Decision time.

She grinned at him. "I suppose if I refuse, you'll blame it on your appearance."

He grinned back. "Anything that works, Doc."

Allegro offered only two places to eat the midday meal on Sunday: a really good restaurant in the downtown business district that catered to the after-church crowd, and a rustic looking but also excellent restaurant at the lake where casual clothes were the norm, not the exception. They opted for the lake.

The hostess was not a patient of Anne's, although Anne did recognize her. She glanced from Anne to David, cocked her head, and pursed her lips, but she didn't say anything until she had seated them beside a wall of windows overlooking the wooded hillside and a cove of the lake below. They were well away from, but not out of sight of, the table where Anne's cousin Joe sat with a group of men, engaged in an avid discussion.

She'd heard rumors that Joe was going after a state

senate seat in the next election, his reason having more to do with proposed oil and gas legislation that threatened his mineral holdings than with a need to serve. It looked as though the rumors might be right. The group with him consisted of the powers that be, the movers and shakers of the south end of Pitchlyn County.

Joe broke off his part of the conversation long enough to shoot Anne a long, unwelcoming stare not seen, she hoped, by anyone but her. Then the hostess called out to a passing waitress, "Hey, Susie. Come take care of Doc Anne and the Dallas cop. And be nice," she added as she plopped their menus down on the table. "We want him to have a better impression of us than the one Hank must have left him with."

Anne saw David's lips twitch, but he controlled them and gave the hostess no more than a polite smile before he hid his face behind the menu.

"I didn't think Allegro had a Sunday paper," he said.

That was just what she needed to take her mind away from why Joe Hansom couldn't even pretend to be friendly. "It doesn't," she told him, feeling a smile of her own threatening to get out of control. "It doesn't need one."

She glanced at her menu. "The catfish is always good," she said. "It's local, and fresh. So is the prime rib. Good, that is. Although I'm pretty sure it has seen the inside of at least one freezer." She read further, sharing her knowledge of the offerings because she knew how wary one could get of strange restaurants. "The German fries are to die for, and—oh, great. They do have it today. Sometimes they don't—save room for the deep-dish apple pie. They serve it heated with a scoop of double-rich French vanilla ice cream."

She heard what could have been a cough, could have been the sound of someone choking, and looked up to see David Huerra watching her cautiously. "Doc?" he said when he saw he had her attention. He raked an appraising glance down all of her he could see, from forehead to tabletop, then back up to her face, and she felt the warmth of a flush threatening her embarrassingly fair complexion and the freckles that no makeup, even if she had been wearing any, could hide.

His appraisal wasn't blatant, but neither was it dismissive. And it didn't offend her. Well, well. Imagine that. Maybe she was coming back to life after all.

"I thought anybody coming out of med school these days had to swear allegiance to the carrot stick and celery brigade. Did you miss a few nutrition classes? Or maybe learn something that the American Medical Association isn't letting the rest of us in on?"

She grinned at him. She'd heard that question before. "Or maybe the rest of us just haven't listened to?" she asked him. "Such as 'moderation'?"

He raised an eyebrow, silently requesting her to explain.

She moved her hand in a sweeping gesture to catalogue her less-than-imposing features. "I weigh a hundred and ten pounds. I don't have an exercise regime, but I park at the back of the lot when I do go to a mall, rarely take an elevator when the stairs are accessible, and walk to work five days a week. Those same five days I eat baked, broiled, or low fat. On the weekends I usually wear myself out toting, sawing, and hammering in my house, so if I want to treat myself, I don't think I'm hurting my chances for a long and healthy life.

"Besides," she added, "I was just telling you what's good on the menu. *I'm* having the baked chicken."

He gave her a rueful grin and a two-finger salute, and she realized that once again, with little or no provocation, she'd climbed on a soapbox. She dropped the menu onto the table. "Sorry," she told him, giving him a rueful grin of her own. "If you push the right button, I can argue the flip side of that, but probably not with as much fervor."

They were laughing when Susie came to take their order. They both had the baked chicken. And the German fries. And the deep-dish apple pie. They talked with an ease and companionship that Anne had found with very few people. It was almost as though they had known each other forever instead of barely twenty-four hours, yet with an underlying awareness of each other as strangers: distant, somewhat mysterious, possibly dangerous to each other's peace of mind. That awareness was visible, in an occasional sharp glance, a marginally nervous handling of the flatware or dishes, a shifting in the mismatched but comfortable chairs. But it was unspoken, as were other things.

She learned that David Huerra, surprise of surprises, had actually seen Placido Domingo in *La Traviata*, that he frequented museums in Dallas and elsewhere, that he had seen the Tutankhamen exhibit, had been to Teotihuacán, and had even been dragged to the Thorne room display in Chicago by a niece who had then demanded that her father, his brother Patrick, build her dollhouse furniture that looked like the museum-quality miniatures she had seen on display. He glossed over his childhood, but he said enough for her to understand what he wasn't saying: for a man who had been raised on what he called a west Texas dirt farm, he and some members of his family had ranged far and wide from their beginnings.

She didn't learn why he had chosen to take a vacation in November, nor did she learn why his expression became withdrawn, almost painfully so, when he mentioned his job. That was all right. She really didn't want to learn too much about the pressures of the Dallas P.D., any more than she wanted to reflect on why she had really left the clinic in Chicago. She did share the story of how she had come to own a sprawling purple monstrosity on a hillside in downtown Allegro.

"My mother put the bid in for me," she said.

"She what?"

Anne nodded. "I didn't even know about the family's lawsuit to partition the property, only that I wanted to come home. At least for a while. I had no idea that I would enjoy renovating an old house. I did ask Mom why, if she thought the house was such a great buy, she didn't buy it herself. She just said that she knew herself as well as she knew me; she'd found her haven and now it was my turn." Anne smiled with the memory of her mother's impassioned speech. "She said that even though Allegro hadn't been particularly good for her, it was probably just what I needed. At least for now."

"So you bought it?"

"Once I saw it, I knew she was right. Purple paint and all." Anne laughed in self-conscious acknowledgment of Joe and all the unpleasantness. "But along with it, I have acquired what appears to be a family feud. It seems they were a package deal, and if my mother knew about it, she kept that knowledge to herself."

"Is this a long-standing feud?"

"I don't know. No one seems willing to admit it exists, much less talk about it."

For a moment she glimpsed the cop in him. "Is it a dangerous one?"

Loud laughter erupted from across the room. In one of those odd coincidences no one would believe, the laughter came from the men with Joe, the main perpetrator of the very feud they were discussing. Their party was breaking up, and Joe, after ignoring her, this time for more than a month, stood up, snagged his leather jacket from the back of his chair, and walked to where she sat.

He stood there with his jacket caught by one finger over his shoulder, pearl snaps gleaming on his white-on-white western shirt, knife-edge creases accenting black denim jeans, tooled leather and triple-stitching marking his boots as custom-made.

"Anne," he said, with all the warmth of an IRS auditor.

"Joe," she answered, marginally warmer.

"I hear you've had more trouble up at the house."

Now where would he have heard a thing like that?

"No," she said. "Not that I know of."

"You haven't lost another crew?"

As if he didn't know. He probably had a pipeline to the lumberyard, if not to the carpenters themselves. "Why, Joe, I'm getting so used to that, I don't consider it trouble any more, just a fact of life. Let me guess—you're starting a new project, and my two carpenters were the very ones you needed for a special phase of that job."

"Winter's coming, Anne," he said, ignoring her gibe. "I worry about you up there all alone. That house has to be almost uninhabitable. When are you going to give up in this effort to inconvenience me?"

"Joe, Joe," she chided. "If you hadn't been so sure of yourself that you only bid ten cents on the dollar, you'd own the house now."

His smile slipped slightly. "Yeah, but that was all it was worth, sitting there going to ruin. I bid fair market value for the land. I suppose you're going to want a profit on what you've done—"

When she shook her head, he grimaced. "You won't last the winter," he said. "You might as well get someplace comfortable before it gets really cold."

David picked up his coffee cup and set it back in the saucer, a nonthreatening action that somehow managed to convey all sorts of unspoken menace. Joe wasn't unaware of him; he'd just been ignoring him. Now he glanced down, taking in David's desperado appearance in one sweeping, disdainful glimpse. He had to know who David was—everyone in the restaurant did—but he chose to pretend that he didn't. That didn't surprise her; his words did.

"You're starting a little early, aren't you? Even for someone with your track record."

No. Winter wasn't coming early; it was already here. Anne felt the chill clear through her bones. What had she ever done to Joe Hansom that would cause him to make such a malicious, mean-spirited attack? Other than buying a house that was up for grabs anyway? Nothing. At least nothing that she was aware of.

She saw David lean forward in his chair and wondered if they were going to have a major scene in the Lake Café. No. She wouldn't give Joe that satisfaction. She smiled at him. "I got a letter from my mother last week. From Australia? You do remember that's where she lives now, don't you, Joe? She asked me to give her regards to your grandmother. Since you won't tell me where she is, please pass the message on to her for me, will you? Or maybe I should just ask around until I find her."

Joe's smug grin became a little strained. He nodded abruptly and left without saying another word.

David Huerra studied her silently for a moment. He glanced in the direction of the door to make sure Joe had left, then rose and held his hand out for her. "I think it's time for us to leave, too."

Yes, it was.

The rain had eased, but the wind was just as cold as they drove back toward town.

"I take it that was an example of the feud," David said.

She nodded. "It's a lovely family, isn't it?"

"Obviously you were adopted."

"Thanks." She sank back against the cracked seat and looked out the window, silent for perhaps another mile, debating with herself, knowing she had to tell him. "Joe has a vicious mouth."

"You don't owe me any explanation," he said, and she knew by the way he said it he'd thought Joe had been making some sort of sexual innuendo. And maybe he'd already heard the stories circulating about her birth. About her mother. "By this time tomorrow everyone else in Pitchlyn County is going to know what he said and what he was talking about. I'd rather at least one person heard it from me," she said, hoping she didn't sound as weary of Joe's unending rumors and innuendos as she felt.

They were still a couple of miles outside of town. Huerra found a wide shoulder and pulled off the road, set the emergency brake and flashers, and turned in the seat to face her. "Okay," he said. "Shock my socks off me."

"I wish." Was there any good way to say this? Damn Joe anyway. She sucked in a deep breath. "He was making allusions to your visible injuries, not to the fact that we were sharing a meal. It seems I— Well, the men in my life . . . They die."

She'd shocked him all right. Maybe he still had on his socks, but for several seconds it seemed he'd lost his voice. "Oh, hell, Annie. Damn that son of a bitch!"

She tried to rake her hand through her hair, got it caught in the pins and gave up. "The first one was in high school. We'd gone steady for three years, two eggheads who didn't fit in with anyone else. Someone decided it would be fun to spike his drink to see how a nerd acted drunk. Then they put him in his car and let him go off alone. He drove off the side of a mountain."

"Annie—"

"It's all right," she said. "I can tell you. Maybe I need to tell you. The other one was a man I had been engaged to. We'd decided we didn't really have what it took to make a marriage work, but Anthony and I did have a fine friendship and a good working relationship. He was murdered—killed in a clinic robbery."

"Hell."

"Yeah."

She thought for a minute that David was going to reach for her. She thought for a minute she needed him to do just that. She hadn't talked about Anthony in months—not to anyone—and just mentioning him brought back too-vivid memories that had stubbornly refused to fade. Instead, David turned in the seat and started the Blazer back toward Allegro with what she suspected to be an uncharacteristic clashing of gears.

David stayed silent—so did she—until they were back in her kitchen. There, he looked at the supplies spilling from the tool room. "Joe is responsible for your crews being hired away from you, isn't he?"

"No one will admit it, but, yes, I think he is. Men who haven't worked for weeks, some of them for months, are suddenly offered long-term projects just as I get them lined up out here."

"What does he want with this place?"

"I think he really does just want the land. Willie Johnson at the sawmill told me Joe wanted to put up another set of apartments like the ones south of town."

"You mean the ones that look like prefab mini-storage buildings?"

She caught her hand to her mouth as an unexpected laugh broke from her. "Yes," she said. "That's exactly what they look like."

He pulled off his windbreaker and draped it over a kitchen chair. "Why don't you show me what needs to be done?"

"Why—"

"I don't like your cousin Joe," he said. "Your cousin Joe is not a nice man, and he's had everything his way for much too long."

"But you're on vacation."

"Yeah," he said, and grinned. It was not a nice grin, not at all like the easy, companionable ones he had shared with her and that had coaxed return smiles from her. No. This one gave her a glimpse of a side of David Huerra she wasn't sure she was ready to know. "Against my will and for a month. And it just so happens that this west Texas farmboy worked his way through night school on a construction crew."

"You're injured. And you came here to fish."

"Wrong," he said. "I came here to think, and I can do that just as well helping you as I can killing bait. Besides, you were the one who told me my brain was still working. Do you remember what the weather is like outside? With the windchill it's about ten degrees, and that's on dry land. God only knows what it is out on the lake in a boat. Come on, Annie, isn't there some part of you, buried way down deep, that wants to rub good old Joe's face in it? Let's do it, Annie. Let's fix up this house. And let's see who offers me what to leave you stranded."

He was offering her retribution for all the slights and slurs Joe had been responsible for giving her since she'd inadvertently thwarted his latest plans. Already he knew her well enough to know what her answer had to be.

Knew it before she did.

And he was right.

In spite of his stated intent, David Huerra didn't start work on Anne's house that Sunday. After a tour and a discussion of what had been done and what remained to be done, after a slice of Sara Lee pound cake topped with the last of her precious stash of Häagen-Dazs, after a yawn and a stretch and a groan she knew he didn't intend for her to hear, he left, banished by her to his rented cabin on the lake for much needed rest.

What she wanted but wasn't able to do that afternoon was to finish lowering the kitchen ceiling so that she'd have one room where the heat didn't hover twelve feet above the floor. What she was able but didn't want to do that afternoon was some minor finish work in the butler's pantry, which, until she'd knocked the doorway through to the hall, had been the only access to the kitchen from the rest of the house.

What she did was something she hadn't done in years. Her things were packed away in a jumble of unlabeled boxes in an abandoned parlor off the living room, and it took some time to locate them, and then to drag the kitchen table closer to the gas heater, and to find a floor lamp to use until her magnifier surfaced.

Her tools and supplies were in three modified tackle boxes. She scooted her pile of invoices and bills to one side and arranged all three cases on the kitchen table within easy reach.

Anne opened the first tackle box and glanced at the battered and well-used metal snips, shears, and soldering irons. She hadn't been able to spend a lot of money on her hobby, and for the last few years she hadn't even been able to spend a lot of time on it. For Anne's high school graduation, her mother had presented her with an unorthodox gift. Anne lifted the fitted case from the bottom of the tackle box's deep tray and opened it, too, tracing her fingers over the matching precision scaled awls and punches and rasps, the calipers and pliers and hand drill with its assorted bits.

Her mother *did* know her well. Any doubts Anne might have harbored about that disappeared when she touched the set of tools that she had coveted for years but had never mentioned to her mother, had no idea her mother knew anything about, until she had opened her gift expecting to see something imminently practical for college and found these.

Somewhere Anne had a padded work surface, but she hadn't uncovered that or her anvil or grinder in her search through the packing crates. She took a folded jeweler's cloth from the second of the boxes, spread it on the table in front of her and began opening the trays and drawers of this case. She'd never used many stones in her work, preferring the beauty of the metal she'd worked with, but she did have a small hoard of them. She lifted them to the cloth, along with the few finished pieces she hadn't yet given away, a couple of partially completed pins, and a scattering of loose findings.

Then she opened the third box.

And knew what had compelled her to drag out these icons of her youth.

But not why.

Not yet why.

She felt a strange tightness in her throat and chest—apprehension or anticipation?—and a betraying tremor in her hands as she lifted the carefully wrapped bundle from the third box and placed it on the cloth in front of her. She'd foregone lunches and movies in high school, and later even necessities, to keep herself supplied with what she'd long ago determined was as essential to her well-being as the air she breathed.

And she hadn't even looked at it in years.

Did she want to now?

This wasn't the material she had cut so that she could shape the smaller pieces. This was intact, although some of it—very little—was worked. She remembered that, too well, and how she had agonized over the designs and the execution. But the other was clean, pristine, just waiting for—for what? For a skill greater than hers had been or probably ever would be, she suspected.

Another gust of rain battered the windows, and in it she heard what she very much feared was ice. What little daylight there had been was fading fast, and the kitchen was illuminated now only by the circle of light from the floor lamp and from the open gas flames of the heater and range. She shivered, cold again, even in her heavy sweater. The chill extended to her fingers. She flexed them once, twice, before reaching again for the bundle and folding back the cloth.

The metal should have been cold. Everything she knew or had been taught told her that. Each exquisite and finely prepared leaf should have absorbed the chill from the unheated room where it had been stored, from the draft now scooting across the kitchen, from the years of having been abandoned to the darkness. But it wasn't. She dropped her hands to the top sheet, unmindful for the moment of fingerprints and damaging oils, and felt the warmth and the soft, beckoning glow of the copper fill her with the same inexplicable longing it always had.

5

1935

 Son of a bitch, but it was cold. Ralph Hansom leaned against the truck and shrugged deeper into the long wool coat he'd bought on one of his trips back east. The hicks in Allegro had laughed at him the first time he'd worn it on the streets there. No one would ever need a coat like that this far south, they'd told him. Well, he was the one laughing now. Maybe they hadn't had so much as a killing frost until a week ago, but those bastards digging and crawling through the tunnels not a quarter of a mile away were freezing their asses off now.

 He stamped his feet, feeling the crunch of frozen grass beneath them. There was one blessing to the cold. With all the rain they'd had, even the abandoned roadbed where they'd parked wouldn't have been protection enough, but maybe Jackson wouldn't get mired down trying to get out of here after all.

 Not that he was worried about Tom Jackson. He'd paid the man enough over the years for him to take the risk. And if Jackson hadn't figured out he was risking

more than losing his new truck in the river bottoms if it
mired down, if the men who owned the leases for digging found out what he was doing—and had been
doing since long before they had taken steps to legit-
imize their own plundering—then who was he to tell
him?

Should he be here? He hadn't bothered to return
since his first visit two years ago, when dealers had been
invited but were treated like beggars for the grave
goods being brought out. He'd long before learned the
general location of where Jackson was obtaining the
objects he'd been bringing him for almost a decade, just
not exactly where and how, something he'd rather not
be too familiar with. Rather than submit himself to the
haggling, the bickering, the total lack of respect he'd
found on that one trip, he'd decided to continue his
more than lucrative association with the one-time dirt
farmer. And Jackson hadn't been averse to doing so.
Granted, it was a little more risky for him than it had
once been, but the artifacts more than made up for the
increased sums the man demanded.

Ralph could see the flare of bonfires from the site,
smell—what? cedar?—burning, and hear the noises
from the digging, oaths and groans and shouts all carried on the wind from the northwest that hurried across
the river but seemed to gather strength when it reached
the grove where Hansom and the truck waited.

Oaths and groans and shouts and—and what? For a
moment Hansom thought he heard footsteps in the frost-
bitten underbrush beneath the trees surrounding him.
The footsteps of something large and restless. Pacing.
Pacing. Back and forth. Back and forth. For a moment he
thought he saw a glow— Someone coming with a torch?
But that was gone. And then it wasn't his eyes that were
alerted to strange goings-on but his ears. A growl?

The wind.

Moaning through the dead leaves still clinging to otherwise bare branches.

Moaning around the hills to the west that had been built by a race far removed from the one that now scrabbled to find the treasures hidden there.

Moaning in the dips and hollows of the river-bottom lands and erosion creeks.

Still—

A branch snapped beneath something heavy, and Ralph Hansom swung around with an oath of his own.

Another branch broke in the underbrush. Hansom twisted in that direction, reaching for the Colt revolver in his overcoat's deep pocket. This time he was sure he heard a growl. Mountain lion? It was possible farther south, but here, along the river? Whatever it was, it was big. Damned big.

He heard the wind moan again, recognizing it this time for what it was, and told himself to relax. He was getting too old for skulking in the bushes. If tonight hadn't been the last chance, if Jackson hadn't sworn it would be worth his while, if he hadn't had a buyer with more money than China had people, he wouldn't be here now. If he hadn't been here before, if he hadn't known what was causing those sporadic leaps of flames, his imagination might not be playing these tricks on him.

He understood the diggers burning the cedar poles and beams they brought out of the mound. Unless they were written on or painted or carved, they had no value except as firewood, and God knew the diggers needed something to burn for heat.

But the bones?

He didn't want them; no buyer he knew of wanted them. What the hell did he expect the diggers to do with them? Take them back into the mound after they'd made sure they contained nothing of value? Call a preacher out here to say prayers over the heathens? They didn't have time for that. Ralph knew it, even understood it. Midnight, which was coming soon, marked the end of the lease and the end of the only job the few, trusted hired workmen had been able to find in months. Marked the end of the time the state of Oklahoma had insisted the leaseholders had before they had to stop, forever, the private excavations regardless of what kind of a deal they could work out with the landowners. Marked the end of the time that Hansom, with Tom Jackson's help, would be able to provide his carefully cultivated group of collectors with the items they had grown to covet.

Well, hell, whoever the bones had belonged to was dead. Long dead. Each and every one of them. Think of this as a delayed cremation. Some ancient civilizations had cremated their dead, hadn't they? He wasn't too sure of that. He could recite the going price for an Egyptian scarab or a Mayan celt or a Spiro gorget dead drunk or in his sleep; his knowledge didn't extend to the people who had made these things. Hadn't had to. Wouldn't need to.

It was just a bone pile, he told himself. Just a damned bone pile. Every rancher he knew had one. A place in a ravine or gully or grove of trees, where he dragged the carcasses of his disease- or predator-killed livestock and left them there to rot or be scavenged, until the ravine or gully or copse was full of bleached white skulls and bones.

It meant nothing there; it meant nothing here.

What did mean something here was that one strange, carved pipe and the wealth of arrowheads and pots and engraved shells that Jackson had been bringing him for almost a decade.

What meant something here was the comfortable lifestyle he had made for himself placing those arrowheads and shells and heathen treasures with so-called connoisseurs of history. Connoisseurs, hell. They were greedy bastards, every one of them. But they had served him well. Ellie's family didn't dare look down on him now, didn't dare say that he wouldn't have a home or two dimes to rub together if it hadn't been for her land and money.

Some said the people who had built these mounds were the ancestors of Ellie's people, not that anybody knew for sure, but wouldn't that be justice of the nicest kind—that in the long run the very people who had proved so tight-fisted with the money from their land and coal and gas royalties had provided him with the means to tell them all to go to hell, that he didn't need them anymore? Not them. Not Ellie. Not the brat she had presented him with.

He heard a shout from the direction of the mounds and a strange silence before voices broke out in a confusing babble of sound, and then a crashing through the underbrush as of something heavy running. He felt a bead of sweat pop out on his upper lip and chill in the night air. He yanked the Colt out of his pocket even as he opened the truck door, preparing to leap into the cab.

Jackson. Ralph sagged against the truck door. Only Jackson. Running. For his life? And then Ralph noticed what he should have seen at once. Jackson was empty-handed.

"Get in the truck," Jackson called out in an urgent hiss. "Now!"

Other sounds intruded over the calls from the excavation, and three men broke from the woods carrying a strange, long litter of some sort, canvas covered, sagging between the poles and with at least three baskets jumbled on top. Ralph hesitated at the truck door while Jackson lowered the tailgate and directed the dumping of whatever the men carried into the bed of the truck. One man crawled in with the litter, but when the other two tried, Jackson waved them back. "On the running boards," he told them. "And for God's sake, be quiet."

Ralph slipped into the cab of the truck and eased his door shut. Jackson leapt into the driver's side, glanced at Hansom and jerked Ralph's hat down to cover his eyes just as one of the men jumped up onto the running board beside Jackson, the other beside Hansom and looked into the cab. "Who's this?"

"Never mind, Billy Ray. You don't want him to know who you are, either."

The man called Billy Ray grunted an acknowledgment. "You got that right. Let's get the hell out of here."

"Not yet," Jackson said grimly.

Jackson sat in tense silence behind the wheel, not reaching for the starter, obviously waiting. But for what, Ralph wondered.

When the explosion rocked the ground even as far away as they were parked, he had his answer. And the leaseholders had their revenge. Jackson fired the engine and spun them out of their hiding place, slewing chert and shale and frozen mud behind them as the two on the running boards swore and grabbed for purchase. Jackson didn't stop or slow down until they reached the old Fort Coffee cemetery, where he wheeled in and skidded to a stop.

Jackson left the engine running while he got out of the truck and joined the three men at the back. Ralph stepped out in time to see Jackson lift a basket from the back and hand it to the one he'd called Billy Ray.

"There's enough here to keep the two of you well for a long time," Jackson said. "Just don't be in too big a hurry to let anyone know you've got it. And if you're thinking about coming back on me for more, I can see that the other men who paid your wages tonight find out that you were working for more than one. You got that clear in your minds?"

Ralph caught only a glimpse of the contents of the basket. Beads, pearls, a few broken shells. For a moment he considered arguing Jackson's method of payment, but he recognized the wisdom of it. What the men were taking wasn't that valuable in the overall scheme of things, depending on what was in the other baskets and under the canvas, and giving it to them made them more active participants than just hired hands. Well, well, maybe the dirt farmer had learned a few of the finer points of stealth and deception while he was grubbing around in the back of a man-made hill. Of course, knowing that made Hansom realize just how much he'd have to keep his eye on Jackson.

Two of the men left. When Jackson turned to get in the truck, he waved the third man from the back with a gesture that said plainly he was to ride up front. "My son," Jackson told him.

"Am I going to get a chance to look at what you've got before we get out of here?"

Jackson laughed. "What difference does it make now? We've got it, and if that blast was half as successful as I think it was, we're not going to have a chance to get more. Let's head to your place before someone from the site stumbles on us and decides they want to have a look at our cargo, too. I don't think either one of us would like what would happen if we're caught."

Ten miles outside of Allegro, on a muddy and potholed mountain switchback with no way to go but down, Jackson again stopped the truck and turned in the seat to look at Hansom.

"I've been thinking," Jackson said, "that I've learned a little about the stuff I've been hauling down to you over the years. I've been thinking that I've learned a little about the other folks that deal in this kind of stuff."

Ralph tensed. Maybe he'd been too trusting for too long. Maybe he should have started watching out for Jackson a lot sooner than this abandoned road in the predawn hours. Cautiously he felt for the Colt in his pocket. How big a shakedown was coming? Casually, almost without effort, a hand came from behind him and clamped his in place before it ever reached his pocket. Jackson's son. Shit.

"What else have you been thinking, Tom?"

Jackson smiled at him, his teeth white in the darkness of the cab. "I've been thinking that all in all, except for the first few loads when you cheated my socks off me, you've been fair. Fair enough so that I'd hate to have to break in that fellow down in El Dorado, or one of those men from Missouri. But those first few loads do stick in my craw, Hansom. You know, like something you just have to drag out and chew on every once in a while? It leaves a bad taste, a sour stomach, and sometimes even a hangover. I sure don't want to have to add to that mess of stuff I'm already chewing on. Sure would appreciate it if I could get rid of some of the old stuff, too. So I figured I'd talk to you, maybe come to a real clear understanding about what this night is going to mean to me, especially now that I won't be able to get anything else."

Hansom drew in a shallow breath, trying not to suck in air, trying to ignore the hand clamped on his. "I thought we'd come to an agreement about what the different things were worth. Are you suggesting that we change that agreement now?"

Jackson shook his head. "No. I've been talking, casual like and real careful. I figure you were paying me right for them. It's just that I ain't never brought you anything quite like I've brought you tonight, and I think we ought to have an understanding before we get to your place."

"Or?"

"Or I let you out here, you walk home, and me and my boy drive to Missouri."

Hansom relaxed marginally. As a shakedown, it wasn't too bad, nothing, maybe, that he couldn't talk his way out of. "Just what in the hell do you have back there?"

As he appeared to relax, so did Jackson. He leaned back against the door. "There's been an archaeologist fellow there, wringing his hands and watching us dig. He even went in once, but when he found out we weren't shoring up the tunnels, he backed right out and went to moaning and groaning about the way we were treating stuff, first of all by even daring to touch it, and then in the way we handled it when it came out. You'd have thought we were in his grandmother's casket the way he carried on.

"Well, what I learned from him was that these things have more value if they're treated a certain way. Like records kept of where they were found. Like some things being kept together. He kept talking about 'intact burials' and 'integrity of the find,' or dictionary words something like that. So when we found what we found, I knew what I had to do. I'd have liked to get that other one. Whooee, that cloak was something else, all feathers and beads woven in with only God knows what. Must have been seven, eight feet long, but somebody else grabbed that right off the skeleton, and I knew I couldn't take the chance of trying to get it back.

"So me and the boys, we threw a little dirt over this one then hauled it out in wheelbarrows until I could get the tarps laced onto the poles—we got all of them, too, that archaeologist would be right proud of the way we made sure of that—and hauled it out. It's all there—or most of it. We dropped some, and then we had to give that little stuff to the crew—"

Hansom leaned forward. Jackson's enthusiasm was catching. "What are you saying? Just what did you bring out?"

Jackson grinned. "Hey, partner," he said, and Hansom didn't bother to correct him, "I think we got ourselves one of their gods."

6

Anne didn't expect David Huerra to arrive the next morning. That's what she told herself as she leaned against the sink while she ate her English muffin, surveying the wreck of her kitchen and listening to the rain as it battered the windows.

She hadn't expected him, but when she heard the knock on the back door, she wasn't surprised.

He wore a disreputable pair of jeans and his boots— not the cowboy kind she was used to seeing around Allegro, but a pair that made her wonder if he'd ever done motorcycle patrol—his blue windbreaker, a gimme cap from Tompkins fish camp, and of course his spectacular bruise that tied his bad-guy-run-amok costume all together.

"Don't even think about walking to work today," David said as he took off his cap and hit it against his thigh, sending raindrops and ice pellets scattering on the porch.

She stepped back to let him enter the kitchen then hurriedly closed the door behind him.

He stopped just inside, sniffed deeply, and smiled at her. "Good. Real coffee. I knew you couldn't be the early-morning-instant type."

Anne nodded toward the counter, feeling a reluctant smile of her own. What was there about this man that gave him the ability to creep behind her armor? What was there about him that she found so appealing? Especially since she suspected that with any encouragement he could be totally overbearing. "Help yourself," she told him. "And by the way, good morning to you, too."

She heard a mumble from him that could have been a belated greeting. So David wasn't a morning person? That did surprise her. She studied him a little more carefully as he reached into the cabinet for a cup and poured himself some coffee, noticing then the care with which he moved. Men! Why on earth did they have to be so—so damned macho? And why on earth did David Huerra think he had to hide his physical discomfort from her? After all, she'd been there when the accident happened. She'd cared for him then and since, and she'd continue to—

Whoa!

She'd continue to *what?* The eerie feeling of déjà vu, of having cared for this man before, hovered around her. For a moment she fought it but when that did no good, she searched frantically for a logical reason for the feeling. When she found it, she couldn't stop the relieved laugh that broke from her. Saturday. Of course. When she had found herself completely and uncharacteristically tending to more than his health needs.

He turned and peered at her over the rim of his cup. "Are you okay?"

Maybe she wasn't, because it seemed so natural for her to go to the fridge, take out another muffin, split it, and drop it into the toaster. For him.

"Sure. What brings you out this early? What brings you out in this weather at all?"

"Cabin fever," he said. "And the fact that your place is warmer than mine."

She raised an eyebrow at that and glanced pointedly at all four of the burners on her kitchen range, which were turned up to maximum, one of them with an upended clay flowerpot on top to act as an improvised radiant.

"And to take you to work," he added.

She'd started to tell him she hadn't planned on walking that morning, that she'd already decided to drive Agnes. His next words stopped her.

"It looks as if that four-wheel drive Blazer is going to come in handy after all."

"The roads are icy?"

He nodded. "The highway and downtown streets are bad enough, but that ski slope you call a driveway is nearly impassable."

"In November?" she asked, incredulous. "I thought this was the South."

The muffin popped up from the toaster. He looked at her questioningly. "For you," she said. "I've already eaten."

He slathered butter on it from the open container and munched reflectively. "Texas is south, Doc," he told her finally. "I'm not sure what this place is anymore." So saying, he carried both muffin halves and his coffee across the room and backed up to the gas heater. "So what time do you have to be at the clinic?"

"Soon," she said, and glanced at her watch. "Oh lord, yes. Real soon." If the streets were as bad as David said, most of her morning appointments would probably cancel, but that time was sure to be filled with work-ins of people who didn't have enough sense to stay in off the ice. "Let me get my snow boots," she told him, glad that she hadn't gotten rid of them when she made the move from Chicago.

When she returned to the kitchen, wrapped and bundled like she'd thought she'd never have to be again and carrying her bag, she found David standing at the table, gently tracing his finger along the narrow sheet of copper with the design she had worked on until well past midnight. She'd mentioned to him Sunday that she'd once worked at jewelry-making, but she had been deliberately vague about the depth of her interest; it wasn't something she had shared with many people. At least not since starting med school.

Now she wondered why.

Slowly, almost reluctantly, he turned his attention from the sheet of copper to her. "You're good, Doc. Real good."

His words warmed her more than her down-filled coat and fleece-lined boots. "Thanks."

"It reminds me of—" He hesitated. "I'm not sure just what it reminds me of. It's vaguely meso-American, but not really Aztec. Not really Mayan. Not really anything I've seen before."

She knew what he meant, because when she had first begun the series of designs, of which this was but one of many, she'd wondered if she was being derivative, and if so, of what.

"Maybe it's just 'Anne Locke,'" she said.

He touched the design once again: a salute? a farewell? "Maybe it is at that." He pulled the folded cap from his jacket pocket and settled it on his head, but waited while she put her supplies back into the tackle boxes and closed them. "So what would you like me to work on first, boss? I'm not sure I'm up to putting in the ceiling without a helper, but I'm game for just about anything else."

Anne might as well have stayed at home. She ran the clinic with the help of Margaret Samuels, an extremely efficient registered nurse who had been out of the workforce for almost a decade, but had kept her license and her training up to date and announced she was ready to return to work when Anne arrived in Allegro looking for an office assistant. Margaret had the doors unlocked, the heater turned up, and the coffee made by the time David Huerra delivered Anne to the front steps and into the building before leaving.

Margaret had also noted the cancellations who had already called, and had begun a list of those she was willing to wager a week's worth of coffee-making just wouldn't show up.

One of those who didn't show up, but who did eventually telephone—just before Anne called Blake Foresman's office to get someone to search for her—was Nellie Flynn, part-time office help, inexperienced, never before employed, who had turned out to be as dependable as the chimes in the Methodist Church in Fairview and, after an almost nonexistent training period, as competent at her job as Margaret and Anne were at theirs. Nellie had slid her car into a ditch halfway down the mountain between her house and the highway and had walked back home before she'd been able to call. After Nellie assured Anne that she wasn't hurt, and that she had a neighbor who could retrieve her car for her, Anne made her promise to stay home until the roads thawed, which Margaret assured her would be soon.

Not soon enough, Anne thought with grim resignation as the day dragged on and she realized that she might have been overly optimistic about how well the people of Allegro had welcomed her. In a day when only three patients showed up, she had to admit that her practice wasn't exactly growing by leaps and bounds. While she undoubtedly got to treat most of the kids for colds and sprains and childhood diseases, and even their mothers for viruses or confirming pregnancy, she seldom saw anything serious walk through her clinic doors. If it was serious, if there was even the slightest suspicion that it might be, the patient bypassed her, usually bypassed the facilities in Fairview, too, and went directly to Fort Smith or to Texarkana.

But that was what Anne had wanted, wasn't it? She'd certainly told herself it was when she'd turned down a position on staff at an Indianapolis hospital and another with an aggressive and growing clinic in Lincoln—both among the places she'd applied while her life was in the process of going to hell but before it actually got all the way down there.

At three o'clock the snow started. All day the rain had been mixed with freezing rain and sleet. It gave way entirely to big white flakes that quickly built up on fences, tree branches, and windowsills. Margaret and Anne shared a long, discouraging minute in front of the rapidly fogging doors.

"Well, hell," Margaret said, sighing. "Three days before Thanksgiving. Who'd have thought it?" She grinned. "I sure hope the deer hunters are having a good time."

Knowing the hunters she'd met in Allegro, who seemed to live for deer season, or turkey season, or some even for no season, Anne suspected a little friendly malice in Margaret's words. "You'd better get home while you still can," she told her nurse. "I can take care of things here for the rest of the day."

Margaret laughed in that earthy, abrupt way Anne had first resented because she didn't understand and now had come to appreciate. "Honey, the roaches from that closed-down tavern out on Highway 59 can take care of all the business that's going to come through this door today. Grab your coat while I turn on the answering machine and tell the county to call you just in case there is an emergency, and then I'll give you a lift home.

Unless you want to call tall, dark, and dangerous to come after you."

Anne shot her a glance, but Margaret was all innocence as she turned on the answering machine, made her telephone call to the sheriff's dispatcher, and began turning off lights. Tall, dark, and dangerous, huh? Anne wondered what David Huerra would think of that description.

Margaret drove an oversized truck as down to earth and as efficient as she was. But she didn't immediately point it toward her house. When Anne turned to her to question her, Margaret shrugged. "Bet you don't have your holiday groceries bought yet, do you?"

Holiday groceries? For whom? And while Anne couldn't quite imagine turkey for one, she resisted the impulse to feel sorry for herself. Her mother, her stepfather, and her two half-brothers were on the other side of the world, the cousins her age had all moved away to find work, and Joe's part of the family hadn't seen fit to do any inviting.

"You've got that right," Anne said. "As a matter of fact, I don't even have my weekly groceries bought yet."

"Busy weekend?" Margaret asked, doing her best to leer suggestively.

Anne spluttered out a laugh. "Don't tell me the stories made it all the way up your hill. And you didn't say a word all day?"

"I was waiting for you to," she said. "Especially after I saw how you got to work."

"But—"

"Easy, Doc," she said. "Everybody in town may know he drove you to work today, but they also know he spent the night in Gretta Tompkins's Number 4 cabin. Alone.

"They also know your latest crew quit on you. And that Joe stopped to say sweet, loving words to you at the Lake Café yesterday."

Anne shook her head. "Is anything ever kept secret around here?"

"Nope," Margaret told her. "Not unless you work at it real hard." She frowned. "Some do." After another moment she added, "Joe usually does."

The truck skidded a bit as Margaret turned into a half-empty parking lot. She tapped the brakes lightly and brought her truck to a stop four spaces from the front door of the grocery store. "We're either real lucky or real late," she said. "Whichever, we need to stock up while there are still groceries of any sort available."

"Stock up? You sound like we're in for a blizzard," Anne protested. "Isn't this supposed to go away in a matter of hours?"

"It isn't supposed to happen at all," Margaret admitted. "Not this early. But since it has, you've got to realize that nobody knows how to drive on ice down here so you might as well be prepared. Then if the temperature goes up to seventy tomorrow, the worst that can happen is you'll have a full pantry, but if it stays cold or gets worse, you're ready for it." She grinned. "Especially if you just happen to get iced in with someone who can't get back out to a certain uninsulated cabin on a very bad road."

The house smelled like fresh paint and turpentine and simmering, spicy chicken when Margaret and Anne made the slippery run from the truck into the kitchen. Best of all, it felt blessedly warm after the buffeting they had taken from the wind in just the short distance from the truck to the porch.

And when Anne saw David Huerra standing at the kitchen sink, it felt like home.

She didn't have time to explore that, though. David whirled around from the sink when they came bursting through the door, but when he saw her he leaned back against the counter, drying his hands. "You're home early."

"Yes," Margaret said, giving him a blatant once-over. "That's because we wanted to get home. Hello." She bumped the two grocery bags she carried up onto the counter beside the ones Anne had just placed there and thrust out her hand. "I'm Margaret Samuels, Doc Anne's nurse. You left the clinic before I got to meet you this morning."

David returned her admiring smile, but Anne saw an easy humor in his eyes, not seduction. "My loss," he said, taking Margaret's hand. "I'm David Huerra—"

"The Dallas cop," Margaret finished for him. She gave a deep sigh and patted his hand. "Why couldn't it have been me out at Willie Johnson's sawmill Saturday?" She glanced at the paintbrushes that lay on the counter beside the sink, and the open toolbox that sat beside them. "I'll bet Joe's wishing pretty much the same thing."

David chuckled before he turned serious. "How bad are the roads?"

"Strictly four-wheel drive," Margaret told him. "But the snow's actually helping by covering up some of the ice. Or at least it will until it freezes over, too." She shrugged and drew her hand from his. "And I'd better get back out on them if I'm to have any hope of getting up my hill tonight."

"You could stay," Anne offered, remembering how cautiously Margaret had had to drive to get the short distance from the clinic and up her potholed driveway and dreading the thought of the miles the woman still had to travel. "I have plenty of room."

Had Anne surprised her nurse? Was her offer of hospitality so out of line? Maybe. Margaret seemed startled for a moment, but shook her head. "Thanks, anyway. But I have—responsibilities. Livestock, you know. Chickens."

Margaret left in a flurry of admonitions and cautions and promises to be careful. When Anne turned from the door and at last began unbundling from scarf and gloves and coat, she realized how much Margaret's presence had filled the room and how inexplicably awkward she felt being alone with David Huerra as the snow swirled outside and early darkness threatened.

Awkward. How strange. Especially after that one burst of . . . of belonging she had felt only minutes before.

"I'd better change clothes," she said, clutching her coat to her chest.

David looked at her, cocked his head to one side and tugged at his earlobe, but all he said was, "Watch out for the wet paint."

Awkward. Since she had met him she had felt many things, but always she'd had this underlying sense of having known this man forever, and well. What had changed? What could have changed in the few hours since he had left her at the clinic door? Nothing, she told herself. Not a thing. She dredged up a smile for him and left the room.

He'd told her to watch out for wet paint. She just hadn't realized how much of it there was. He'd finished framing and hanging the new kitchen/hallway door and replacing the trim along the hallway wainscoting and bathroom door. All of it gleamed with new gloss enamel. But that wasn't what drew her attention.

Anne stopped at the bottom of the stairwell, her attention drawn upward. For a moment she stood there with her hand on the old age-blackened varnish of the railing and her foot on the bottom step, listening—longing. Had she heard something? Or had she only wanted to hear something?

And then she realized how bizarre the last few minutes would seem to anyone else—as bizarre as David Huerra's first reaction to her house?—and gave a self-conscious chuckle as she forced herself to turn away from the stairs and go on into the bedroom to change into jeans and a sweatshirt so that she could rejoin David in the warmth of the kitchen and get on with the never-ending project of making this old house into a home.

If anyone had asked her the previous Saturday morning before she went to Willie Johnson's sawmill, Anne would have said she didn't want a man in her life. She didn't need a man in her life. She didn't need anyone in her life until she figured out what *she* was doing in her life.

After having had seven roommates while in med school, and never a moment to herself afterward because of the pressures of her practice and her clinic work, and the sheer number of other people who lived in the building where she had finally leased a tiny one-bedroom apartment that was all her own, after she'd seen how crowding too many persons in too small a space with no hope for more destroyed the humanity in those crowded, Anne had hoped she would be forever happy, or at least content, to rattle around in her small town and her big old house without having to worry about offending, bothering, or annoying anyone else. Or being offended, bothered, or annoyed by someone.

David Huerra didn't offend or annoy her. Bother her, yes. But that was something she was trying very hard not to think about.

There was something pleasant about coming home

from work and finding him there, something familiar about working together and sharing with him the meal that he had begun but that together they finished preparing; something almost . . . almost intimate about how easily they settled into each other's lives while the evening settled around them. At least that was how it seemed until he pushed back from the table after their meal and walked over to the pile of drywall and rolled insulation.

"You had company today, Doc."

"Here? At the house? Everybody knows I'm at the clinic on Mondays."

He nodded. "That's what I thought. But I couldn't be sure whether his surprise was at seeing me here, or at seeing anybody at all when the house was supposed to be empty. He covered it real well, though."

"He?" Anne had lived in the city too long. Her paranoia was working overtime. "I don't suppose it was my loving cousin Joe with an invitation to Thanksgiving dinner?"

David quirked a grin at her. "What? You'd accept and waste that runt bird I saw you stash in the freezer?"

She shook her head. There'd be no invitation to join that part of the family. She'd known that since the day she won the bid on the house. "Don't malign that bird," she said. "If you're really good, I might decide it's big enough to share with you."

His grin softened. "Thanks, Doc. And if *you're* really good, I might share my Aunt Elena's cranberry relish recipe with you. But no, it wasn't your loving cousin Joe. At least not in person."

It looked as though she wasn't the only one suffering from a little paranoia. "Then who? The weather today certainly wasn't conducive to casual, drop-in visitation."

He nodded. "Our buddy Hank."

"Hank Foresman?" That made absolutely no sense.

"He's never so much as spoken to me if he had to cross the street to do it. What on earth did he want?"

"Work."

"Work? Here? Why?"

David snagged a card of paint samples and brought it to the table. "He said—" He set the card on the table and himself in his chair. "He said he was in Alcoholics Anonymous. You may not know, but one of the twelve steps to sobriety is to make amends for any harm you've caused."

Anne nodded. She was familiar with a number of twelve-step programs. "But he hasn't—"

"He said he'd fallen off the wagon and that his wife— Ida?"

She nodded again. Ida Foresman was as straitlaced and honest as any woman her patriarchal God ever created.

"Ida," David continued. "Anyway, apparently Ida tore a strip off him once Blake brought him home Saturday. Said he could either get back in the program or find a new home. And since I was up here helping you, he'd be able to make some amends to me by helping me out."

"Right," Anne muttered into her coffee cup. "Did you believe him?"

"For about thirty seconds. Until I saw how he looked when I explained how I could use him to help hang the new ceiling in here. And until I realized he was a lot more interested in what you were doing upstairs than in what I was so obviously doing down here."

"What are you doing upstairs, Doc?"

"You didn't take him up there?"

"I took him down in the cellar, which needs a new door, out to that old garage or barn on the back property line, which needs a new roof, even to the well house, which only needs a good shoveling out, but we just never got around to going upstairs before I told him

I'd have to check with you about giving him a definite answer. But I was tempted. Real tempted. If for no other reason than to see what he thought was of so much interest up there. What do you think it could be?"

"Nothing." But Anne shivered as she remembered the feeling that had gripped her as she stood with her foot poised on the first stair, that sense of being both drawn and repelled by something unnamed and unnamable. "Absolutely nothing. There's only more old house and . . . "

"And? Come on Annie."

She grimaced. Why was she stretching for an explanation when she probably didn't even need one? "And one strange room that makes no sense."

"Strange? In what way?"

"Just—" How did she explain it? "Didn't you go upstairs at all?"

He shook his head, but not before she noticed an uneasiness in him, too. At least she thought she did.

"Then let's go upstairs and I'll show you. I need to check on a stove anyway."

Yep. There was an uneasiness all right. He stood, but not quickly, and he walked to the front of the house with her, but not with any enthusiasm, and when they got to the base of the stairs, he rested his hand on the newel post but kept both feet firmly planted on the old pine floor.

And she knew why. In no way did she want to walk up those stairs in the dark of the night. Something was up there. Something that was going to change her life. And if David felt it, did that mean his life would be changed, too?

She forced a laugh and turned toward him. "It's all your fault," she said. "If it hadn't been for your comment about someone walking over my grave, my imagination wouldn't have gone wild."

But it hadn't. She'd gone up those stairs last night without so much as a quiver and lighted the stove. Only tonight, with him in the house, had she felt any uneasiness.

"My fault, is it?" he said as he reached for her hand. "I'm not the one who bought a haunted house."

His hand enveloped hers, holding it, wrapping it in familiarity and—and safety. "Haunted house?" she managed to splutter. "Where did you get an idea like that?"

He tugged on her hand, pulling her closer, and they started up the steps together. "From your buddy Hank. He kept making all sorts of allusions to mysteries and danger and an Indian curse."

"And he was sober?"

David chuckled. "If your cousin Joe was trying to scare me away, it didn't work, Doc."

Amazing. Anne felt her own answering laughter. Why had she feared going upstairs with this man?

"It didn't work with me either," she told him. "Especially since I think it was all an invention of Joe's to keep anyone from wanting this wonderful old house."

There were five bedrooms upstairs, two bathrooms, a sleeping porch, attic stairway, a couple of rooms not large enough for anything but storage, and the room where Anne had left the stove burning the night before. They poked their heads into each room, turning on lights where there were working bulbs, rattling dresser drawers, cabinet doors, and windows, and opening the rare closet door, and finally she led him to the one room in question.

An ornate art deco light fixture hung from the ceiling, about three-quarters of the way across the room. The art deco vanity backed up to the wall that adjoined the bathroom in that end of the hall and had probably been installed about the same time as the light fixture. Instead of having, at the most, an old wardrobe or a corner that had been framed in for a closet, the entire back wall of the room had been converted into a closet. The decorative little stove that at one time must have seemed the height of sophistication glowed merrily. Instead of the floral paper she had found in every other room, this one held the remnants of a boldly striped paper with a swag border, except in one corner where it was shredded as though someone, at some time, had made a valiant, if heedless, attempt, at stripping it from the wall.

The furniture remained. All art deco. A long couch that had once probably matched a stripe in the wallpaper, although both were now badly faded. A couple of chairs. An octagonal table with a stained-glass lamp and huge ashtray. A mirrored dressing table with its matching bench. All of it lay covered with a grime that not even the years of neglect the rest of the house had suffered could explain.

David looked around the room with what Anne recognized as his cop's eyes. "I don't suppose there's a lock on the outside of that door."

"No." She could answer that. "At least, not one that can't be opened from the inside with a key. But there is a slide bolt on the inside."

"And the closets? Was anything left in them?"

"No."

Still holding David's hand, she led him to the nearest door and opened it. Light from the room went only partially into the closet, but it was enough to see that it was one deep closet extending the width of the room, empty of anything except a single, long rod and a few bare wire hangers below a narrow shelf.

"This is the back of the house, isn't it?" he asked. "The outside wall with no windows?"

"Yes." She'd known he'd realize where they were, even though they'd gone almost in a circle upstairs.

He stepped back and appraised the overhead light,

then looked back into the closet. "If the closet was added later, that might explain why the light's not centered."

He'd noticed that, too.

"But not why they took out windows for this closet when there's a perfectly good inside wall," he said. He stepped into the closet and then back out, pacing the distance between the closet's back wall and the overhead fixture, then the distance from the fixture to the opposite wall. "It's short a few feet."

"I know."

"I thought you would. Any ideas?"

"No." The room wasn't cold, but Anne was. She tugged on David's hand but found him almost as reluctant to leave as he had been to climb the stairs. Eventually, though, he did follow.

"That was what I was going to do this past weekend," she told him. "Explore the possibilities."

Once again in the kitchen, both of them backed up to the stove, fighting a chill.

"How?" David asked. "How were you going to explore the possibilities?"

Anne should have known he wouldn't drop the subject. Why should he, when it was still so very much on her mind?

"I thought I'd go up into the attic," she told him. "Maybe measure the distance from the ceiling fixture wiring to the outside wall of the house."

"And if there's a discrepancy? What then?"

She shrugged, as though it really wasn't too important. But it was. She knew it, and apparently so did David Huerra. "And then, maybe knock a hole in a closet wall and see why."

"When?"

Restrained impatience. How interesting. And how

very much like her own feeling. "Wednesday," she said. "I close the clinic at noon. There'll still be daylight. And maybe it will be warmer." Then, knowing on some level that she was probably doing the worst thing possible, that she hadn't felt any of these strange reactions until David Huerra came to this house, she looked up at him and said it anyway. "Want to help?"

"Yeah." He turned slightly, looking down at her upturned face. "Yeah, I do." Then as casually as if he'd been doing it all his life, he gave her a quick but thorough kiss. A kiss that went from casual to heated in the space of a heartbeat. A kiss that lasted no more than half a minute but seemed to have gone on for centuries.

"Damn," he swore softly as he clamped his hands on her arms and pulled away from her. "I don't . . . "

Then, before she found her voice or any words to use with it, he grabbed up his jacket and let himself out. Anne watched as he skidded across the backyard, buckled himself into the world's oldest Blazer, and slid his way down her hill.

And that's when her questions, and doubts and—yes—longings really began.

Longings that weren't based on the physical.

Yeah, right.

David Huerra was a literate, sensitive, attractive man. And in the six months she'd been in Allegro she hadn't even been out for a drink with a man. Let alone a literate, sensitive, attractive one. Now she'd had him in her house from daylight until long after dark, and to herself for most of the evening hours.

And what had they done? They'd talked, yes. They'd laughed. Yes, that, too. And they'd worked on woodwork and insulation and drywall and old wiring.

All of that she could have taken in stride. All of that she could have accepted as nothing—well, not too much, anyway—out of the ordinary. But then he'd kissed her, and she realized that she'd been lying to herself since the moment she helped pull him from his mangled car.

Oh, God, she didn't want to feel this. She didn't want to feel anything. Not yet. Maybe not ever. And not for someone who regularly and consistently put himself in danger.

But when he was with her, she didn't slink back into any of those pseudo-healthy techniques she'd developed to keep from thinking about what had really brought her back to Allegro. She didn't have to. When David was with her, she didn't think about screaming children or fear or even about Anthony, her fiancé for all of six days, and how he had died.

So maybe it was a decent trade-off. A little feeling—surely she could restrain herself to that—in exchange for a little, maybe a lot of, peace.

7

1935

    Lucy loved the garage—at least the loft of it,
all quiet and dimly lighted and private. There wasn't any
place private in the house anymore, not even her hidey
hole in the attic, since Aunt Marian and the baby had
come to live with them.

Lucy tried to like the baby, she really did. It would
have been easy to love the little boy, if Aunt Marian had
just let her hold him once in a while, if she had just let
her play with him, if she wasn't always telling her to be
quiet or still so she wouldn't bother him.

If Papa hadn't liked the baby better than he liked her,
and Aunt Marian better than he liked Mama.

Lucy felt guilty for thinking that, just like she felt
guilty for not really liking her little cousin. It wasn't *his*
fault. But was it hers? Had she done something that
made her papa not love her?

It was all right, she told herself. She had Mama to
love her, and Mama was better than Papa and Aunt
Marian and Cousin Joseph all put together.

And now she had Walter, too.

Walter sat in the desk beside her at school. He was new this year. He didn't have a papa to buy him new clothes or shoes and sometimes he looked like he was hungry, but he didn't make fun of her when she couldn't spell the words or make the reading behave and he wouldn't let the others make fun of her either.

She didn't think he was going to have a Thanksgiving dinner, and she knew Papa wouldn't let her invite him and his mother to theirs, but Mama had made an extra pie for her to give to them. Just as soon as he got here. Just as soon as she showed him the secret she had hidden in the loft over the garage.

Papa kept the garage locked, even when his big, new car wasn't in there, but he didn't know about the two boards at the back, under the window, he didn't know that she came in here whenever Aunt Marian got just too bossy to stand, and he didn't know about the mama cat and the kitten upstairs in the loft.

Papa was gone now. Lucy didn't think he'd come home all night. Maybe he wouldn't come home. Would Mama make Aunt Marian leave if he didn't? She'd heard her grandpa talking once—more than once—telling Mama it was her house, that she didn't have to be a servant to any white man. Mama had always hushed him when she saw Lucy, so Lucy wasn't too sure what Grandpa meant—not about the white part, but about the servant. Wasn't Mama just doing what mamas did?

Lucy hopped up and down, stomping her feet. Her coat was warm, and the garage walls kept out most of the wind, but Mama wouldn't let her wear overalls except when she visited Grandma and Grandpa, and her legs were cold. And if Walter didn't get here soon, everybody else would be here and she wouldn't be able to show him the mama cat and kitten.

She heard a two-note whistle outside and looked out

the window. Yes. There was Walter coming through their secret place in the hedge. Lucy inched the first board to one side and answered his whistle, and in a moment Walter squeezed through into the garage.

"Wow," he said. "This is big. Almost as big as a barn."

"It used to be a barn—well, a stable, anyway," she told him as she led him to the ladder in the corner and up to the darkened loft that created a ceiling over half of the building. She couldn't really remember when, that was when she was a real little girl, but Mama had told her it was, and that was why there was still some hay up in the loft. "I wish it still was. I'd sure like to have a horse."

"In town?" Walter asked. "Could you do that now?"

Lucy nodded. "Out here. If my papa would let me. Grandpa told me."

Walter scuffed his already worn shoe in the dry, loose hay scattered across the floor. "Bet you'd have a whole lot of friends if you had a horse."

Lucy might not be real smart, she'd heard Papa tell Mama she wasn't, but she knew why Walter hung his head and kind of shriveled away from her. "They wouldn't be real friends," she told him. "Not like you. And you'd always be my best friend."

He didn't look real convinced. "Promise?"

Lucy nodded.

"Blood brothers?"

"Ah, Walter, we don't do things like that." At least she didn't think they did. None of her cousins from her mama's family ever told her if they did. Hunting for words that were for now as slow in coming as they always were when trying to read, she pushed aside a stack of old feed sacks. The mama cat looked up and gave a welcoming twitch of her tail but didn't try to raise up on the injured leg Lucy had cleaned and bandaged. She was yellow and scrawny, not at all like

Mama's fat tabby. Quickly Lucy checked the dishes of food and water, then petted the cat. The kitten was getting braver every day. It crept toward her. Lucy curled her fingers gently around the wiggling, mewling little ball of yellow fluff and pulled it out of the shadows. "And besides," she said, offering her treasure to Walter, "I'm showing you my best secret even without that."

"I don't care," he told her, obstinately stubborn as she had learned he could be. He gave the mama cat a comforting pat before he tickled the tiny little kitten on the belly and under the chin, and she saw his smile dart out of hiding for only a moment. He shrugged and pulled out a scratched up pocketknife. "I been thinking about it, and I want us to make an oath that we're always going to be best friends. And I figure the best way to do that is share blood. That way when Harvey Skinner tells me I don't have any right to butt in when he's giving you a hard time, I will, too, have."

Lucy looked at the knife and shivered. It wouldn't do to let anyone, even Walter, know she was afraid. But she was. Oh, yes, she was. "You mean cut each other? Like in the movies?" She dragged her head slowly from one side to the other and held the kitten closer. "I don't think so. Mama would be real mad if I got blood on my clean dress."

"Come on, Lucy." He opened the knife and held the blade against his finger. "It would only be a little bitty cut, it's not like we're going to cut open our arms or anything—"

"Hush!" Lucy twisted away from him and the sight of the knife. Something scarier than that was getting ready to happen. "Someone's coming."

"We've got to get out of here."

Lucy heard the scrape of the padlock. "It's too late,"

she said, dropping to her knees in the hay and scooting back from the edge. "Quick. Get back here, out of sight."

It wasn't her papa's car. Instead of the big black Buick, a new but unbelievably muddy pickup truck that she recognized as belonging to Tom Jackson backed into the garage. Three men, her papa, Mr. Jackson, and someone she didn't know, got out of the truck and pulled the garage doors shut, sliding a board through the braces to keep them shut, and walked to the back of the truck.

Quickly Papa pulled the baskets off whatever was wrapped up in a big piece of canvas and tugged the canvas away.

Silence. Utter silence.

And they were too far back from the edge to see what kept her papa and Mr. Jackson and that other man so quiet. She and Walter shared a questioning look. She put the kitten to one side and quietly, stealthily she and her best friend slithered to the edge of the loft to look down.

Oohh.

Lucy pressed her lips together and prayed she hadn't let that moan escape.

A man lay in the back of the truck, all crumpled, surrounded by what looked like a whole lot of Papa's treasures, and covered in that metal that Papa always threw away when Mr. Jackson brought some to him. But this was different. It wasn't all green and mangled and stuck together. It glowed, and there were designs on it, strange drawings of the big birds she had seen in some of the shells Papa sometimes had out on his desk, and cats, big cats like she had never seen before. And it covered him from the top of his head right down to his feet.

Then Papa reached into the truck and picked up something and moved something else, and she saw that the man wasn't a man—well, wasn't still—

She felt that funny sound trying to get out of her

again when she saw that beneath the copper he was just bones. White bones. Bones that seemed to her to gleam with as much life as the copper. But not to her papa she guessed, because he tossed what looked like an arm bone to one side while he looked at the metal and then snatched up a—a what?—a statue and turned it from side to side.

"Didn't I tell you I did good?" Mr. Jackson asked. He reached into the back of the truck, too, and raked up a double handful of those round shell things Papa got so much money for when he sold them, put them down and lifted up two big shells—really big shells—that looked like dippers or gourds or pots, and turned them over and spilled out the beads Papa called pearls.

Papa put the statue down. He was trying to look like he wasn't impressed, but Lucy knew better. She'd seen him look like that sometimes when Grandpa would be talking about how much coal they were taking out of the mines on the land he had bought next to his allotment.

"It will take some time to move all this," he said. "If I even can. I know where it came from, but some folks might question it, except for the regular stuff, since I doubt anybody's seen anything quite like—

"What about the other one? The one you couldn't get. Did he have these copper plates all over him, too?"

"Nah," Mr. Jackson told him. "Just that big feather cape I told you about. And piles of stuff like these beads and shells and pipes. But it was broken. All broken. I ain't never seen so much unbroken stuff at one time before."

"Neither has anybody else," Papa told him.

"And they just let you walk out of there with it?" Now her Papa had his disgusted tone of voice, the one he used when he told her how bad her teacher said her reading was. That one. Had Mr. Jackson done something wrong, too? Was that why Papa was trying to make him feel bad?

"Hell, no, they didn't just let me walk out of there. I told you how we got it. And you were there, so don't think you're going to be able to weasel out of being part of it. If someone else just happens to figure out what I've done, I figure they'll be able to figure out who I did it with."

"I'm not trying to weasel out, Jackson. I'm just trying to be fair about what it's worth, and I'm afraid we won't know that until I manage to move it."

"Until you— Oh, no," Mr. Jackson said. "I'm not leaving this with you, so you can just forget all about trying that. You take it, all of it, now, and pay me for it like we talked about."

"It's Thanksgiving Day. The banks are closed. Where do you expect me to get any kind of serious money?"

Mr. Jackson smiled, but it was not a smile Lucy would like to see aimed at her. "I expect you to get it from that safe in your office. The place where you keep the money you don't want the taxman or your wife to know about. And I think I'll just go along with you to make sure you don't try to send anybody around to pay a surprise visit on me or my boy."

Papa had a safe in his office? With money in it? Was that where it all was? She'd heard her Grandpa ask her mother once what happened to all of Papa's money so that he never had any extra to spend on his family. Nobody knew. But Mr. Jackson did. How?

Unless it was just a guess, and a wrong one at that.

She hoped her papa would tell him he didn't have a safe and that he wasn't going to buy the dead man in the truck. She hoped her papa hadn't already done something real wrong, like helping to steal the dead man in the first place.

Her papa stood up real tall. He looked at Mr. Jackson first and then at the dead man in the truck for a long time. Finally he nodded his head, just once. "Come on then," he said.

The third man, the one Mr. Jackson had called his boy, stayed in the garage with the truck, keeping her and Walter trapped in the loft. Walter looked at her while the man locked the doors back, and she could see the worry and questions in his face.

She shook her head, wanting to tell him not to worry, that they'd get out just as soon as Papa finished his business. She wanted to tell him to be quiet because she knew her papa would be real mad if he caught them watching what he was doing today. It was wrong. Real wrong. And nothing anybody could say to her would convince her it wasn't. But it was a big secret that she knew they all had to keep or something real bad would happen to all of them.

She felt the soft brush of fur against her cheek and reached out to catch the kitten before it fell off the edge of the loft. A little hay slithered down, dropping into the back of the truck. Mr. Jackson's son didn't see it though. He was staring at the door. Until he turned and went back to the side of the truck and looked in at the dead man.

He had his papa's nasty smile. Lucy saw that as he stuck his hand into the pile of treasures and pulled out a small carved piece and stuck it in his jacket pocket.

The growl seemed to come from everywhere.

She felt Walter jerk to attention at her side and clutch her hand. But he didn't say anything. Maybe he couldn't. She sure didn't think she could.

What was it? And where was it?

Mr. Jackson's son looked around, nervous like, then shrugged and, trying to act like he wasn't as scared as she was by the sound that shouldn't have been there, reached back into the truck for another piece and stuck it in his pocket, too. Maybe he wasn't. Maybe he didn't hear it. Maybe he just felt them watching him as he stole that stuff from the dead man.

It was inside the garage. Downstairs, under the part the loft covered. And it was not mad, not yet, but getting there. The kitten Lucy clutched in her hand heard it, too, and its little ears flattened back and the fur rose up on its neck. Walter's hand tightened on hers.

Mr. Jackson's son grabbed a third piece of the treasure and eased his way to the doors, looking around a little, even up toward the loft before he scooted outside and slammed the doors shut behind him. Lucy heard the bar go across outside just as the cat—it had to be a cat, a big cat, maybe more than one—downstairs growled again. Over the pounding of her heart, and Walter's because she could hear that too, she heard the sound of restless pacing and then—silence.

The kitten relaxed in her grasp and began purring. Walter released her hand, slowly, and pulled himself closer to the edge so he could hang his head over and look back into the part of the garage beneath them.

He jerked back with a a nervous laugh and scrambled to his knees. "There's nothing down there."

"What do you mean there's nothing down there?" Lucy put the kitten down, crawled forward, and peered over the edge and into the corners. "I heard it. You heard it. Even the kitten heard it."

But there was nothing there. Only a pile of tires and tools in the corner and a bunch of old harness and tack hanging on the wall. And the man, the dead man, gleaming and glowing with the warmth of copper, jumbled and hurting and all alone in the truck.

"We've got to get out of here," Walter whispered. "While we can."

She didn't seem to be able to move.

"Come on, Lucy!" He tugged at the collar of her coat, pulling her back from the edge. "They'll be back after a while, and maybe that thing will be, too."

He pulled her to her feet and half pushed, half carried her to the ladder. "Hurry!"

"Wait!" No matter how much she wanted to run, she paused long enough to put the kitten back, safe with its mama.

She scrambled down the ladder, not believing until she looked around that the cat or whatever it had been was really gone. Walter scrambled after her and took her arm, tugging her toward the window and the loose boards at the back of the garage. But she couldn't go. Not yet. Digging her feet into the dirt of the floor, she stopped. Walter turned to see why.

She couldn't leave him. Not that way. There wasn't much she could do about him being all jumbled up like that, but she climbed up on the sideboard and reached in and put his arm back with the rest of him, only shivering a little when she touched the bare bone. When Walter saw what she was doing, he took a deep breath but climbed up to help her.

She had to touch the metal. Just like she'd had to touch it all those other times when Mr. Jackson brought some. This was different from all those other times. This was warm. Even though it couldn't be. Even though everything else in the garage was cold. Slowly she traced her fingers over one design—a cat, pacing, mouth open in an eternal growl.

She heard voices outside the door, and Walter tugged on her arm. She nodded. But before she left, she took the edge of the canvas and tossed it over the dead man.

It only partly covered him, but when she reached for the other end of it, to toss it, too, Walter already had the corner in his hand. He looked at her, not smiling, then climbed into the back of the truck and finished the job of covering the corpse.

Maybe she would trade some blood with him, after all, Lucy thought. Anyone who knew her as well as he did, who knew without her saying anything that she couldn't go off and leave the dead man like so much trash, had to be worth a little pain, a little blood. But she had a feeling that what she and Walter had shared this day in the garage was worth a lot more than any oath would have been before—

Before what, she didn't get a chance to explore. The voices outside the garage were getting closer. Walter jumped from the back of the truck and held his hand out to her. She smiled, quick like, because there wasn't time for much else, and jumped down, too. Then they slipped out beneath the loose boards, hearing what Lucy thought sounded like the low warning growl of the kitten's mama, only bigger, coming once more from inside the garage. Because they couldn't leave the boards dangling open to tattle on their having been there, they slid them into position and ran together for their secret place in the hedge, just as the garage doors banged open.

Lucy whirled around. "Papa," she whispered. "Will it hurt Papa?"

Walter dragged her down into the undergrowth beneath the hedge. "Sshh. Listen."

But there was nothing to hear. Nothing but the muted sound of voices within the garage. Then she saw Mr. Jackson's son walk to the shed beside the henhouse and come back dragging two big barrels, returning again to the shed for packing crates.

"What are they doing?" Walter asked.

Lucy shook her head. Were they putting him in a barrel? Was that what—

Her papa came out of the garage and marched up to the back porch. "Ellie!" he called out. "Ellie, get out here now!"

Mama came out onto the porch, wearing her apron.

"I want you to go the post office," Papa told her. "And then I want you to run over to McPherson's and pick up that book I lent him last week."

"Now? We have company coming in less than an hour. I have dinner on the stove."

"Marian will watch it," Papa said. "Take her Ford and go. And take Lucy with you."

Mama didn't like it when Papa talked to her like that. Now she stood up straight. "Lucy isn't here right now. And Marian can run your errands."

"Marian can't leave the baby. Just go. For once don't give me grief in front of my associates. Just go and get the mail and get the book so I can lend it to Jackson here."

She might not like it when he ordered her, but she always did what he said. Frowning, she took off her apron and stepped back into the kitchen, saying something, probably to Aunt Marian, before she went and got into Aunt Marian's spotless new Ford and left.

Aunt Marian came out of the house and said something to Papa that Lucy couldn't hear. Papa hugged her and whispered something to her. Aunt Marian laughed, and then Mr. Jackson and his son drove away in their dirty, empty truck, and Papa and Aunt Marian began hauling barrels and crates into the house.

"What do you suppose he told her?" Walter asked in a whisper.

"I don't know," Lucy said. "She never laughs. Never.

Walter? Did they put him in those barrels? Did they break him up even more and stuff him in those boxes?"

"I don't know. Wait here while I go see."

"No—"

But it was too late to warn him to be careful. Walter crouched and ran for the back of the garage and pushed aside one of the boards to peek inside. He was there for a long time, quiet, and Lucy saw him kind of slump there until he turned and then not even trying to hide came back to the hedge and sat down heavily beside her.

"Well," she asked when he just sat there saying nothing.

"Yep. That's what they did all right," he said, and his voice sounded strange. "Every bit of him and all the stuff that was with him is—is gone, out of sight, probably in the crates. Except for those long poles that were in the truck. Those are stacked up against the wall."

"But he's too big to fit in just one of them, unless . . . unless . . ."

"Yeah," Walter said. "I know."

"It's not right," she whispered. "It's not right to do that to someone!"

"Lucy, he's dead. He's been dead a long time."

"I don't care. Papa's wrong. Mr. Jackson's wrong. We've got to do something."

"We're just kids," Walter said. "Your papa isn't going to give him back just because we say to, and even if he would, who would he give him back to? So what are we going to do about it?" Walter asked. "What can we do? What will whatever it was that made that noise let us do?"

"I don't know." For the moment, Lucy admitted defeat. For a moment she believed all the things her teacher and her papa said about her being dumb or stupid. But she wasn't. She just couldn't read too good. Lots of folks couldn't read. That didn't mean she couldn't think. "I don't know," she repeated. "But there's got to be something."

8

Wednesday finally arrived—cold, but not as cold as Monday. And clear, with enough sunshine to filter through the ancient windows and vents of the attic. A perfect day for prowling.

In the day and a half since that brief and unexpectedly devastating kiss, David had managed to act as though it had never happened. Because his actions echoed her own admittedly conflicting desires, she had done the same. At least she hoped she had. She wasn't looking forward to an entire afternoon of guarding her words and emotions, but she also wasn't looking forward to an afternoon of searching out a mystery without David's steady presence beside her.

The attic stairs took them up into the northeast corner of the house, completely opposite to the area they needed. She had been up there, once before, right after she took possession of the house, but the profusion of actual walls, as well as those created by the studs of the walls below rising to the roof trusses, had confused her then, and it confused her now.

"My God," David said when she led him through a cut in what had to be the original wooden-shingled roof into the main part of the attic. "You have enough floor space for most small city halls. How many rooms are there up here?"

"I don't know. Not as many as it looks right now. If I remember correctly, the area we want is in the original part of the house, and it's basically open."

"Let's hope so," he said, testing the flooring beneath him with a cautious foot before he trusted it with his weight.

The attic wasn't completely floored, and in those parts where it wasn't they stepped over the roll insulation someone had installed long enough ago for the pink to be distinctly gray, making their way carefully along planks laid across thick, sturdy cross members.

Considering the condition of the rest of the house, the attic was surprisingly free of clutter. But then, except for furniture and some household goods, Anne had found nothing resembling Great Aunt Ellie's personal property, and she wondered, not for the first time, who had come for it and when. Since her bid had been for the house and furnishings only, she supposed she didn't really care who had divided up the essence of Ellie Hansom that probably had remained in the house after her death.

There were no halls, but brick chimneys, sloping ceilings, and, of course, the rising studs helped guide her, until they reached the south side of the house. A change in the roof line placed what windows there were in the end wall at the front of the house, and only a slatted vent lighted the rear. Cautiously, carefully, Anne made her way to the chimney flue for the small parlor stove below, and directed the beam of her flashlight along wires she found snaking their way across studs and insulation toward the wiring box for what she suspected must be the art deco light fixture.

They'd brought a metal tape measure with them, but they didn't really need it. The box lay off-center of what was clearly a rectangular area approximating that of the room below. And what she had thought to be a framed-in closet wall rose as a stud wall through the ceiling of the floor below, as did the walls of all the other rooms of the second floor.

"Another room?" she asked David, who had made his way to the other side of the stud wall.

"Yeah." He knelt down and began pulling at the insulation until he uncovered some ancient electrical wiring and followed it to a lighting box. "And it looks as though it's been wired."

She walked to the stud wall and looked toward the back of the house. There was enough space for a good-sized bedroom behind that wall, not just a three-foot-deep closet. "Why?"

David pulled back the insulation. There, as in the rest of the house, the ceilings were solidly framed and covered with thick boards. He knocked on it, and she almost expected an echo, but all they heard in the silence was the sound of their breath.

"Want to go find out?" he asked.

Anne shook her head, a reflex action, surely, because at that moment she didn't want to find out. She wanted to leave the mystery of that back wall in limbo as it had to have been for fifty years or so. But she couldn't. And David couldn't either.

The room was as eerie as it had been Monday night. She glanced at David and found him studying her. He felt it. Oh, yes, he felt it too, but neither of them said anything.

Taking a deep breath for the courage she suddenly needed, she opened the closet door and stepped in. The back wall inside the closet had been papered-over drywall. David knocked around on it looking for studs, tapping on it and the front wall, listening for differences. Even she could hear them.

She hefted the hammer. "Anywhere?" she asked.

"Looks like it."

She found a spot out of sight of the open door and waited for David to come to her side. Now that the moment had come, she didn't want to do this—but she knew she had to.

She raised the hammer, gripping it, and swung it. The ease with which it penetrated the wall stunned her. For some reason she had almost been expecting a vault or a fortress. She stepped back, and David bent to step closer beneath the rod and looked into the gaping hole before he moved aside for her. Nothing but darkness greeted her. Darkness, a chill, and that same attracting, repelling force that had gripped her Monday night at the foot of the stairs.

She handed the hammer to David. He nodded, and began knocking hunks out of the drywall, while she switched on a flashlight.

This time, the hole was large enough for both of them to look through it at the same time. The circle of light from the flashlight played across windows, still in place but covered on the outside by the wooden shiplap exterior siding, across a small floral paper, across a bare bulb hanging from a broken fixture in the ceiling, across years of dust on the bare pine floor, across something that gleamed faintly from that floor in the far corner of the room.

Anne dropped the flashlight.

"Was that—"

"I don't know," she said quickly. "I don't know."

Both of them stood silently for a moment, then, without speaking, they began tearing chunks of drywall away. Why, she didn't know. She wanted to run away, to leave the room as they had found it, to forget all about windows and measurements and secrets. God, yes, secrets. And she suspected David did, too. Instead, they worked silently but almost frantically at enlarging the opening while the beam of the flashlight reflected off whatever it was that lay in the corner.

Once they'd torn away enough drywall to make an opening large enough to squeeze through, David laid a restraining hand on her shoulder. Foolish man. Did he think she was going to argue with him about who went through first? She didn't want to go through that opening at all. But she did, easing her way in behind him as he stooped and retrieved the flashlight. Instead of doing the obvious, going immediately to the corner, he shined the light on the bare bulb and broken fixture above them. A long cord dangled from it. Miraculously, when David pulled on the cord, the bulb lighted, casting its forty-watt glare into all corners of the small room.

Illuminating what lay there on the floor.

"Oh, my God." Anne caught her hand to her mouth, tasting the chalk of drywall as she fought to hold in a moan.

Four wooden poles outlined a large rectangle covered with beads, pottery, shells, weapons—axes, celts, maces, and assorted blades and points—and what appeared to be small statues. Two others served as bracing. And in the center, covered with glowing, engraved copper plates—

"It's a body," she whispered.

"No." David spoke softly. He walked to the edge of the first pole and knelt down, reaching out but not touching the abundance of artifacts that surrounded what her eyes told her was definitely a skeleton. A human skeleton.

"It's a burial," he said, his voice hushed. "My God, it's a—it can't be—complete archaeological burial. But who? What? He must be—what do you think, Anne? Six feet seven? Eight?"

He. Yes, this was—had been—a man. A tall man by anyone's standards. The copper that covered him had to be a form of armor. Thin, engraved with warlike hawks and snarling, prowling cats, it was impractical for any protection so it had to be ceremonial. It had to be . . .

And then she recognized the copper feathers that sprang from his mask, the human representations with their distinctively outlined eye that adorned a breastplate, the almost abstract snakes, the swirling repeated designs, and most of all, the cats. It couldn't be. But it was.

"My designs."

Slowly she sank to her knees at the foot of this impossible find. She too stretched out her hands, drawn to the man but like David, unable to bring herself to touch him.

"Who—" She lost her voice entirely for a moment and only managed to recover a small part of it. "Who is he?" Did she know? *Should* she know? Somehow she thought she must. But *how?*

"A monarch of some sort. Obviously a powerful warrior, because of his armor and the number of weapons." David shook his head, still speaking in hushed tones. "But how did he get here? Into a closed-off room in Allegro, Oklahoma. How did he get into your house, Annie? And why is he still here and not in some museum?"

A small box rested near the warrior's left foot, from which the covering had long ago disintegrated, leaving the bones visible and strangely vulnerable. Cautiously Anne reached for the box, almost expecting a crack of thunder or an ominous voice demanding that she stop.

The box appeared to be—cedar? It was hard to tell. It had a fitted, almost transparent top, with a design etched in it. She held it for David's inspection. He touched it as cautiously as she had lifted it.

"The top is mica, I think," he said.

She nodded, swallowed, and began carefully working the top from the box. The inside of the box was lined with copper and contained only two items. Small shell cameos lay among the remains of some woven fabric. They were perhaps two inches in diameter, each bearing the representation of a person: a man and a woman. The man pictured was this one. She knew it. She felt it in every chilled inch of her being. She looked at the items surrounding him. Possessions. Awesome in their diversity and antiquity, but only possessions. "But where is she?" Anne asked.

She sensed David's eyes on her and looked up to see him watching her warily. She tried to smile. When that didn't work, she handed him the box containing the two cameos. "The woman whose likeness accompanied him," she explained.

David took the box from her and lifted one of the cameos, turning it in the light of the bare bulb. Carefully he replaced it and the mica lid and settled it back in its original place.

"Come on, Annie," he said, rising to his feet and putting his hand on her arm. "Let's get out of here for a minute."

"No, I—"

"Come on, Annie," he said more forcefully. "We need to get out of here."

He sounded so convinced she hadn't the heart to argue with him, until he reached to turn off the overhead light.

"No—"

He shook his head, but he pulled the cord, plunging the room into darkness except for the small beam of light that seeped through the opening they had made. Then, holding her arm firmly—for her support or his?—he walked her to the opening and all but pushed her through it.

They didn't make it to the warmth and familiarity of the kitchen. At the base of the stairs, Anne stumbled. David stopped and turned to look at her. He muttered an oath and threw his arm around her, almost dragging her to the front of the house, to the safety and sanity of her bedroom. There, he pushed her down on the side of the bed and shoved her head down between her knees.

Anne sucked in a deep breath and tried to raise her head. His hand on the back of it wouldn't let her. "I'm not going to faint," she protested.

"Could have fooled me. Breathe. Slowly."

As she struggled for air, she dimly realized that his words were as ragged as hers. "I've seen worse," she choked out.

"Yeah. Me, too."

She felt the pressure on the back of her head ease and the mattress dip slightly as he sat beside her, heard him working as hard at controlling his breathing as she was, and knew as she fought her reaction that it was all out of proportion to what had gone before. And that David Huerra, the big-city cop who had to have seen more carnage and mayhem than even she, had reacted just as strongly.

Eventually his hand slid from the back of her head to the nape of her neck, and his touch gentled. Eventually her breathing settled into a rhythm that would supply her body with the oxygen it needed. Eventually she heard him draw a deep breath.

She looked over at him to find him pale beneath his bruises. Paler even than when she had pulled him from his car. He looked back at her. Both of them had questions; neither of them had answers.

And at almost the same time, both of them realized that David's hand had begun tracing a pattern on her neck that was more sensuous than protective.

Anne tensed. He withdrew his hand. And she once again felt the chill of the house. But at last she was able to begin to identify the emotion that had gripped her so strongly when she looked at what remained of that bare, vulnerable foot. Not horror. Or perhaps, not entirely horror, because that was mixed in with it. But grief. A grief so intense, so all-encompassing, that it threatened to paralyze her.

Fighting it, she reached for the bedside telephone.

"What are you doing?"

"I'm calling the sheriff," she said. For the moment that seemed the only thing to do. "We've got to report this."

"Annie, however he got there, he's been there for a long time. A few more minutes won't make any difference. Let's think about this. Blake Foresman is a good man, but I'm not sure his department is what we need right now. I'm not sure he's up to handling what—whatever it is that we just exhumed."

He was right, of course. Anne knew that. A few more minutes wouldn't make any difference. Whoever was up there had been there for—what?—fifty years or so, and, if she allowed herself to think clearly about him, had probably been dead for a lot longer than that.

He was definitely not anything Blake Foresman would want to be responsible for.

She sighed and slumped back onto the bed, releasing the telephone, and nodded. They did need to think about this. About who and what and when. And about why it had affected both of them the way it had. David squeezed her hand and released it with a sigh of his own.

"Good girl."

Anne glared at him. "Don't be patronizing, David Huerra. I'm not the only person in this room who just fell apart."

He managed a grin, a lopsided one that didn't quite disguise the fact that he was still as deeply affected by their find as she was. "Damn," he said. "I was hoping you hadn't noticed."

Her laugh surprised her. And as weak as it was, as reluctant as it was, it was enough to bring them both out of the morass of emotions and into a semblance of normality.

Anne had no alcohol in the house. David brewed coffee so strong she choked on the first swallow. But that jolt of caffeine was what she needed. That, and his touch, which she no longer had. Even though he sat beside her at the round kitchen table with its familiar nonmealtime clutter of phone books and construction invoices and a pile of opened but unsorted mail, he kept his hands securely wrapped around his mug of coffee. As she did.

She was weakening though. She could tell that at any moment she would give way and act on her uncharacteristic need to be connected to someone, anyone.

David stood and paced the length of the room before returning to the table. "You worked the emergency room during your internship, didn't you?" he asked.

"Yes."

"And I've been in homicide for five years." He sat down. "So why did we react the way we did?"

She looked up to find him fighting to find answers that just weren't there. To hell with it, she thought. She needed human touch regardless of how proud or stubborn he thought he had to be. She reached for his hand. Without looking, he grasped hers, and slowly, gradually, she felt the tension begin to leave her, begin to leave him.

Remembering his words the first time he saw her house, she attempted a lightness she didn't feel. "Maybe someone walked over our graves?"

He smiled, or grimaced. It was difficult to tell which. "Maybe," he said. "But it felt more as if *we* were the ones doing the walking."

Yes. Now that he mentioned it. Yes it had. And the graves had been their own.

"I don't suppose this uncle of yours was a grave-robber?" he asked tentatively.

She shook her head. "I don't know much about him. Only that for a while he was, or at least was thought to be, extremely wealthy. He owned half the town. And then he lost his money, had to sell off his holdings."

"But not this place?"

"No, and I think everyone wondered why. But we found out, just months ago in fact, that this was always Aunt Ellie's place, part of her allotment from the Choctaw Nation, and he never owned any part of it."

David glanced around the kitchen, and she knew he was seeing the size and scope of the house of which this room was just a part. "Somebody had some money."

Yes, someone did. "He did, early on. And of course her family had coal and gas and lots of timberland."

"When?" David asked.

He hadn't released his grip on her hand, but he turned over an envelope from her untidy pile of mail and began, idly, she thought at first, drawing a design on the stark white with a fine-line black pen.

"When what?" she asked as she watched a design

emerge. A design she had just seen upstairs on a round piece of shell.

"When did he lose his money? The depression? That far back?"

"I don't know. Is it important?"

"I don't know. I don't know what is and what isn't anymore. Damn!"

"David?" What was happening here was serious enough, but she sensed his frustration came from more than just—just?—this afternoon's bizarre happenings.

Again he smiled. Or grimaced. "I told you I came to Lake Allegro to think, didn't I?"

She nodded.

"But not what I had to think about."

He knew he hadn't. That was one of those secrets she had sensed in him.

"I blew a case, really blew it, because I had closed myself off in my preconceived notions."

She didn't see the relevance, not really, and he must have sensed that she didn't.

"I almost cost a couple of nice people their lives, maybe did cost one woman hers, because I insisted on seeing something the way *I* knew it had to be. And then I learned that I didn't know it all after all."

"So you came here to—?"

This time it was definitely a grimace. "To learn whether or not I could ever be a cop again. To learn whether or not there was enough left in me after fifteen years on the force to rejoin the human race.

"I didn't want to," he continued slowly, "but I was ordered to come here or someplace like this. I thought I'd spend my thirty days staring at strange walls and feeling my brain turn to mush. I had no idea that I would have to face something that had no apparent logical explanation."

She had to set aside what he said about self-discovery, for the moment, to address the second part of his statement. "There's a logical explanation," she insisted. "Just because we don't know what it is—"

"I'm not talking about just what we found upstairs, Annie. Or maybe I am. Maybe it's all tied together."

And of course, she had no answer for that.

David squeezed her hand. "Okay," he said. "For now, let's not dwell on our reaction to what we found in that room. If we do that, maybe we *can* find something logical in why there's a copper-armored skeleton with most, if not all, of his grave goods surrounding him in a carefully constructed secret room in your house."

"Uncle Ralph was a grave-robber?" she offered tentatively.

"Maybe."

"David, I was not serious."

He flashed a wry grin at her. "There are different kinds of grave-robbers," he told her. "Some of them operate within the law. Maybe your uncle was a collector. The question is, which particular set of graves did our friend upstairs come from?"

"No. The question is, why is he still here? I may not be knowledgeable about archaeology and artifacts, but it seems to me that there's a fortune hidden here. Supposedly, Uncle Ralph sold everything of value he owned, so why didn't he sell what . . . what we found upstairs? Unless there's something really bizarre going on and the skeleton isn't as old as we think it is."

"Good point, Annie. Let's find out."

"Right. And just how are we going to do that?"

He scooted the drawing toward her. "I know a collector. I wouldn't call him a friend, but he's reputable, probably even honest. Let's ask him—discreetly—

about some of these designs. They seem familiar, but I can't place them. Maybe he can."

She thought about that for a moment. *Discreetly* was the operative word here. Since he'd stopped her from calling Blake, she'd realized she didn't want cops, or now collectors or reporters, crawling all over her house. Finally she nodded. "And I have a friend who just finished a residency in pathology. I can ask her to assure us we're not dealing with a reportable corpse."

"Is there any way you can get more information about your uncle?"

"Maybe. Probably not from anyone around here," she admitted. "But maybe my mother knows something."

"Okay." He chuffed out a breath. "If we hurry we can get this started before the holiday officially begins so that maybe by Monday we might know something."

She glanced at her watch, knowing it was far too late to accomplish anything before Monday, only to find that barely an hour had passed since they had started their search. "You first," she said.

David brought the phone to the table and dialed information in Dallas, asking for the number of the collector he knew, while she dug through her junk drawer for her address book containing Karen Ready's new, unlisted Chicago phone number. David had his number before she found hers and had dialed by the time she returned to the table. While the telephone rang at the other end of the line, he continued drawing on the sketch he had started.

"Jack?" he said. "David Huerra." He laughed. "Yes, it has been a long time. How was your trip to Peru? Oh, really. I'm sorry to hear that. Maybe next year."

He waited, listening for a moment. "Well, yes, there is something you can do. I'm hoping you can identify an artifact for me.

"No, not official business. As a matter of fact, I'm on

vacation. It's something that's— Well, hell, Jack. It's personal."

David laughed again, but the pen in his hand pressed down on the envelope. "How about me sending you a drawing—okay, a tracing of a shell gorget?"

He frowned slightly. "Oh, yeah, it's engraved all right. . . . A couple of heavily dressed figures with speech symbols. They're holding some sort of vessel with a cat-headed snake, the world or four winds symbol and a couple of other things I don't remember seeing before.

"Yes. Oh, yes, there's enough to identify. It's intact. No, it hasn't been killed. I don't know. Let me check."

He held his hand over the mouthpiece and frowned at her. "He's excited, but trying to hide it. He says he needs to see the real thing."

"Should we send it to him? Can he be trusted?"

"Probably," David said. "And it's either send him a piece or invite him here if we want any kind of positive I.D."

"Not here." That much she was sure of.

David nodded. "FedEx? UPS? Do we have time to make their pickup schedule?"

"No, not this late. We'd have to drive to Fort Smith. How about overnight mail? It takes two days to get most places from here, but that would put it there Friday."

"You're sure?"

She wasn't, but they had to do something. This at least was a start. "Yes."

He lifted his hand to her cheek and held it there for a second. Encouragement? Who knew why at that time? She didn't; David probably didn't either. But that small gentle contact was needed, oh, so needed.

Slowly he withdrew his hand and lifted the receiver. "Okay," he said to the man on the line. "We'll get this out to you tonight. Where do you want it sent?" He scrawled the address on the envelope beneath his sketch. "Right. No, I don't know whether the owner will want to sell or not. I'll ask, and I'll certainly recommend you. Yeah, thanks. Right. I'll call you what—Sunday morning? Will that give you enough time? Okay. Thanks again, Jack. I really appreciate this."

Reflective, David replaced the receiver and scooted the telephone toward her. "Your turn."

She reached Karen at the apartment she still shared with two of their original roommates, although that would change soon. Anne knew Karen had been chasing a slot at a university med center somewhere in the west—Wyoming, Montana, Utah, Colorado. Anywhere closer to the mountains she loved and away from the man she didn't.

"It's about time you contacted somebody, Locke," Karen told her with a laugh. "We were all beginning to think you'd either fallen in that lake down there, or taken root and started to sprout. How the hell are you? And what's it like not to have to chase yourself around the clock?"

"Excuse me," Anne said. "I thought I'd reached the mature and eminently respected Dr. K. Ready. I must have misdialed."

"So, kiddo." Karen dropped her voice half an octave and affected a mixed-eastern European accent. "You call, you joke, you must vant somet'ing. Tell Dr. Ready how she may help. But remember—none of my patients survive."

Karen had been the one who held the roommates together back in those early crowded years. When tempers, already short because of stress and long hours, threatened to get out of control over whose turn it was for the shower or who should have carried out the trash, she was always there with a joke when needed, a soft word, or even an occasional dressing-down.

Anne and Karen had gone through a residency in internal medicine together, but Karen had learned early on she couldn't stand losing a patient. She was the only person Anne knew who'd gone into pathology because she was too softhearted to watch the living die. In pathology, Karen swore, she'd have a chance at finding out how to fight disease and trauma without risking her heart. Knowing Karen, Anne thought she probably would.

"I've missed you," Anne told her friend.

"Yeah." Karen lost the accent. "Me, too. Damn." Anne heard a strange muffled noise and then a sniff. "Did you just call so we could have a good cry together, or was there a more important—excuse me—*another* reason for you spending long distance dollars I know that practice down there doesn't provide?"

That comment was part of one of Karen's ongoing gibes, made without malice, and Anne let it slide. Besides, Karen's opinion of her practice wasn't so very far off the mark. "Yeah," Anne said. Now that the moment had come, she almost relished her reaction. It was all too seldom that she got the best of Karen Ready. "I want you to look at a bone and tell me if I have to call the cops."

Absolute silence filled the line. Finally, Karen whispered softly, "You're serious?"

"Yeah."

"But you're qualified. Surely you can tell if it's—"

"I can tell that it's human, and that it's dead. Long-time dead. But I need your expertise to tell me how long, and whether I need to call a homicide division or a museum."

Anne looked at David to see him frowning and shaking his head as though to tell her to be careful about how much she said. But this was Karen, someone she'd trust with her life. Still, when he leaned closer she held the receiver so he could hear both parts of their conversation.

"Oh. Oh, well, sure I can do that. I do that a lot. But generally it's the cops who bring me the bone. Are you sure you don't want to go the regular route—of course, you're sure. I'm sorry Anne. You have a reason for not contacting the cops, right? Something to do with that godawful old house you bought and that mean-spirited cousin of yours?"

David glanced at Anne and grinned, and his eyes taunted her with his knowledge that no matter how circumspect she had tried to be with him about her family, she had not suffered in complete silence.

"I can send you a right femur," Anne said.

Again silence filled the line. "You have more than the one bone, don't you?" Karen asked. "You have the whole damned thing. What did you do, literally find the skeleton in the closet?"

David's frown grew fierce. And not without cause. He didn't have any kind of shared history with Karen on which to base trust. And for now, maybe the less Karen knew, the better—for her own sake, if they were wrong about the age of the man upstairs.

"I have a right femur," Anne repeated. "Will you look at it for me?"

"Oh, hell yes, you know I will," Karen said with only mild exasperation blunting her words. "I suppose you want it yesterday, and in complete confidence, too?"

"Got it in one," Anne told her and laughed softly, knowing Karen's eyes were dancing and her mouth was drawn in a mock pout. "With overnight mail to your door, it should get there Friday morning, and I'll call you Sunday morning for an unofficial report. Okay?"

"You're damned right it will be unofficial. Do you have any idea—"

"Lots and lots of ideas, Karen. You know that. It's the reason you put up with me all these years. When you couldn't get into enough trouble on your own, I was always able to help you out. And I'll owe you for this. Big time."

"Big time and big explanation," Karen added. "Anne . . ." Her voice was hesitant. Anne knew why, of course. Karen couldn't fail to ask, yet she didn't want to bring up harsh memories. "Are you all right? Really all right? We worried about you so much when you left. You know, you had some pretty serious injuries, lady. Physical and, well, and otherwise."

Anne didn't miss David's sharp glance. Only inches away from her, his already dark eyes took on an even darker glitter. She wanted to take the telephone receiver and pull away from him, but the damage had already been done.

"I'm fine, Karen," she told her. "Really. The practice is every bit as slow as we thought it would be, and so is the town. I've had lots of time to rest. And to heal."

"And to find skeletons in the closet," Karen added dryly. "Yeah, it sounds as though you've found a perfect place to recuperate."

"Better dead skeletons in the closet, than live, persistent secret admirers. Have you found out who he is, yet?"

"Pu-leeze, Anne. Jeeze. You could have gone all day without mentioning that."

Anne chuckled. Karen still sounded more provoked than frightened by this unknown suitor. "More flowers?"

"Twice a week," Karen told her. Maybe provoked wasn't a strong enough word, because Anne definitely heard more in her friend's voice than that. She also heard hesitation, as though Karen were holding something back.

"And what else?"

"Nothing," Karen said. "Nothing except my paranoia. You know I never could keep track of my things. And with Rae and Molly in the apartment, it's no wonder that I occasionally lose something."

Anne felt David tense beside her. She shook her head as she saw him reaching for the receiver. "Well, if it's clothes, check Molly's closet," she told Karen. "And if it's more serious than that, maybe you'd better reconsider talking to the police."

"Yeah. I can just see the headlines on something like that: 'Bone doctor blows whistle; flowers mask scent of formaldehyde.'"

"Karen—"

"It's okay," she said. "I promise. Now send me your femur and start practicing for the time when you're going to give me this wonderful explanation. Is it too much to hope there's a living man mixed up in it somewhere?"

"Dream on. I'll talk to you Sunday, but let's keep in touch, okay? I worry about you. And thanks."

Anne sank back in her chair after she hung up, as drained as if she had just taken a major test. Concerned, David asked, "Are you up to calling your mom now?"

"Doesn't matter whether I am or not," she told him after a glance at her watch. "I never can remember whether it's a seven-and-a-half or an eight-and-a-half hour time difference. They get up early, but if I call them now, Mom's fully capable of putting a contract out on my life."

He had to have heard the affection in her voice in spite of her words. "You love her, don't you?"

"Yeah," she told him. "A lot. And I miss her. A lot. But I'm so damned glad she's happy at last."

David dropped his hand to her shoulder, and it was like his touch to her cheek had been earlier. Necessary. Too much. Not enough.

"Okay," he said, squeezing her shoulder gently before

releasing it and standing. "Let's go get the stuff to send."

Anne didn't want to. God knew she never wanted to go back into that room. But she knew they had to. "Right," she said. "Just let me find some boxes first."

The two items they were mailing were fragile and would need a lot of protection. She grabbed two boxes left over from her move and scooped up a double handful of polystyrene peanuts and a couple of lengths of bubblewrap.

David stopped her as she was reaching for tape and scissors. Stilling what even she recognized as nervous procrastination, he put everything but the boxes on the table. Those he took from her. "This is all we need for now," he said. "We'll bring them down here to pack."

She stood looking at him in silence, every fiber of her being rejecting her conscious decision to go back upstairs. *We'll bring them down here to pack.* David had said that, linking himself with her even though she knew he didn't want to return to that travesty of a grave either. She swallowed once, still silent, wishing he didn't have his hands full with the boxes so that he could at least touch her, and then realized that she could reach out. She could offer the touch that maybe he needed, too. She rested her hand on his arm. He glanced at it then back at her eyes. "Okay," she said abruptly, sounding much braver than she felt. "Let's get this over with."

9

What waited in the secret room was as overwhelming as it had been earlier. For both of them. Anne felt David standing close behind her at the foot of the array heaped up around the copper-covered skeleton within the confines outlined by the cedar poles.

But maybe it was getting easier to view this scene, or maybe her eyes were just becoming more accustomed to the forty-watt lightbulb.

The area defined by the cedar poles was perhaps six feet by eight feet. The body—she couldn't think of it in any less personal terms—lay in the center of that area on the remains of what appeared to be some kind of mat, although it was difficult to see for the profusion of items piled upon it.

She saw two wooden barrels and several boxes in the corner of the room. She made her way over to them and found them empty except for a small amount of dirt in the bottom of each of them. The same dirt, probably, that she felt sliding beneath the soles of her shoes. The same dirt that she saw in small piles among the artifacts and which lightly dusted everything within the boundaries of the cedar poles.

"Did you find anything?" David asked from the other side of the burial.

"No. Just dirt. And maybe the way he was brought up here."

"Then let's get on with it."

The harsh, bleak sound of his voice echoed her own emotions too closely for her to begin to examine. Deciding it fell in that area of things they wouldn't dwell on, she nodded, carefully walked around the perimeter of the burial and knelt beside David.

Almost reverently, he touched a round, engraved object four inches or so in diameter that rested on top of a pile of other engraved shells. Anne recognized the design on it as he lifted it and held it so the uneven light could illuminate it. "This is a gorget," he told her, again turning the item in the light so that she could see. "It's engraved on a circle of conch shell and made to be worn as a neckpiece. These two small holes here?" He pointed at a place near the top of the disk. "These were drilled so that a thong could be inserted." For a moment she thought he was going to place it back with the others. "I hate to separate this," he said.

"I know."

"I'll want to make a tracing of this before we send it away."

"Is it very valuable?" she asked.

"Yeah. Oh, yeah. If it's authentic, and I don't think there's any doubt of that, it won't really matter where it originally came from. It— Yeah. It's valuable."

"Something your friend Jack might decide actually belonged to him?"

He was silent for a moment. "I don't think so, Annie, but greed's a strange thing. It can make thieves of people you'd swear on your life were honest. So just to make sure Jack stays honest, we'll do the tracing, or photocopy it if we can find a copier, and— I don't know. Can you register overnight mail?"

"I don't know. I've never tried. Doesn't it have to be signed for anyway?"

He didn't answer, but he put the disk in the small box she had selected for it and then moved the larger box closer to her. "Do you want me to get it?" he asked.

He didn't have to say what "it" was. The unspoken words hung between them, all out of proportion, as everything had been since they'd pounded their way into this room. Leg. Thigh. *Femur.* She snatched onto that clean, impersonal word, hoping it would bring reality into their own private twilight zone. It didn't.

Did she want David to get it? Did she want David to be the one who desecrated an already desecrated grave? Anne didn't want either one of them to, but that was irrelevant now. She shook her head, trying to erase images of the skeleton before them as he once must have been—living, vital, dynamic—and leaned forward.

The copper plate covering the warrior's right thigh was in two pieces. It had been hinged. The remains of what appeared to have been leather thongs were still clearly visible. It also mirrored the copper plate on his left thigh. Two cats looked out from the armor, upright on their haunches. Their bodies twisted to one side for protection, but they were writhing, snarling, ready for battle. And she didn't want to touch either of them, but she knew she must. As reverently as David had lifted the gorget, she lifted the copper plate and lay it beside the thigh.

As much as she could see of the femur was intact. Part of it was still hidden by the copper plates that had covered the man's abdomen and groin. All connecting muscle, all flesh, had been gone for years, for centuries, but without the harsh intrusion of weather, the bone had taken on a soft, white patina, curiously unmarred by the green tinge ancient copper should have given it. Hesitantly, she reached for it.

A low growl seemed to come from all around them. Anne jerked her hands away and her head up, to meet David's frantic search of the room.

"What was that?" she whispered.

But then the wind rose outside and she recognized the scrape of that branch from the pecan tree that periodically threatened the roof as it raked against the side of the house. And sighed. "Wind," she said. "Just wind."

But still, she didn't want to go on. "Do we have to do this?" she asked David. "Can't we just sheetrock and paper over the closet wall and pretend we never found him?"

"And leave him here for your cousin Joe or someone else out for the quick buck to find?" David asked. "How long do you think it would take him and your buddy Hank Foresman to pick through and scatter this collection?"

Not long, Anne knew, and not with any respect. She reached again for the femur and couldn't help apologizing. "I'm sorry. I wouldn't do this if it wasn't absolutely necessary, and I promise to put it back just as soon as I can."

Walking over a grave? Yeah. They were doing that. Big time. And it didn't help that she felt an undue bond with the long-dead man whose grave they were desecrating. It didn't help that she sensed that David felt that bond, too.

David's hand covered hers as she placed the femur in the box. His sigh echoed hers as they released the partially calcified bone. They remained kneeling there for a moment, then stood, not speaking. David was the one who reached over and replaced the copper armor to cover the length of missing bone. He picked up the boxes and stood, but waited until Anne had passed through the opening into the closet before he turned out the light and followed her.

Downstairs, the kitchen seemed abnormally normal. Anne left the room long enough to locate a package of white tissue paper in her gift-wrapping supplies. She gave it to David and he carried it to the round oak table where he made a tracing of the gorget. Together they located a box more suitable for the femur and carefully wrapped the bone and the gorget. They packed with the hope the fragile items would reach their destinations without damage and that the recipients would treat them with equal respect.

"I have labels and postage at the clinic," she told him when the items were wrapped and securely taped into their boxes.

"Good. It will mean Jack knows about you, but it might be better if it looks like these are really going out from the clinic. That way, no one around here will be curious about what we're sending overnight delivery on a holiday weekend."

"Do you really think anyone would even notice?"

"Annie, Annie," David said, with a grim sort of humor. "This is your small town. You know someone would. And if Cousin Joe is already suspicious about what you're doing in the house, you know it would be only a matter of hours before he or one of his friends began to wonder what you'd shipped off, and why."

David was right, of course. Joe might not know about their friend upstairs, but since he'd so obviously sent Hank around to snoop he probably suspected something. And wasn't that a nice little piece of a puzzle she hadn't even been aware of until David Huerra came crashing into her life?

Anne looked at the long, squat box with the femur in it. Strangely, handling it, being responsible for it, caused her more concern than any thought of the small artifact David had said was so valuable. "You'll go with me?" she asked, but it wasn't really a question. She couldn't visualize carrying those two boxes through town without him by her side. She couldn't visualize him letting her do so.

"I don't think that's such a good idea. Not with that hole in the wall upstairs and with at least one person real curious about what's up there."

"Oh." He was right again, damn it.

David carried the packages for her, out to where she had parked Agnes, near the old barn. He opened the driver's side door, slid both boxes over the center hump until they rested on the floor on the other side, and turned to her. "Be careful."

For a moment as she looked up at him, she considered pleading with him to reconsider, to go with her. Pleading. Her. She had begged exactly once in her life. It had done no good. She couldn't suppress the shudder that ran through her.

"Annie?"

She shook her head. She couldn't bring herself to tell him that nothing was wrong, because she wasn't sure that everything wasn't wrong. But there wasn't anything either one of them could do about it right now except exactly what they were doing. "I'll be all right," she said as she climbed into the truck. "You be careful, too."

David watched until Anne had backed her truck to the wide, sparsely graveled area nearer the house, turned, and disappeared down the driveway.

Be careful.

His warning? Or hers? His concern? Or hers?

Did it matter?

Was it necessary?

He felt an all-too-familiar prickling along the back of his neck. Carefully, but with all appearances of casualness, he turned. Nothing. Nothing but the old barn, weathered, decrepit, all but falling down. Unless there was something or someone inside. He'd walked out here with Hank Foresman Monday, but they'd done little more than crack open one of the hinge-sprung doors.

Cautiously he began walking, pacing off his steps to the north wall and then to the rear of the barn.

Nothing. Nothing except a hastily made but ancient repair to the board and batten siding beneath the grime-blackened window on the rear wall: four one-by-fours laid unevenly across the siding and hammered in place with oversized nails. Nothing in the now bare, skeletal branches of the overgrown hedge.

He continued on around the barn until he once again stood in front of the doors.

Inside then?

Because the sensation of being watched was as real as when he first felt it. Because he had been through this too many times to disregard whatever warning system sparked this feeling.

Inside then.

He faced the doors. His service revolver lay safely stashed beneath the seat in the Blazer, half the oversized yard away. The locked Blazer. And the keys were on Anne's kitchen table. Whoever or whatever could be long gone by the time he retrieved them and his revolver.

He could risk a quick look. Joe was a bully but not necessarily dangerous. Hank was a blowhard and so out of shape David could outmaneuver him easily. The odds of him being physically harmed were minuscule so long as he wasn't taken by surprise, and there was little chance of that now that his early warning system had kicked in.

He stopped for a second with his hand on the ancient

door. What an interesting qualifier his thoughts had just produced. Physically harmed. He shook off that thought and lifted the crossbar. He pulled one of the double doors open, keeping it between himself and the dark interior of the building. Then, moving quickly, he stepped to the other side and pulled that door open, too.

A hole in the roof helped light the back of the barn, although an old loft kept the north side in shadows. He stepped to one side to look into the dim interior to make sure that no one waited in ambush there, and saw only the rusted remains of an abandoned car, wheels and rotted tires sunk into half-composted leaves. It was an old Ford—fifty years or so old—with its windows rolled tightly up and covered with decades of grime. No one had touched those doors in years, just as no one had cleaned those windows, but to be on the safe side, he yanked down on the door handle, finding it every bit as filthy as it had looked. Finding it locked. He eased around the car. The other door was locked too, but the vent window on the passenger side cocked out at a slight angle. He found it stuck, but not locked, pushed it open and bent to look inside.

The car was empty, a rusting, mostly rotted hulk. He reached inside and jerked up on the door handle to free the lock. Damn. It didn't budge. He wiped at the lower corner of the window, smearing the dirt. The lock button sat squat and fat and still down, and what appeared to be an acre away from the vent window opening. He grimaced, but there was no other way. Leaning sideways against the filthy car, he stretched his arm inside along the base of the window until he felt his fingers touch the flattened top of the lock button. Thank God it was still there. He caught it, scissors fashion, between two fingers. Now, if he could just—yes! He felt a stubborn tension on it, but it did ease up. He sagged against the car for a moment, and then withdrew his arm and opened the door.

What had he expected to find? He and Anne had used their quota of surprises in an upstairs bedroom. Or had they? A miasma of despair pervaded the interior, from the oversized dashboard with a key protruding from the ignition next to the starter button, to the small rear bench seat with its rusted springs clearly visible. Years of despair. A lifetime of despair.

Swearing, David slammed the car door, holding it shut with splayed hands as he leaned against it.

And then he realized what he had seen but not noticed before. Rust. In the humidity of this town, of this entire area, anything not zealously protected would rust and corrode in record time. Why hadn't the copper corroded? Other than the light sprinkling of dirt, barely more than dust, the entire hidden trove in that upstairs room had remained remarkably clean. Pristine. New.

Even the conch shell core pendants had still carried the opalescent glow of new shell.

Why? How?

Not now! he told himself as he felt the despair from the car leaching its way out into his hands, up his arms. He jerked away and turned to continue his study of the barn. Four rotting tires without wheels rested against the wall along with what appeared to have once been harness and tack that had fallen from hooks on those walls.

Behind him, ladder-type stairs led to the loft.

And the back of his neck still warned him of something . . . Something.

He tested the flattened rungs of the ladder and found them surprisingly secure, and when he gripped them and released them, his hands came away covered with still more previously undisturbed dirt.

He looked at his hands, at the ladder, and up toward

the loft. Nothing was up there. Nothing could be up there unless it had wings. But still he climbed up and cautiously peered over the ledge into the loft. It was empty, entirely visible except for one corner which housed a pile of wooden boxes. David eased himself onto the flooring. Testing it, he found it sturdy. Sturdy enough, he thought, for a quick but careful examination of those boxes.

If the boxes contained anything, examination would have to wait, he decided when he reached the corner and discovered their primary purpose. Stacked as they were, they created an alcove, hidden from view, just large enough for—*for what?*

A gust of wind whistled through the barn, bringing in a chill and a scattering of dead leaves, and sounding at one moment suspiciously like the furtive laughter of young children, at the next like the sigh of a lover. David turned rapidly and felt the floor, not so sturdy after all, shake beneath his feet.

"There's nothing here." He spoke aloud, and the sound of his voice startled him almost as much as the wind had. But there *was* nothing there. If ever there had been, it was gone. Long gone.

He eased his way back to the ladder and down to the ground. Little remained in the rest of the barn. A pile of rotted lumber, a stack of discarded, beyond saving, furniture, the frame of what looked like an old hospital bed, an ancient trunk, empty, with the lock missing and the lid hanging crazily from one hinge. Nothing to explain the warning he'd been given.

Nothing.

Nothing except the car. The rusting, dead car. And the depression it had invoked in him.

Enough!

David whirled and marched out of the barn. He and

Anne had enough to worry about without adding an abandoned car to the list.

Unless the car was part of the mystery.

He stopped. They had no way of ever learning if it was. Did they?

More carefully than he had opened them, mindful now of their age and disrepair, David closed the double doors and dropped the wooden brace into position, sealing whatever was in there, if anything was in there, securely inside.

Where the hell was Annie?

It was getting dark. Not really late, but dark. Too dark to be working in an unlighted closet, and David didn't want to open the frayed draperies in the upstairs sitting room or turn on any lights to advertise to anyone who watched that he was in that room.

And hell, yes, it was late. Too much time had passed since Anne left with the packages. She could have driven them to Fort Smith in the hours she'd been gone. She'd had more than enough time to fill in a couple of labels and waltz those two boxes over to the post office.

Unless something had happened to her.

"Damn!" The staple gun twisted in his hand, slamming his thumb between its handle and the edge of the panel he was constructing. He shook his hand, muttering at the minor pain. Carelessness. Stupidity on his part. He should have gone with her, would have gone with her if it hadn't been for that hole in the wall.

Well, that was just about fixed.

He had prenailed the remaining piece of trim. Now he aligned it along the edge of the paper-covered drywall and tapped it into place. He carried the drywall into the closet and fitted it over the opening that he had enlarged until it stretched between the two-foot centered studs, from the base nailed to the floor to the brace he had nailed between the existing studs just below the closet shelf. The paper matched, compliments of a cheesecloth backed strip he'd cut from the inside closet front wall above one of the doors. And the trim matched those pieces he had nailed in place over each of the studs, making the stained vertical strips appear to be part of the original finish of the closet rather than an afterthought.

It would do, he thought, as the makeshift door eased snugly into place and blended into the surrounding wall.

Like it had never been disturbed.

He'd done most of the cutting and trimming downstairs, so with a minimum of pickup, this room would look like it had never been disturbed, either.

And then, by God, if she wasn't back, he was going after Annie.

He was returning the last of his tools to the converted sleeping porch adjacent to the kitchen when he heard the kitchen door open.

"David?"

"Where the hell have you been?" His growl burst from him before he'd even thought the words, surprising him as much as it must have surprised Anne. He dropped the armload of tools and drywall leavings and trim and whirled to face her.

And saw the blood.

"Annie?" His voice came out soft and shocked.

"Annie," he said again, louder but still not much more than a whisper as he moved into the kitchen, as he crossed to where she stood, as he gripped her shoulders. "What happened?"

"What?"

She followed the direction of his eyes, to the blood splattered on her shirt, clearly visible between the edges of her open jacket. "Oh, damn. That."

"Hell, yes, that," he said, drawing her toward the table. "Sit. Are you all right? What happened?"

With his hands still clutching her shoulders, he used his foot to nudge a chair out from the table and pushed her onto it. God, she was small. Why hadn't he ever noticed before just how small? Just how fragile? He felt the bones of her shoulders, of her arms, beneath his hands, but he couldn't ease his hold on her, not even to pull her jacket away and search for her injury. He shouldn't have let her go on alone . . . go *out* alone. She wasn't prepared for the dangers. "Who did this?"

"David." Anne looked up at him with confusion at first darkening her eyes, then concern, before she smiled gently. "Bobby Preston. It's his blood, not mine. He was playing Superman and tried to fly off his parents' garage. He landed in his mother's rosebushes. He's the reason I'm so late. Now. Are *you* all right?"

Was he? Or had he gone completely over the edge? He didn't like not being in control, and he hadn't been. Not once today. Not since finding the body. Not in the barn. Not even now when any fool could look past the blood splattered on Anne Locke's shirt and see that she was not bleeding from any wound but that she was pale and drawn and that probably the last thing she needed was some madman interrogating her and shaking her hard enough to dislodge the pins in her hair.

And any fool could also see she was trying desperately to distract him from the subject of his interrogation.

He dropped his hands from her shoulders and spun around. "Yeah. Oh, hell yeah. I'm just dandy."

"Then why—" Her voice cracked, hoarsened. "Then why are you carrying your revolver?"

Damn! He felt for the small of his back, where he had tucked the revolver into his jeans.

"What happened while I was gone?"

He looked at her and tried for a grin—anything—to erase her worried frown. "Would you believe nothing? At least, nothing with a rational explanation."

She shook her head, and her chin came up a notch. "Everything has a rational explanation. Sometimes we just have to look harder for it than at others."

"Like our friend upstairs?"

He saw the change that clouded her face, saw the shudder she couldn't quite suppress. *Low blow, Huerra,* he thought. *What are you going to do next? Find a puppy to kick?*

"Yes," she said firmly. "Exactly like our friend upstairs. Now, please tell me what else has happened."

He sighed, dragged out a chair and sank onto it. "Nothing, Annie. Absolutely nothing. I guess I just let my paranoia get out of control."

"How?"

Let it go, he wanted to tell her. But he sensed she wouldn't. And maybe she ought to know how far out of control he had let his imagination get.

"I— When you left today, I had a bad feeling about your garage."

"Bad enough so that you armed yourself to investigate?"

"Bad enough that I would have, if my weapon hadn't been so far away and if I hadn't been so sure the intruder would escape if I took the time to go get it."

"And did he?"

"Hell, Annie, there wasn't anyone there. Just a falling down barn, a rusted-out, locked hulk of a car, and a pile of clutter."

"Then what was the problem?"

"The problem was—" He reached across the table for the envelope with the drawing he had sketched only hours earlier, but he couldn't hide behind studying it.

Not now. "The problem was, it felt as though there was someone there. There was no reason for the emotions I felt as I broke into that car."

"Like upstairs."

He heard no question in her soft voice, only a resigned statement of fact. For a while, he'd wondered if maybe he'd imagined the intensity of feelings—his and hers—in that upstairs room. Now he knew he hadn't.

"Yeah," he said. "Like upstairs."

"God." Anne folded her hands in her lap and sat up very straight. "Do I have to go out there, too?"

"No. Not now. Maybe not ever. But haven't you been in there? Haven't you—"

"I've been in there," she said. "Six months ago. I wondered about hauling off the old car. I considered trying some kind of renovation on the trunk but decided it was too far gone. And I climbed far enough up the ladder to see that the loft probably wasn't secure enough for exploring, and that except for those boxes in the back, it was empty."

"And felt nothing?"

She shook her head. "But then—and you're not going to like this—I never felt anything strange in this house or around it, until last Saturday morning."

She was right; he didn't like it. Whatever was here had been here a lot longer than a few days. It had been firmly in place before he felt the first chill shudder over him as he stepped down from Anne's truck. Unless— Unless Anne wasn't being as forthright as he had thought. Unless Anne had an agenda of her own that he knew nothing about. And now he needed to change the subject.

"With all the excitement at the clinic, were you able to get to the post office?"

She grimaced. "Not exactly. But I did get them mailed," she said quickly. "Margaret—you remember my nurse?—saw the crowd at the clinic and stopped to help. I had the packages ready to go when Bobby's family brought him in. I'll admit, I worried about it, but it was either that or run the risk of letting them sit until Friday, so I asked Margaret to carry them to the post office for me."

"And she did? You're sure?"

"Yeah, you're right," Annie said. "Your paranoia is working overtime. You met Margaret. What's not to trust? Besides," Anne fumbled in the pocket of her jacket and dropped a square of folded paper onto the pile of invoices, "she brought me the receipts."

He tried for a grin. Maybe he made it. "Once upon a time," he told her, "I was a reasonable, sensible person."

"You're sure about that?" She delivered the words deadpan, but he saw a glimmer of humor in her eyes.

"Come on," he said. "I'll show you what I've done while you've been off hobnobbing with the small and famous. And run something past you that I think will provide some additional protection as well as a reason for you to be up in the sitting room at odd hours."

"Do you really think someone is keeping tabs?"

"Do you want to accept at face value that Cousin Joe really doesn't suspect anything about our friend, and that Hank Foresman is just trying to make amends?"

She didn't answer, but she didn't have to use words to tell him that she trusted Joe and Hank no more than he did.

10

Woman-From-The-West lay on the robes near the fire. That she lay in the same place where the Warrior had died brought her scant comfort. Soon she would die. As he had. As their child within her had.

And their separation would be for nothing. *Nothing.*

Would she be allowed to join him in the hereafter if she had not kept her promise to him? Or would she be forever separated from the man who had grown to mean more to her than her own soul?

His burial chamber was covered now but no one had yet smoothed the top of the sacred mound. No one had yet begun to build another mortuary house.

Just as no one had burned this house and all its contents after his death.

As no one had killed the grave goods that accompanied him on his journey.

As no one had been allowed to disturb him once his armor-clad body had been placed in the chamber with the ceremonially robed body of the Priest.

The Guardians would not allow it.

They had allowed no one to approach him, to harm

him, to touch him in any way, since she had knelt by his side and returned to him the small cedar box he had given her containing their images on shell.

And they had allowed no one to approach her, to harm her, to touch her in any way she did not wish while she wore the medallion, while she carried his child. But even they were not powerful enough to force someone to give her aid.

The pain came in unrelenting waves now as her body tried futilely to expel the body of their child. He was dead; he must be. Too many hours had passed since he began his journey into this world.

Too many hours had passed since she'd sent her sweet child of a maid to find help for her. Too many hours had passed since the one still living member of the Warrior's guard had come to her side bringing his own mate, telling her the maid would not be allowed to return. Too many hours had passed since she'd heard the last of their moans and cries as they had died, poisoned before they even came to her, she was sure—not by the black drink of honorable death but with something sly and secret—to prevent them from offering her even succor in her last moments.

And for what?

More power for one person?

Three had ruled when she came to these people. The Chieftain, the Priest, and her mate, the Warrior. They had ruled well; their people had prospered.

Now, only one ruled. And greed ruled that one.

No Priest had been allowed to rise up.

If the Warrior had lived, he could have confronted the despot the Chieftain had become, could perhaps have prevented it happening.

But he had not lived. And his successor had not been allowed to be born.

What would happen to his people now?

When the greed of one destroyed the hope of many, would they all just cease to be? Would they fade from the earth as though they had never been?

What would happen to her?

Would she float in limbo, forever alone?

The Warrior was safe. She held onto that thought as the last light in the house faded. He was beyond the touch of the Chieftain, in the hereafter. And his body was safe from depredation and degradation. The Guardians would see to that. Yes. She raised her hand to the likeness of the Warrior she wore on her breast. As was hers. *He* had seen to that in his last moment. And his likeness was all of this earth she needed to accompany her.

Even in limbo. Even alone.

11

Anne had spent too many years getting up before dawn for something as sane as a holiday to keep her lazing in bed. She didn't like it, but she was up and dressed in jeans and a sweatshirt, leaning against the kitchen sink, not quite awake enough yet to tackle any work on the house, and waiting for the coffee to finish dripping into the pot long before eight o'clock Thanksgiving morning.

David hadn't returned to his cabin until after midnight the night before. Even then, he hadn't been happy about leaving her alone in the house with the warrior and at the whim of whoever might decide to come looking for him. Which was pretty silly, Anne thought in the dim, cool light of early morning as she rubbed her neck and stretched and tried to wake up.

She'd been alone in the house with the body upstairs for the past six months. And vulnerable to whoever decided to come looking for him. She shuddered at that sudden thought. Maybe David hadn't been quite as arbitrary as she had believed last night.

She wondered where David was. She wondered why, for probably the ninetieth time, she hadn't told him she didn't give a hang what small-town gossips said and asked that he stay with her last night. She wondered why—and how—he had so quickly become a part of her life.

She heard the groan of an engine and pushed aside the faded kitchen curtain to look out the window over the sink, just as the gray-green Blazer David drove topped the hill of her driveway.

She dragged open the back door just as he stepped onto the porch. "Morning."

"Good morning to you, too," he said as he thrust a brown paper bag at her.

She took the bag and stepped back in mock alarm. "My God, you're actually awake. What happened?" She opened the bag enough to glance inside. "And doughnuts? Where on earth did you find someplace open this morning?"

He headed directly to the coffeepot, eased the carafe from under the stream of dripping coffee and one of the waiting cups into its place. While the cup slowly filled, he stood facing the window, not looking at her. "Are you in a better mood this morning, Doc?"

Uh oh. *Doc* not *Annie.* And she heard no teasing in his voice, only a weariness that might be explained by lack of sleep last night. He had thought she'd been incredibly stupid in refusing his protection last night.

But he had brought a peace offering.

"Yes," she said quietly, "I am." She extended the bag toward him. "And thank you for breakfast."

He did a quick juggling act with the two cups and the coffeepot and turned, handing her a filled cup. "Come on," he said. "There's something we both need to see."

Maybe if he'd pulled her along behind him, she'd have protested. He didn't; he simply led the way out of the kitchen and down the long, wide hall.

What did they need to see? To visit the room upstairs again? Nope. David passed the stairwell. And before she could become even remotely suspicious, he passed the door to her bedroom, too.

The door to the front porch was a massive, carved relic from an older age, complete with an etched glass window showing a woman in a rose garden. Anne had fallen in love with the window the first time she saw it but in the go-for-nothing pace her life had once again assumed—couldn't seem to get away from—she seldom really saw the door any more, simply passed it on her way from one job in the house to another.

And if she seldom paused long enough to admire the door she loved, she certainly hadn't taken the time to open it and step out onto the long covered porch. Now David did, and led her outside into the brisk November morning.

A grouping of nondescript chairs and a settee made of what appeared to be small branches had been left on the porch. Anne noticed that a tarp had been thrown over the settee. David gestured toward it and with more than one unspoken question, Anne sat.

So did David. Close enough to her on the small settee that only inches separated them.

"I'll take one of those doughnuts now," he said, leaning against the tarp-covered back of the settee and drawing in a deep breath.

Anne handed him the bag. "So what is it we need to see?"

David stopped with his hand half in the bag and looked at her incredulously. "Annie. Oh, Annie. You can't still be that asleep." He lifted his hand and pointed toward her front yard and beyond. "Open your eyes."

Maybe she was asleep. Maybe she had been asleep most of her life. She had marveled over the view once, twice, maybe even three times when she first moved into the house, had promised herself that she would never grow used to it, and then, like the door, it had become a mere prop in the background of busy work. She gave David an apologetic smile and leaned back against the tarp, looking out into the distance.

The town of Allegro, with its ancient brick buildings and tree-lined residential area, sat on the edge of a hillside, the hillside her house topped. The lake was farther to the south, in the valley, fed by a northern flowing river that, once freed by the dam, continued its meander north, marked in the distance by a tree line not visible at this early hour because of the fog rising from the water. Mountains rose on the south and the east, surrounding them like friendly, aged sentinels. The sun had already risen far enough to have lost the miraculous glowing colors she had once—but only once—seen from this porch, but its early morning slant lighted and highlighted the various shades of green and tan of forest and cleared field on the closest mountains.

Now Anne, too, took a deep, cleansing breath. "Thank you."

She heard the rustle of the paper bag, then felt it as David nudged it back toward her hand. "My pleasure," he told her.

Not willing to look away from the peace of the view, Anne groped in the bag and retrieved a doughnut. The two of them sat there in companionable silence, until Anne shivered, and David shifted his weight beside her.

"Cold?" he asked."

"A little."

"Here." She felt his arm settle around her shoulder and draw her against his side. She tensed slightly, until she realized he offered nothing but warmth, then relaxed against him, loathe to give up the peace they had found on the porch. Not yet. And at the same time

realizing David was merely continuing—on a different
level—the campaign she had recognized and rebelled
against last night: protecting her.

Well, this protection she could take.

"So what do we do now?"

His words were an intrusion and a reminder that she
didn't want. Once again she tensed. This time, she
moved away from him. And he let her go.

She sighed, stood, and gave one last, reluctant glance
at the valley before turning toward the door. "Now, I
start cooking. And getting the house as ready as I can
for Thanksgiving dinner."

The fool woman had invited people for dinner. And not
just dinner—televised football and parades and all the
attendant folderol of a holiday feast.

David lugged the last packing crate from the downstairs sitting room into place in the upstairs sitting
room.

People who would want to see what she had done
with the house.

People who would be marching through room after
room, opening closet doors, and giving in to natural
curiosity. Or maybe not so natural.

He straightened and stretched and looked around the
now carefully cluttered room.

Well, this would help. Moving Anne's unpacked
goods up here had freed a reasonably sized room downstairs for her television and had given her a reason for
the lights in this room to be on at night. And the things
he had stacked in the closet helped hide the back wall
from any but the most determined of searchers.

Maybe it wasn't such a bad idea after all, he thought.
Maybe a little enthusiastic gossip about how normal

everything up here looked was just what the doctor needed.

He heard footsteps behind him and turned as Anne entered the room. She paused at the doorway and looked around, at the boxes so neatly stacked, at the portable sewing machine he had found and opened and set on a small side table he'd brought in from another upstairs room, at the small stove he'd lighted to heat the room and the bar of soap and clean towel he'd placed on the vanity. At what had become a cozy and efficient work room, a place to sort through boxes and yet keep the clutter from the rest of the house. A place to be comfortable and warm while doing so. A place to clean up afterward.

"Oh," she said. "Oh my. You have been busy."

Almost as though against her will, she crossed the room and opened the closet door. The boxes he'd stacked there were not heavy, could easily be moved, even by her, but seemed to fill most of the closet. She stepped inside, silent, looking at the boxes, then placed her hands on the small portion of the back wall not covered by crates and stood there for a moment, head bowed, quiet.

"He's—all right?"

David knew the emotion that fueled her question; he'd felt it, too, as he'd begun the job of further hiding the warrior. He knew it, but didn't like at all the fact that Annie felt it.

"Annie. He's dead."

She whirled to face him. "I know that!"

But did she? he wondered. Did *he*? Because even he had to admit what they were doing seemed much more personal than hiding an already hidden treasure.

The kitchen was redolent with the aromas of Anne's childhood and as sparkling clean as two people could make it. The supplies had all been either stashed in the room off the kitchen or hidden away elsewhere. The small sitting room had been dusted and swept and the dining room truly cleaned for the first time since she'd moved into the house. And her plain white china looked almost festive on her grandmother's Battenburg lace tablecloth.

She didn't know why David had fallen so willingly into helping her prepare for this meal, but she knew she couldn't have done it without him. She doubted that she *would* have done it without him, but knowing he would be alone for Thanksgiving unless she invited him to dine with her, knowing that *she* would be alone, had started her thinking about others who might be alone. Nellie, her receptionist, and her small daughter, and Margaret, her nurse.

But it seemed Margaret wouldn't have been alone. Not according her response to Anne's invitation. She wanted to come, but she wasn't sure about other plans—and if she did come, could she bring someone.

Anne heard the first car groan up the drive just as she and David stashed the last tool and closed the double doors to the supply room. Anne wiped her hands on the dishtowel she had tied around her waist, then, after looking around distractedly, dropped the towel into the hamper by the washing machine.

"Nervous, Annie?" David asked. "Don't tell me you've never entertained."

Anne shook her head. "Not for a major holiday. Not anyone other than roommates or close family."

He dropped his hand onto her shoulder and gave her a gentle push toward the door. "You'll do fine."

She shot him a disbelieving look. "And what if I burn

the pie, or the turkey's dry? What if I absolutely ruin this meal?"

"Then we'll eat cornbread dressing and Aunt Elena's cranberry relish and start practicing the stories we'll tell for the rest of our lives about your first Thanksgiving feast." He grinned at her. "Provided, of course, you ever open the door and let your guests in."

Nellie Flynn stood on the porch with her hand resting protectively on a four-year-old, scrubbed clean, wide-eyed, miniature version of herself.

The little girl smiled shyly and held out the pie carrier she held. "Mama said be real careful, 'cause this is special for Doc Anne. Are you Doc Anne?"

Anne knelt and took the carrier from the little girl. "Yes, I am. And who are you?"

"I'm Lilly, silly." The girl giggled. "I made a poem."

"Oh, my word." Nellie shook her head and sighed. "It's Lilly that's being silly. You know better than that, cupcake. Apologize to Dr. Locke."

"Grownups aren't silly?"

Anne chuckled. "Sometimes grownups are very silly. Just like we are right now for standing out here in the cold." She stood, lifting the carrier, and stepped to one side. "Why don't we go on in so I can see what's in here that smells so good. You know you didn't have to bring anything, Nellie, but I think I'm going to be real glad you did."

When Nellie didn't move except for her hand tightening on her daughter's shoulder, Anne looked up to see her staring into the house. At David. In all his bruised and battered glory.

She had no idea what caused Nellie's tension, but worked quickly to defuse it. "Nellie Flynn, meet David Huerra." She smiled at David and handed him the pie carrier. He lifted an eyebrow but dropped right into the domestic role she had just assigned him as though he suspected Nellie might not set foot in the house if he didn't.

"Nellie's my receptionist," she told him. She turned her smile on Lilly and took her hand. "David is the Dallas police officer who was hurt in the wreck with Hank Foresman. He's been helping me with the house. My goodness, you're a big girl, Lilly. Your mother tells me you're four?"

"Yes." Nellie held up four fingers. "This many. Are we going to have turkey and gravy?"

"You bet," Anne told her, at last ushering the small party into her kitchen.

"I like the leg."

Anne laughed and bent to help the little girl with her jacket. David set the pie carrier on the table. She noticed that although he stood close, he made no effort to help Nellie with her jacket until she had freed herself from it and was looking for a place to put it down.

"Why don't I hang those up?" he asked, holding out his hand but not aggressively reaching for them.

Nellie kept the large bag she had carried and slung it once again over her shoulder as she handed him her coat. She then turned quickly to her daughter, fumbled in the bag and brought out an obviously well-loved rag doll.

He'd just hung the two coats over pegs in the battered coat rack on the wall next to the back door when the sound of another engine, this one considerably more powerful than Nellie's Escort, announced the arrival of her other guests.

"It must be Margaret," Anne told him. "She was able to come after all."

Not only had Margaret managed to come for dinner, she had brought the "someone" she'd mentioned. When Anne opened the back door, she found her nurse and a tall, lanky man with hard, suspicious eyes standing on her back porch. And in a replay of the earlier arrival, he, too, was staring over her shoulder. At David.

Margaret thrust a covered casserole dish at Anne. "Thanks for inviting us," she said. "Anne Locke, this is my husband, Wayne Samuels."

Anne didn't let her eyes widen, but she knew her shock must be evident. Husband? Margaret?

Instead, she took the dish and smiled at the man. "I'm happy you could come today, Wayne." Then, because he was still staring past her, she half turned. "Have you met David Huerra yet?" she asked, knowing that he probably hadn't. "David's—" For some reason she didn't examine, she didn't want to tell this man that David was a police officer. "David's a friend of mine who's been helping me with renovating the house."

"Huerra." The man's voice was abrupt, almost curt, and rusty as though little used.

"Samuels."

Anne looked from one to the other of them. Honestly! she thought. Men! They were facing each other, measuring each other, like a couple of territorial dogs. She stepped between them and considered handing David the casserole the way she had the pie carrier, but decided she probably wouldn't get away with it this time.

"Come on in," she said. "We finally got the television tuned in, and it's almost time for the parade. I know Lilly is really looking forward to seeing it."

With relief she saw Margaret's lip lift in a shadow of a smile, acknowledging Anne's diversion. "Lilly isn't the only one," she said as she entered the kitchen and held the door open, encouraging the man she called husband to follow her. "I love the Thanksgiving parade, too, but there's no way on earth we can tune it in at our place enough to tell even one band from another."

Anne set the casserole on the table and watched as the man entered cautiously. With great care and gentleness for such a dark, rough-looking man, he helped Margaret remove her coat and hung it on the rack before removing his own.

David closed the kitchen door but stood braced in front of it, Margaret spoke quietly but with what could almost have been forced cheer about how much better the kitchen looked than it had only days before, and Nellie looked as though she wanted to run away.

"Doc Anne? Doc Anne?"

Anne felt a tug on her skirt and looked down to find Lilly pulling on it.

"Are we going to watch the parade, Doc Anne? Really?"

Thank heavens for babies and their sublime self-absorption. "You bet, cupcake," she told Lilly. She glanced up at her assorted guests. Had this been such a good idea? She wasn't sure now, but she was in for the duration. Unless Nellie bolted or—good grief, who was Margaret to call David *tall, dark, and dangerous* when she had her own edition of that hidden away on her mountaintop?

"How about something to drink?" she asked. "I have coffee, hot cider, and tea. David, would you mind showing everyone the way to the small parlor while I fix a tray?"

"Let me help," Margaret said.

Anne looked toward Nellie and doubted that she would walk through a strange house with two strange men. "No," she said. "Thanks, Nellie will help me. But why don't you make sure that Lilly doesn't miss anything?"

Nellie shot her a look of pure gratitude and turned toward the cabinets as the others left the kitchen. Anne considered asking her why she was so uneasy. Was it because of David, or this house, or even something that had happened before she arrived, but decided that Nellie would only speak when she felt safe in doing so.

The little downstairs sitting room was really quite pleasant, Anne admitted later as she and Nellie carried the trays containing beverages and snacks into the room. At the end of the living room, it had double windows that faced the long front porch, French doors that faced the covered porch that wrapped around from the dining room, and a wall of fireplace and book shelves.

Unfortunately, until she had a chance to check out the chimney, the room had no heat. David had solved that by somehow coercing Gretta Tompkins into letting him borrow a kerosene heater, which he had set in front of the open fireplace.

A heater which he and Wayne Samuels were standing by, discussing, just before coming to words about when Anne entered the room.

"Let me ask her."

And before she had time to more than set the tray on a small table, David grasped her arm and led her from the room.

"That's quite a crowd you called together today, Annie," he said when they reached the front hall, well away from any chance of being overheard.

"Ask me what?" she said, deciding that might be a safer topic than her guest list.

"You know he's done time, don't you? Hard time, and I suspect not too long ago."

"No. I— He's— Well hell, David." Sometimes there was nothing to do but swear. "I thought Margaret was a widow. I didn't even know he existed until ten minutes ago."

David looked at her in silence for a moment before he chuckled and pulled her head against his shoulder.

"Well hell, Annie," he said, mimicking the exasperation in her voice. "A woman who can keep a secret better than I can, a hard-time con, a woman who's either been raped or seriously assaulted, and a four year old. Nobody's ever going to accuse you of a dull mix at your parties."

"Nellie—"

"Sshh. I shouldn't have said that."

"But—"

"Annie, if she wants you to know, she'll tell you."

"But—" How on earth had she worked with the woman and not picked up on anything even hinting at that kind of past until today?

"We have something more immediate to discuss," he told her. "Samuels doesn't like kerosene heaters. Says he doesn't think they're safe. He's volunteered to help me check out the chimneys."

His shoulder was nice. Too nice. And she shouldn't be leaning on it. Even if he had tucked her head against him, he obviously had meant nothing by it. Anne pulled away.

"You don't have to if you don't want to."

David shook his head. "That's not the point."

Confused, she looked at him. "What is?"

"We'll have to go on the roof," David told her. "And in the attic."

"Oh." Now she understood his reluctance.

"And he volunteered."

"Oh, dear. Do you think— No. Not if he's with Margaret. She— If she doesn't hate Joe, she at least considers him a lower life form than algae."

"I don't know what I think, Annie. I do know there's nothing in the attic for him to see. Maybe he needs to know that, too. And maybe I need to check him out some. Working together, I could do that."

"Is he— Do you think he's dangerous?"

"Who the hell knows, Annie? But the next time my captain tells me to go off and rest for a month, I'm going to introduce him to you and tell him about this trip."

Samuels knew what he was doing. That didn't surprise David. A man as hardened as Wayne Samuels wouldn't suggest doing something he wasn't competent to do. Not even as an excuse to snoop where ordinarily he wouldn't be able to.

He didn't appear to be snooping. That didn't surprise David either. Any man as hardened as Samuels would know how to hide his interest.

It seemed that his only interest in the dim light of the attic was the construction of the old house. He played his flashlight beam across the unplaned lumber of a massive roof truss and a smile as unexpected as a bolt of lightning cracked his hard face.

"They knew how to build," he said, then fell silent and stonefaced again as he went unerringly to the chimney for the downstairs sitting room.

David was respectably familiar with modern chimney construction, but he stood back and watched as Samuels inspected the bricks for discoloration and the mortar for failure. "This one looks okay, at least under the roof. You want to check out the other ones while we're up here?"

There were three other chimneys for wood or coal fireplaces, and two chimney flues for stoves, including the one for the small upstairs sitting room. David shrugged. He knew how to hide his interest, too. "Might as well."

So they did, finding all the brick unstained, all the mortar intact, and David learned absolutely nothing about Wayne Samuels other than that he knew chimneys, he worked with an intensity that blocked out everything else, and he showed no interest in Annie's attic other than an appreciation for the craftsmanship that had gone into building it.

Well, hell.

Well double hell, he thought when they walked out to Samuels's truck and he saw, stashed neatly under the low camper shell, all the equipment necessary for cleaning the chimneys, and most of the supplies for any repair they might have decided was necessary.

Maybe he had lost more than just his edge.

"You always come to dinner ready to clean and repoint chimneys?"

Samuels had draped a coil of rope over his shoulder and had begun pulling an extension ladder from the back of the truck. He stopped and leaned against the tailgate. "Maggie said the doc was cold." Whatever accent the man had had once had long since vanished into his rusty voice. "You got a problem with neighborly help for your lady? Or is this just your cop working its way out?"

His lady. The town gossips had been working overtime if they'd already paired the two of them, in spite of all his precautions about going back to that permanently air-conditioned cabin each night. But the gossips weren't the issue here. And neither was his relationship, or lack of one, with Anne. Or his right to question any guest of hers. Damn. He had no *right* to do what he was doing, but it sure seemed as if he did.

"Maybe both," he told Samuels, in a voice as uninflected as the other man's had been. "Where'd you do your time?"

For the first time he saw life in Samuels's eyes. A glimmer of what vaguely resembled humor lighted them for a moment before fading back into their flat darkness.

"Not did I do time? Or why did I do time? But where?"

It had seemed a logical question to David. He knew it had happened, and he wasn't interested in any explanation of mix-up or setup. A nice clean *where* would give him all the information he needed for finding out the rest. "Yeah."

Samuels bent back to the truck and hauled out a stack of plastic sheeting, a long-bristled chimney brush, and a burlap-covered weight on another length of rope. He hefted the burlap and pushed the sheeting at David. "Take this to Maggie. She knows how to set it so we won't have rooms full of carbon and soot and bird skeletons to clean up. Then come back for this stuff. I'll meet you on the roof."

Neatly done. David watched Samuels slowly but deliberately walk away. He hadn't argued or denied David's assumption; he'd just acknowledged and then ignored it. But the day wasn't over yet.

Margaret—there was no way he could think of that stately woman as Maggie—met him on the back porch and took the pile of plastic from him. He knew she'd watched his brief exchange with her husband; the tension in her eyes, her hands, and the set of her jaw all told him she had. She glanced once toward the side of the house where Samuels had passed on his way to the front chimney. "He's a good man, David Huerra. Don't ever doubt that. Not for a minute."

Maybe he was a good man, but maybe Margaret only thought he was. And what the hell difference did it make to him anyway? If the man wasn't interested in the secret in the closet, he could keep all of the secrets he wanted to. After today he'd be gone and Annie—and *he* would never see Samuels again. Right? Right.

Then what the hell did he care if the man had a rap sheet three miles long?

Because he was married to Annie's nurse. Because he would be in Annie's life long after David had gone back to Dallas. Because—

"Ready down here." Margaret's voice floated up the chimney only seconds after David had climbed to where Samuels waited.

Samuels stood staring at the overgrown, wooded area beyond the back hedge. With visible reluctance he turned his attention from the hillside to the chimney. "All right," he called down the open flue. "We can handle it from here, but it will be a minute."

A minute? Why the wait, David wondered as he hefted the long-handled brush up onto the roof and glanced pointedly at the weight and rope. It looked to him as if their party was all ready and waiting.

But maybe not for chimney cleaning. At least not yet.

Samuels stared once again at the hillside. This time, David followed his example, seeing nothing but wild land. "Is there a problem?"

"Maybe," Samuels said. "Maybe not." He stooped, picked up the brush, and looked at it as though wondering how it came to be there, how he came to hold it. "But I reckon you've got a right to know. I'd want to know if my lady was at risk.

"I wasn't going to come today. I don't get out much, don't mix with folks too well, didn't figure I needed the hassle of you asking me all sorts of questions I don't plan to answer. But Maggie likes the doc. Maggie wanted to come. So I drove up last night just to look around, check out the place.

"It was late. Your Blazer was gone, and the house was dark except for a light from a downstairs room about there." He pointed to the opposite side of the house, in the general direction of Anne's bedroom. "And one from an upstairs room at the back. I thought at first that one was from a television but the color was wrong, more amber than blue. Outside it was dark. Real dark. So I could be mistaken about what I saw."

David's warning signals kicked in with a vengeance as the back of his neck started its too-familiar prickle. "You saw someone?"

"Nope." Samuels put down the brush and picked up the weighted bag, resting it on the chimney ledge. "Something. Two actually. Might have been mountain lions. Big ones. But I don't recall ever hearing about them coming this close to town before. At least, not in any way I believed. Just thought you ought to know," he said, tightening his hold on the rope and lowering the bag into the chimney. "Maggie'd be real upset if something happened to Doc Anne."

David turned once more to look at the hillside, remembering the sound he'd thought he'd heard the day before but had dismissed as only a trick of the wind. "Maybe we ought to look for tracks," he suggested.

"Already did." Samuels said.

"And?"

Samuels turned to look at him. "There weren't any."

12

The night wrapped itself around the old house. Anne leaned back, making herself as comfortable as possible on the sprung and lumpy Chippendale-style sofa that Ellie Hansom's estate had left in the downstairs sitting room.

The glow from the remains of a fire in her newly cleaned fireplace mingled with the soft, rose-colored circles of light from two fringed and beaded floor lamps, and a Chopin étude whispered from her portable tape player set up on the library table across the room.

The day had been almost perfect, in spite of its rocky beginnings, but now all her guests were gone, Margaret and her desperado who had been so remarkably gentle, Nellie and her delightful daughter, Lilly, who had begged hugs and good-bye sugars from everyone, including an astonished Wayne Samuels. Only David remained—and the man in the closet—to keep her company in the echoing, suddenly lonely rooms.

She knew she ought to be helping David as he made his rounds checking to see that all the doors and windows were locked and secure, but for the moment contentment held her quiet and still. This was why she had returned to Allegro. This sense of belonging. This sense of family that might be only an illusion but seemed so real. This sense of safety, in spite of Joe's continuing feud, that told her that only David's cop persona saw any real need for his double-checking the locks. Here there were no muggers lurking on every corner, no drug dealers invading the school or clinic, no danger waiting to jump out in ambush.

She heard footsteps on the hardwood floor and slanted her head to look at David as he entered the room. He stopped by the French doors leading out to the rear porch and tried the handle, then glanced warily at the old draperies that obviously were meant to frame but never to cover the doors.

The remains of the last log in the fireplace dissolved in a sparkle of glowing embers, sending a few errant flames dancing across the grate before they faded away. David secured the screen in front of the firebox and leaned back, resting his arm on the oak mantel. "I believe your first dinner party was a success, Dr. Locke."

Anne grinned lazily. "Yeah. Which of us did it surprise more? You? Or me?"

He returned her grin before turning serious. "Are you up to trying again to reach your mom?"

A little of her contentment faded, and she sighed, knowing that when she left this room, when she returned to the brightly lighted kitchen and the questions that still had to be answered, the rest of it would, too. She patted the couch beside her. "Sit with me just a while longer?"

David nodded, acknowledging her need to remain cocooned in the peace of this room for at least a few more minutes. He sat on the other end of the sofa, extended his long legs toward the fireplace, and stretched his arm along the back of the sofa, toward her.

"What a mixed bag of people we were to have come together so well," she said softly, remembering how they had at first faced each other warily and then had reached some sort of uncertain truce as the afternoon wore on.

"Not so strange," he said on a sigh and a stretch. "Considering we all had something in common."

She turned her head to look at him and found that he had shifted closer to her. "What?"

His hand dropped to her neck and began kneading muscles she hadn't known were so tight. She closed her eyes and surrendered to the massage, vaguely wondering why the touch of a man she had not known a week ago felt so natural, so familiar, so right.

"What?" Both his voice and his touch remained gentle, but she heard an underlying tension in his words. "Surely you noticed, Annie, that with the exception of Lilly, everyone at your table today was hiding from something."

How had he known?

She gave him the smile that had fooled everyone but Karen and her mother. "Surely not everyone," she said.

He wasn't fooled; she could see that in the speculation in his eyes. "Oh, yes," he said. "Everyone."

And then she realized that not only had he included her in that statement, he had included himself.

"And what are you hiding from, David Huerra?"

"I suspect from the same thing you are, Anne Locke."

No. He couldn't be. He couldn't have the memories she had. Or could he? His hand had stilled on her neck. She leaned against it, needing, wanting his support but not able to take more than this. "Maybe—" she said, groping for a way to deny his words. "Maybe we're not hiding from something so much as we're looking for something."

"Maybe," he said, giving her that much as he moved

and at the same time pulled her toward him until she found herself held tight against his side with his arm around her. "That's better," he said.

Better? For whom? And in what way? Because the comfort she had felt only moments ago had fled. Now her awareness of him was much more primal, much more demanding, and even though she might have told herself she could handle a flirtation with this man, right now she wasn't so sure.

"David," she said, putting her hand against his chest to push away but finding and being trapped by the beat of his heart beneath her palm. "This isn't a good— This isn't wise."

"Don't you think I know that, Annie?"

When he'd kissed her before, she'd been too surprised to savor the touch of his lips and the hard strength of his body. She'd had no warning, no time to anticipate. Now she did. He tightened his arm around her shoulder and lifted his other hand to her cheek, holding her still as he looked down at her in the dim light, searching her eyes for answers, for permission. The music swirled through the room, accenting the moment. "Nothing about this is wise," he said. "We'd both be making a mistake, a big mistake, to get involved with each other. It can't go anywhere, Annie. You know that. In less than a month, I'll leave; you'll stay."

She wanted to deny his words, but she couldn't. She would stay. Allegro was her haven, her safe place. And no matter what demons had brought David here, he would leave. He would have to leave.

"I know," she said.

"Damn, Annie, you're supposed to tell me not to do this."

"I can't."

The music ended, leaving the room in silence as

David stared down at her, as she felt his heart racing beneath her palm.

"Stop me, Annie," he said, bending toward her. "Before we both get hurt."

A sound as sharp as a shot cracked through the hushed room. David jerked away from her and twisted in a warrior's stance, searching the room as he thrust her behind him, protected between his body and the sofa.

For a moment, even Anne didn't recognize the sound. For a moment the adrenaline pumping through her had nothing to do with pheromones and hormones and attraction and fledgling affection and everything to do with fear and blood and the sound of screaming that never seemed to stop. For a moment she was trapped in the nightmare that had brought her back to Allegro and would never let her leave.

For a moment. Then sanity returned and she recognized the sound as the faulty shut-off mechanism on her ancient tape player. "Oh, God," she moaned, sagging back against the sofa. "It's nothing," she told him, gesturing toward the tape player. "It's—nothing."

The tension drained from David as rapidly as it had from her. He glared at the tape player. But he stood, the moment lost, the mood broken, and after a moment he held his hand to her. "Let's go make that call," he said.

She nodded. What else could she do? She couldn't very well drag him back down on the sofa with her; that wouldn't be smart. That wouldn't be wise. That could very possibly be emotional suicide. But she didn't take his hand. Instead, she offered him a tentative smile, one acknowledging her own withdrawal from him, and managed to get herself to her feet.

"Wait," David said as she left the room. When she looked at him questioningly, he again checked the lock on the French doors, went to each of the lamps and turned them off, and as they left the room, he closed and tested the door behind them. "Is there a key for this door?" he asked.

She raised an eyebrow. "There's a whole box of keys in a kitchen drawer," she told him. "Is there a reason to search for one?"

He shrugged, grimaced, and finally gave her a wry smile. "A cop's paranoia?" he offered.

She didn't return the smile. He might be joking about a cop's paranoia, but his request and his words had activated her own, and she didn't like it one bit. Not here in her house. Damn it, until he'd come along she'd seldom worried about keys for the outside doors, let alone for interior ones.

"Good enough for me," she told him. "But I'll let you go through the box."

He dropped his hand onto her once again tense shoulders. "Annie, I'm sorry. There's probably no reason in the world to lock that door."

"But you'd feel better if I did?"

He nodded.

"Are you going to tell me why? Who do you think might try to come through it?"

"Not who," he said. "What. Samuels saw what he thinks were a couple of mountain lions near here last night. All the glass in that room would make easy access. I'd just feel better if you had some solid wood between you and it."

Mountain lions? This close to town? Surely not. And yet— And yet she remembered the sound, so like a growl, that she had heard when they were in the secret room, the sound she had hastily, gratefully attributed to the wind, and shuddered. "Well, hell, David." Once again she threw the words she had heard him mutter under his breath as he worked in the house back at him and laughed weakly. "What else is going to happen? What else can happen?"

He pulled her to him, and she went easily into his arms. Yes, the sensation fluttered through her again— *Natural. Familiar. Right.*

He hugged her quickly, tightly, and released her. "We're going to call your mom for some answers about your uncle," he told her. "Then I'm going to check the locks on all the doors and windows one more time, I'm going to look around outside just to make sure nothing and no one is or has been lurking around out there, and then I'm going back to my cold, drafty cabin, while you get some much needed rest. Okay?"

It wasn't, but she supposed it was what had to be done. "Okay," she said.

"Anne?"

Her mother's voice carried clearly over the long distance lines, and in its soft drawl Anne heard all the sounds of home, though now tinged with the flavor of *down under.* "Honey, what's wrong? Are you— Oh, gosh, it's Thanksgiving Day in the States, isn't it. I'm so sorry. We're in such a rush getting ready to go to the ranch—I mean station—I forgot. Are you all right? Did you have a good day? Did any of the family come through with an invitation for you?"

"I love you, too, mother," Anne said when her mother paused for breath. "And, yes, I'm all right, and no, no one came through with an invitation, so I invited friends to the house and had dinner here."

"You did? In that wonderful old dining room? I just knew that would be a great house for entertaining. I always wondered why Aunt Ellie didn't do more of it. Of course, Marian was a pretty heavy burden on her time, and she was just about as grim as they come, but anybody who would paint a house purple had to have a sense of humor, even if it was dry—"

"Mom?" Anne hated to break in on her mother's enthusiasm—for too many years Katherine Locke had had no time or energy for enthusiasm, only for the fight she waged daily to raise her daughter alone and in a home that Anne would never have reason to be ashamed of. But she wasn't single mother Katherine Locke any longer; she was Katherine Hudson. And she no longer balanced precariously on the edge of poverty. Tom Hudson had seen to that. Sometimes Anne resented Tom for taking her mother so far away, for making the long visits they had once shared impossible, but when she heard the life in Katherine's voice, she knew that the missed visits were small enough payment for the happiness her mother so richly deserved and had at long last found.

"Yes, dear?"

Anne glanced at David, who had pulled his chair close to hers at the kitchen table, and tilted the receiver slightly, wordlessly inviting him to listen in on the conversation. "What do you know about Uncle Ralph?"

"Oh." A faint crackling sound filled the silence. "Is it important?" Her mother laughed abruptly. "Of course it is, or you wouldn't have called. What's happened, Anne? My God, I didn't get you in any trouble, did I? I really thought Allegro would be a safe place for you to recover. Is it Joe? He always was a mean little brat, but I thought surely by now he would have grown out of it."

"No. I'm not in any trouble. At least none that I can't handle, I think. And it's not Joe, not really, although he still is a mean little brat. But there's— We— I need to know what— I need to know everything you know about Uncle Ralph. Do you . . . Do you remember him?

"No. He died when I was still real small. We? Who is *we*, Anne?"

Anne sighed. She loved her mother; she really did. But sometimes she wanted to shake her. Fortunately Katherine was well out of her reach. She looked at David and saw him fighting both a smile and a serious case of frustration.

"Mom, please. Uncle Ralph? What did he do for a living? How did he lose his money? And when?"

"And this is really important to you?"

"Yes."

Anne heard the clink of ice in a glass thousands of miles away while her mother took a sip of her inevitable strong southern sweet tea. "Marian would be the one to talk to about what happened to Ralph's money," Katherine said slowly. "Of course, she's always been crazier than a bessie bug. At least since her accident. And depending on her mood, she might blame it either on the curse or the cats—"

"Mom!"

"But according to the letter I got from Harriet—you know, my cousin who lives in Kansas City—Joe's had her in a nursing home in—where? Jeez—Texarkana, I think, since Christmas. But he may have moved her again. He does that, you know."

"No," Anne said. "I'm afraid I don't know very much about his side of the family."

"Well, honey, they're not family. Not really. Well, maybe . . . "

"Thank God for small favors," David whispered. "But ask her what she meant—"

Anne shook her head and cupped her hand over the telephone speaker but removed it when he gave her a quick, reassuring smile.

"I need answers, Mom, please. And if you don't have facts, would you please let me have the gossip?"

Katherine laughed. "What on earth have you gotten yourself into now?"

"A purple house, remember? You put the bid in for me."

"Yes. I did. Are you sorry?"

"Only when Joe hires another work crew away from me."

"He's done that? Why?"

"He wants the house, Mom. Or the land. I'm not sure which."

"Damn. So did his grandmother. But she wasn't entitled to it, either."

"Because even though she was Ralph's sister, the house belonged to Ellie?"

"Yes. At least that was what the grownups said when there were any outsiders around. But there were a lot of us kids around—at least for a while, before everyone started moving away to find work—and we heard things. So bear in mind that what I can tell you is filtered through a child's perception of cryptic conversations. Except for the things Marian actually said. And God knows how that's been filtered."

Anne could only shake her head. Maybe this meant her mother accepted that she had finally grown up. Amazing. David's hand clamped on hers where she held the receiver and his other caught her chin, stilling her.

"I never knew exactly what he did for a living. Not much at the last, I remember hearing that."

"Did he go broke in the Crash?"

"Oh, no, honey. He came through that like a champ. And he made money hand over fist all during the depression. I remember hearing that said, time after time, and not with any admiration. It seems he had cash—lots of cash that no one really knew where it came from—so he was able to buy up forfeited tax lands and even some delinquent mortgages before the government put the brakes on foreclosures."

"Then what happened?"

"Marian said it was a curse."

"Yeah, right."

"No, just listen, my young skeptic. Ralph dealt in antiquities. Of course, no one I overheard called them that back then. They simply referred to his 'treasures.' But he apparently had quite a little network of sources and markets for archaeological items. Probably a black market network, but a lucrative one just the same. Until he got greedy.

"The story is that he was involved in those excavations at Spiro, on the sly of course, and that he bought a load of contraband that wiped out all his resources and then couldn't get rid of it."

David's hand once again tightened on hers, and he leaned closer. Anne felt her throat go dry. "Why?"

"Why did he buy it? Or why couldn't he get rid of it? Or does it matter? He bought it because he thought he could make a dollar. And if he couldn't get rid of it, it was probably because somebody finally pulled one on him and unloaded a bunch of fakes. Fitting justice, I'd say."

"Spiro?" Anne asked. "As in LeFlore County, just north of here?"

"Yes. There was a big discovery made there in the thirties. Didn't you study that in— Oh. We were in Tennessee by the time you got to state history in school. Anyway, I think he just got caught in a scam and never got over the blow to his ego or his pocketbook. Marian insisted that he had infuriated some ancient god.

"In fact, she insisted that same god, in the guise of giant yellow cats that just happened to be roaming around the upstairs hallway, killed two of his suppliers as well as causing the fall that broke her back."

Anne heard the humor in Katherine's voice. She knew

there was not a malicious bone in her mother's body, not even after the hellacious time she'd gone through as a young woman surrounded by these people she now discussed. She glanced at David. He wasn't smiling.

"Cats?" *Samuels saw what he thinks were a couple of mountain lions near here last night.* Coincidence, surely. She felt her hand slide on the receiver.

"Yeah." Katherine's voice lost its laughter. "Cats. Forgive me, darlin'. I'm sorry Marian broke her back. I'm sorry Ralph died, but Ralph treated Aunt Ellie like dirt. And after he died, Marian kept it up, propped up in that room upstairs, expecting Ellie to wait on her hand and foot—which Ellie did—expecting her to care for her young son—which Ellie did until she just couldn't handle it anymore and sent him to stay with a cousin—refusing even to sell the car that Ralph had bought her, not his wife, to help with the expenses of her care. These things I do know.

"And I know that when Ralph died Marian tried real hard to take Ellie's home away from her, but never produced so much as a birth or baptism or confirmation certificate to prove she was really his sister, and that Joseph, her son, as nice a kid as I could hope to meet when I was growing up, looked a hell of a lot like that framed picture of Ralph that used to dominate the mantel in your living room. I am so damn glad that we're on Ellie's side of the family." Katherine paused to draw in a deep breath and remained silent a moment. "And I am off my soapbox as of now. I'm sorry, Anne. I thought I was over all the hard feelings. I guess I'm not."

From laughter to bleak despair in the space of a heartbeat. So her mother's memories were as sneaky about ambush as Anne's were. "No, Mom. I'm sorry. I shouldn't have dragged you into the past."

"And why not, darlin'? Every family has a skeleton or two in the closet."

Anne turned to David. This was her *mother* for God's sake. If she couldn't trust her, who could she trust? Slowly, almost reluctantly, he nodded his head.

"That's just it, Mom," Anne said. She took a deep breath. "This family— We— It wasn't actually in the closet; it was behind a false wall in an upstairs sitting room."

She heard an abrupt clank—her mom's glass hitting the ceramic tile of her kitchen counter—and a sharp, indrawn breath. "Lucy?" Katherine whispered. "Did you find Lucy? She didn't run away with that Briggs boy? Oh, God, no one really believed she'd go off and leave her mother, even if Marian was doing her best to make her life holy hell, but there wasn't any other answer . . . Have the police identified her? Oh, God. Oh, God. In the house all this time?"

"Mom? Mom, back up a minute. Who is Lucy?"

"Lucy Hansom. Ellie and Ralph's daughter. You found a skeleton? A human skeleton? In Marian's room?"

"No!" Anne shouted the word to break through her mother's frantic questions. "Well, yes. But not— Mom, what we found was probably the contraband you said Ralph got stung with. Not a—not a woman, not anyone we have to call the police about. At least I don't think so. I've asked Karen to give me her opinion so we can be sure. And asked a collector in Dallas for an opinion on one of the items with it. But other than that, I'd just as soon no one else knew about it. At least not yet."

"Oh." Again, only a faint crackle filled the silence for one second, two, three. "Oh. It was true then? He did get stuck with what he thought was treasure? Someone did pull a fast one on Ralph Hansom?"

Again Anne looked at David. He shrugged.

"I don't know, Mom," she said. "I don't know. It sure

looks real to me, but I won't know until some time next week." And then, to keep any more of her mother's questions unspoken, Anne asked one of her own. "That was Marian's room? The art deco one?"

Katherine laughed softly. "Ellie didn't change it? Good. It has to be pretty worn by now, but when I was growing up, I used to peek in the door when Ellie had Marian out for her bath or for some other reason, and I thought that must be the most sophisticated room ever designed.

"You're all right with this, Anne?" she asked abruptly. "Finding it wasn't too much for you so soon after . . . "

"I'm fine, Mom. How are the boys?"

Again Katherine laughed. "They are holy terrors. Tom has them out now for some last minute 'manly' shopping before we take off. They'll be sorry they missed your call."

"I'm sorry, too. How long will you be gone?"

"About a month. You do have the emergency numbers in case you need to contact us?"

"Yes. Yes, I do. But don't worry. Everything here will be fine."

"I just hate it that you're all alone there with this mystery to solve."

"Face it, Mom." Now Anne laughed. "You're just sorry you aren't in the middle of it with me."

"Maybe," Katherine admitted.

"And besides," again Anne looked toward David. Hesitating only slightly, he nodded. "I'm not alone."

"Ah hah! The *we* that kept slipping out when you were talking to me? Who? 'Fess up, Anne."

God! She felt about ten years old. And David's grin didn't make things one bit better. She felt her face turning red and every one of her freckles glowing. "He's a Dallas police officer on vacation, and he's helping me with the house."

"Good. You tell him hello for me. And you tell him to take good care of my little girl."

He'd moved away slightly, she hoped to give her privacy for the rest of her conversation, but she was pretty sure he'd heard that last bit, anyway. She glared at him, even as she softened her words to say good-bye to her mother.

"What else can happen?"

At David's question, she looked up from her studied inspection of the telephone after she had replaced the receiver.

"I believe you asked me that just a few minutes ago," he said.

Sighing, she leaned her elbows on the table and rested her chin on her hands.

"Anne?"

She couldn't answer his question; she couldn't answer her own. And she couldn't sit there pretending that those questions weren't racing through her. She jerked to her feet and paced to the kitchen sink where she gripped the edge and stared out the window. David must have turned off the porch light while making his rounds, because blackness pressed in, capturing the lighted kitchen like a mirror, throwing her image back at her. Throwing the image of David standing behind her back at her.

He dropped his hands to her shoulders, then traced them along her arms, before enfolding her.

"I don't need this," she told him. But she wasn't sure whether she was talking about the complications her mom had just brought up, or the complications that her reaction to his embrace could cause. "I came back because I wanted a slow, uncomplicated life. Not a mystery, not a . . . "

"Not an involvement?" he asked.

She stared at his image in the window and found him

just as intently watching hers. "Not an involvement," she admitted as she released her grip on the sink and raised her hands to capture his arms as they held her.

He didn't comment, not on her words, not that she held him locked in the embrace he had initiated, not that she had leaned back against him, absorbing his warmth. He didn't comment about her crazy aunt, her greedy uncle, her missing cousin, incest, or adultery. He just held her as the two of them stared at their reflections against the midnight black backdrop of the kitchen window. He just held her, until she felt the comfort he offered her turning to something warmer, something more intense. Until she felt the changes in his body signaling that he, too, had taken a step beyond comfort.

No, she definitely didn't need this, she thought, even as she canted her head to one side, exposing her neck as David lowered his head toward her. She felt his breath on her cheek, on her throat, as his arms tightened around her. "David . . ." she murmured in protest.

"I know," he told her. "I know, Annie. I don't want this either. Help me out, here, lady. Tell me to get lost. Tell me that all you want from me is someone to hang drywall. Tell me . . ."

If only she could. Slowly she turned in his arms.

"Tell me why you're running," he persisted on a groan of need. "Tell me what brought you back to Allegro."

And that was all it took. She still stood within his embrace. And she still needed his warmth. But now it was to protect her from the chill that shuddered through her.

"Annie?"

"What makes you think anything happened?"

"Maybe because your best friend and your mother have both been concerned about your recovery? Maybe because when I asked, you tensed up like a rubber band about to snap? Maybe because I sometimes see the weight of the world in your expression? What happened, Annie? Is it so bad that sharing won't make it easier?"

Nothing would ever make it easier. But maybe it was time to share. "I got shot," she said.

She felt his arms tighten around her, felt the protest he wouldn't let himself utter.

"I was lucky," she told him in a soft monotone. "I only lost my spleen. Anthony—the man I had been engaged to—two mothers and four children at the clinic, and eventually two cops, and one of the six young men who were convinced we had to have drugs at the free clinic we staffed twice a week, died."

She heard him moan—for her—and let herself accept that small comfort.

"Sounds to me like you lost a hell of a lot more than your spleen," he said, restraining her when she would have pulled away.

Yes, she had. But those closest to her had not seemed to give more than lip service to the fact that much more than the physical trauma needed healing. How had David? And just how perceptive was he? "Such as?"

"Such as your innocence, a dear friend. Your career, maybe, and the lifestyle you had chosen and cultivated. Those are part of the losses. I imagine you also picked up a trailerload of guilt, too, didn't you? Because you'd worked hard to convince people to take advantage of your clinic?"

He was too damned perceptive. Anne tilted her head back so that she could look into his eyes. They were clouded with pain—for her. And she didn't have to admit anything, because she saw in them his knowledge of just how much of that guilt she carried.

"Yeah."

"So you came home, to lick your wounds, to recover, to assuage your guilt by providing medical care where it hadn't been available before, maybe even to recapture your courage, and ran straight into Cousin Joe and a half-century-old mystery?"

She couldn't have put it more succinctly; she *wouldn't* have, because she couldn't have been that honest with herself. But she could admit the truth when it was slammed down in front of her. She nodded once, a mere jerk of her head.

"And a man who is no more sure of his future than you are."

When she looked up, the pain she saw in his eyes was now his own.

"No, you definitely do not need this, Annie," he said, using his hands on her arms to hold her still while he stepped away from her. "Unfortunately, I don't know how to back up and take the mystery away. And I don't know how to change Joe's attitude. But I can keep from adding myself to the load of stuff piling up on you."

She wanted to argue with him—God it was lonely without his arms around her—but she knew he was right. And she also knew that he didn't need any more of her problems than he had already shouldered; he had his own to work through. That was why *he* was in Allegro.

"I want you to lock the door when I leave. And stay inside. I don't know how much stock to put in Samuels's story about the mountain lions, but it's just too much of a coincidence that your crazy aunt claims they crippled her.

"Tomorrow we'll talk about what your mother said. And we'll try to figure out the what and why of the man upstairs. You'll be all right until then, won't you, Annie?"

Of course she would be. She was strong. Didn't he realize that? Otherwise she would have already broken.

Otherwise she would have given in to the demand she felt rising within her to beg him to stay.

"Of course," she said, and even managed to dredge up a small smile. "And you be careful."

He caught her face in his hands and looked steadily into her eyes. Was he convinced? She wasn't sure. But eventually he nodded and released her.

"I'll be back first thing in the morning," he told her.

Anne watched from the locked screen until the Blazer's taillights disappeared down the drive, then closed and locked the back door and leaned against it.

She hadn't wanted him to leave. But until she was sure why she wanted him to stay—for protection, for comfort in the lonely hours of the night, for physical gratification, or for some reason that was all of those, and more—she couldn't ask him to stay. Wouldn't ask him to stay.

Slowly she crossed the kitchen, turned out the light, and started toward her room. She was at the top of the stairs before she realized it, and then, drawn, she found herself in the upstairs sitting room, opening the closet, stepping into it. She caught the edge of the strip that bordered the drywall insert. Boxes blocked the way. Boxes that she could easily have moved but which provided enough deterrent to bring her to a halt.

She pressed her hands flat and leaned her head against the wall. Why was she doing this? She didn't want to look on what lay beyond this fragile barrier. She never again wanted to see what lay on the cedar litter.

But it seemed that she couldn't raise her head, or move her hands, or leave the chill darkness of the closet. Not yet. But maybe soon . . . soon, she could leave him alone in the dark.

13

1935

The scream echoed through the house, waking Lucy from a troubled sleep and bringing her upright in her bed. It sounded again, this time accompanied by baby Joseph's angry demand for food, or for changing—sometimes they sounded the same—or maybe just for comfort because he had to be frightened; his mama was the one who was screaming. Unless, oh please no, there was something wrong with him.

Lucy swung her legs over the edge of the bed and tugged her long flannel nightgown down to cover them. She shivered in the chill early morning air and made herself hesitate long enough to find her house slippers before she ran toward the screams.

Aunt Marian's room was on the other side of the house, halfway to the back, at the end of the first hall. Papa got there before Lucy did, and neither he nor Aunt Marian saw her when she skidded to a halt in the doorway between Aunt Marian's sitting room and bedroom.

The light on the table beside the bed was on, and Lucy saw Joseph in his crib, screaming and waving his little arms and legs. Aunt Marian was all but collapsed against Papa, crying and every once in a while pointing, but not toward Joseph—toward the other side of the room.

The barrels and crates they had brought in earlier were there, in the corner, only now they were tumbled and open, and between them, in the shadows on the floor—

Lucy sucked in a big breath. There he was. All spread out like he had been in the truck, only better, neater, taking up much more space, with the poles around him making a kind of frame for him, and with all his treasures heaped around him.

Mama came into the room behind her and stopped in the doorway with her hands on Lucy's shoulders. Then Papa noticed the two of them standing there. "Go back downstairs, Ellie," he said, moving a little to stand between Mama and the man on the floor. "Everything's all right up here. Marian just had a scare."

Didn't Mama see it? Maybe not. She just nodded toward the crib and frowned. "Take care of your baby, Marian."

"Go," Papa said again. "And take Lucy with you."

Of course Mama left, using her strong hands on Lucy's shoulders to propel her along with her. She always did what Papa told her to do. But at the top of the stairs, she stopped and looked at Lucy. "Will you go back to sleep if I send you to your room?"

Lucy nodded.

"I mean it, child. I know you've got more curiosity than any ten other girls, but you don't need to be sticking your nose in where you might get it cut off."

Lucy looked up at her mama. She wanted to ask her about the man on the floor, but maybe she hadn't seen him. Maybe Lucy hadn't *really* seen him, not like she'd thought she did. She wanted to ask her what she could poke around in that would get her in trouble, but she knew better than to do that. So she nodded again. Her mama hugged her. Her mama gave the best hugs in the whole world, Lucy knew that for a fact, and this morning she smelled real good, like she'd already been in the kitchen, like cinnamon and apples and nutmeg. "Go back to bed, child."

Lucy didn't say she would; she couldn't say she wouldn't. Instead she smiled and headed down the hall toward her bedroom while Mama went back downstairs. Then Lucy turned around and went back toward Aunt Marian's room.

Joseph was quiet at last. And she didn't hear Marian crying anymore as she slipped into the sitting room and tiptoed across it to the bedroom door. Papa and Aunt Marian were just standing there, staring at the man on the floor, and Papa was not happy.

"What do you mean, you don't know how it happened? You expect me to believe someone came into your room and spread this out and neither you or that screaming kid heard anything?"

"Well, that's exactly what happened, Ralph Hansom. And don't you dare yell at me. I didn't want that dirty old mess in my bedroom anyway—"

"The hell you didn't! You couldn't stand the thought of something worth that much money being out of your control for even a day."

"My control— I'll have you know—"

"And how do I know you didn't do this?" He waved his hand toward the man on the floor. "Why in God's name you'd scream about it, though—"

"Me! You think I had anything to do with—with rearranging that corpse. Oh, wait. Is it all there?"

"How the hell should I know? We didn't inventory, remember? You were in too much of a hurry to get it all stashed before Ellie's family showed up. I doubt anyone knows just what's supposed to be there, even Jackson."

"Jackson." Aunt Marian sounded like Grandpa sometimes did when he said Papa's name. "I wouldn't put it past that piece of white trash to have come looking for a little more of the take."

"Oh, Ralph, do you think it could have been Jackson, that he came in while we were all asleep. My God, he could have killed all of us in our beds."

Now why would Mr. Jackson do a thing like that, Lucy wondered. But she didn't have time to wonder long. Papa turned toward the door and started marching her way.

"I don't know," he said, coming into the sitting room just as Lucy ducked behind the wardrobe. "But I'm damned sure going to find out." He turned and looked at Marian, who was standing, just standing there, staring down at the man on the floor with the strangest, saddest look in her eyes. "Come on," Papa told her. "I'm not leaving you here. Not now anyway. For all I know, you've been prowling through the lot of it half the night. But don't forget, Marian, that no matter what you found or find there, it's not worth a dime to you until *I* find a buyer."

Lucy stayed hidden behind the wardrobe until they'd left the room, until she heard their voices floating up the stairs, still arguing. Still mad. Then she crept out of hiding. She knew where they'd be going. Papa's study. And she knew she couldn't get close enough downstairs to hear what they were saying, and she also knew she had to hear what they were saying.

But first, she had to look once more at the strange, wonderful man on the floor. The copper covering him glowed softly in the dim light. He looked almost peaceful lying there. Slowly, careful not to disturb Joseph, who was now happily sucking at a bottle, Lucy made her way to the foot of the wooden pallet. Papa might not know what had been with the man, but Lucy counted one more basket than she had seen in the truck, and on the very edge of the pallet, half on, half off the cedar rail, sat a carved statue. Just a little one. One that looked just like— Lucy reached out to touch it but couldn't seem to make her fingers work. She shook her head. It looked just like one of the pieces that Mr. Jackson's boy had taken when he didn't think anyone was watching. But it couldn't be.

A small box rested near the man's foot. Lucy knelt and this time had no trouble picking it up. It had a delicate, engraved top, which she touched with gentle fingers then slid open. Inside, in a nest of shattered fabric, lay two small medallions. Lucy turned the box toward the light enough to see that each carried an engraved likeness, one of a man, the other of a woman. And they made her hurt to look at them. Hurt almost to tears, and she didn't know why. She sucked her lower lip between her teeth as she knelt on the wooden floor and rocked back and forth, seeking—comfort?—seeking something she couldn't understand, until Joseph gurgled and tossed his bottle to the floor. Quickly Lucy replaced the box and rose to her feet. Just as quickly, she found Joseph's bottle for him and silenced him as he opened his mouth to wail a protest at being left alone.

Papa's study was at the north end of the house. The room directly above it was a guest room, almost never used even though it had one of the few closets in the house. This one was in the sloping space beneath the attic stairs, and one end wall was made by the brick chimney of Papa's fireplace. She'd found a loose board there ages ago, and while she knew she couldn't see anything—she'd given up even trying to do that—she didn't know if she could hear anything. She'd never tried while Papa was in his room.

Now she thought it was worth the risk of being caught.

She lifted the board and bent down until she had her ear to the opening. She heard Papa cranking the telephone. He didn't like telephones, said he thought the nosy old operators listened to every word, so he had to think this was important.

"Yes, Gladys," he said. Mrs. Porter was the operator. "Get me Tom Jackson at Atwood. I know what time it is. Just ring the number will you? Yes, Gladys, I know it's long distance. My God, woman, I don't care if the Atwood operator is asleep. Wake her up."

Then Papa was quiet for a moment. Aunt Marian said something, but Lucy couldn't understand her words, just her tone, and she was still mad.

"Mrs. Jackson?" She heard her papa's voice distinctly. "I'm sorry to bother you at this— What? No. No, this is Ralph Hansom. I need to talk to Tom. What? I'm sorry. I can't hear you over the static." There was silence, and Lucy strained to hear, to make sure she wasn't missing anything. "I see," her papa said at last, and this time he didn't use his 'important man' voice. "I see. Yes. I'll call back later. No. No, it was no trouble. You— You take care now."

"Well, what did she say?" Aunt Marian all but shouted.

"Tom isn't there."

"So he was here!"

"I don't think so. There was a crash. The brakes on that new truck of his failed, up in that straight, flat farmland, and the car hit the one tree within three hundred yards. Jackson's son was driving. He was alone when it happened, and they only found him an hour or so ago. Jackson's still talking with the sheriff and the undertaker."

14

David awoke long before dawn Friday morning, compliments of the wind-up alarm clock that seemed to be standard issue for the cabins at Tompkins Fish Camp and the nagging feeling that he shouldn't leave Anne alone too long to deal with all the problems her home had brought her.

He turned up the panel heater in what he suspected was a wasted effort to take the chill off the room, and lit the burner under the old blue coffeepot and its two-day-old brew, knowing that if he hurried he could be in and out of the shower before the thing boiled over. Icy cold well water lost most of its appeal when it came straight from the showerhead, but this morning, he needed the extra kick it would give him to get started.

He glanced out the tiny window in the bathroom. Yep, those idiots in the next cabin were already up, probably chomping at the bit to get back out on the lake. He guessed it took all kinds, but why Pete Tompkins had ever thought, and he'd ever agreed that he might be the kind who'd actually enjoy sacrificing helpless bait from a boat in a subfreezing windchill, he'd never know.

He emerged from the shower in time to lift the pot off the burner as it started spewing over and poured himself a cupful of reheated sludge. He needed that extra kick this morning, too.

Gretta Tompkins was just stepping out of her cabin when he drove past. She smiled and waved. His captain's mother was a nice woman, someone who had no bones to pick, no ax to grind, no ox to gore. Just a genuinely good person.

Nice. Not earthshaking. But nice.

Something he hadn't realized he'd needed in his life. Something he hadn't realized had been gone until now.

He'd found the convenience store on Monday, halfway around the lake on the way into town. Straight out of his concept of a step into the past, it offered bare wood floors, a pot-bellied stove, decent coffee, fresh doughnuts, and usually two or three fishermen and local residents gathered around the stove or the live-bait boxes, swapping stories before they started their day. To his surprise, within less than a week, he had become an accepted part of that early morning crowd. He didn't kid himself that anyone was going to spill any deep secrets around him, but the camaraderie was a welcome change, a reminder of early days on the force before even the small talk between officers got dragged down into the cesspool their investigations invariably led to.

That too was nice. Not earthshaking. But nice.

Something else he hadn't realized he'd needed, hadn't realized he'd missed, until he felt the warmth and welcome wrapping itself around him.

Only one car sat outside the store when he arrived. A

sheriff's patrol car. David approached warily, but the car was parked, not slewed in, and the lights and radio were dark and silent.

He eased in the front door. Blake Foresman looked up from his propped-back chair beside the stove and lifted his foam coffee cup in welcome.

"Henry's out in the storage shed," the sheriff said. "It's strictly self-service till he gets back."

David felt the tension release him. He hadn't meant to stick around this morning, only grab a cup of coffee to go, but maybe he ought to take advantage of this chance meeting. He nodded and headed toward the coffee counter.

"You're out early," Foresman said when David settled into the chair next to him.

"So are you. Or is it late?"

Foresman grunted, which David interpreted as meaning late. "I'm two men short," he said on a yawn, "and I like to give the men with families as many holidays as possible."

David's respect for this man had been slowly growing since the day of the accident. Now it took a giant leap. He nodded his understanding and appreciation of Foresman's work assignment and took a cautious sip from his cup. The brew was as hot as asphalt in August and as strong as it could be and still be liquid, but it was fresh. "You make the coffee?" he asked the sheriff.

Foresman grinned at him. "I figured I'd need all the help I could get to make it the rest of the shift and thirty miles home. Too strong for you?"

David returned the grin and they sat there in companionable silence for a few minutes before David broached the first subject. "These woods around here are pretty wild. Ever have any trouble with predators?"

"Every now and then a bear gets curious and we have

to call the wildlife people in to chase him back to his part of the woods."

"How about cats?"

"A bobcat or two has been reported, usually by a tourist who's had too much to drink and can't tell the difference between a wild animal and something like Gretta Tompkins's twenty-pound yellow tabby."

David thought of his neighbors in the next cabin. Yeah. They'd be likely to do something like that. But he was concerned with something much larger than Gretta's house cat. "How about mountain lions?"

Foresman peered at him, not alarmed, but alert. "They're not unheard of around here, just rare enough to make a sighting real newsworthy. Why? You hearing strange noises around your cabin?"

David shook his head. "Wayne Samuels said he thought he spotted a couple on the hill behind Dr. Locke's house."

"Well," the sheriff said. "Well, now. Samuels, huh? Heard he was up at the doc's for dinner yesterday. He ought to know. Well, hell. That's all I need—a couple of wild animals practically in town."

Was there anything this sheriff—anybody in the whole county for that matter—didn't hear within a day? Somehow David doubted that there was. But Blake Foresman didn't ask about Samuels, and he didn't issue any warnings about him either. That silence almost as good as told him he could trust his instincts and trust the man. But almost wasn't good enough if Annie's safety was at risk.

"Anne thought Margaret was a widow."

"So did Margaret."

David waited, silent, and after a moment Foresman shrugged. "I stood beside her six years ago while she buried what was left of a body the army told her was his.

I stood beside her last winter when we dug that body up and gave it back to the army after Wayne showed up on her doorstep one morning more dead than alive."

Damn! Samuels had done hard time all right. He'd done time in hell. "MIA?"

"Nope." Foresman let the legs of his chair drop to the floor. He stood and stretched. "Not even official prisoner of war. He came home, you see. But his brother didn't. His best friend didn't. After a couple of years, he joined up with a bunch to go back in and look for some of those who hadn't made it out. He doesn't have much to do with folks. Won't talk about what happened in those years he was gone. But he'd die for a friend."

Yeah, David thought, he would. He already had.

Which left the next topic. Anne hadn't picked up on it. Or if she had, she hadn't said anything. But Katherine's questions had triggered questions in David. Questions that couldn't be ignored. "What do you know about Lucy Hansom and somebody named Briggs?"

"Lucy?"

"Yeah. She'd have been Anne's great uncle Ralph's daughter."

"Would have been?"

"Or is. Seems she took missing a number of years ago. There might have been a search. Might not have been."

"You've got a need to know?"

David grimaced. "Maybe."

Foresman looked at him. "You got any idea when?"

"Nope."

"I grew up in this county. I've been back for fifteen years. In office for nine. And I don't remember anything about her. I don't suppose you could ask Joe?" When David just looked at him, Blake shrugged. "No. I suppose not." He sighed and crushed his empty cup.

"Give me a couple of days. I've got a room on the third floor of the courthouse bulging with old records. I'll take a look."

"Thanks."

"What the hell are you two doing up at that house, anyway?"

"Just making it livable, Sheriff," David told him while his thoughts jumped from the man in the closet, to Katherine's assumption that they had found Lucy's body, to the eerie and oppressive feeling in the old barn, to the absolutely impractical attraction growing between him and Anne, to the big hole that faced him whenever he thought about his future. "Just making it livable."

David brought doughnuts that morning, and just like the previous morning walked her out onto her front porch and sat with her for a dose of early morning air with their caffeine. But this morning he sat far enough away that they didn't touch. And this morning, although he teased her, even laughed with her as they discussed the day before and their plans for the morning, he looked as though he needed the calming effects of the view of the valley and mountains beyond. He didn't seem agitated so much as troubled, drawn in on himself as though caught in thoughts he didn't much like but couldn't avoid. Like she too often was.

"Want to talk about it?" she asked finally. She wouldn't. But maybe he would. Maybe he needed to.

"About what?"

"About whatever's bothering you this morning?"

"Nope." He stood and tossed the dregs of his coffee into the overgrown flowerbeds fronting the porch. "What I want to do is take a look around the outside of the house to satisfy my paranoia and then finish that kitchen ceiling."

The telephone rang as the lights of Allegro were beginning to dot the darkening landscape below the house. The clutter of their day's work still lingered in swept-up piles, and the remains of their leftover turkey dinner still occupied the table. Anne gazed with satisfaction at her new ceiling, and David, who had finally managed to forget to worry about what he was going to do with the rest of his life, gazed at her and wondered how she had managed to draw him out of his dark mood.

The phone rang a second time, a sharp summons full of its own importance, refusing to be ignored. Anne stiffened, her smile faded, and the animation drained from her face, but she made no move to answer the phone, made no move to quiet the intrusion.

"Are you expecting a call?" he asked.

She shook her head.

"Do you suppose it's an emergency?"

"God, I hope not," she whispered.

He stood when she didn't, walked to the counter, picked up the telephone, and brought it back to the table as it rang still another time. He set it beside her. "Is something wrong, Annie?"

"No. Of course not."

Then why don't you want to answer the telephone? What the hell's going on here, anyway? "You want me to answer that?"

She looked like she wanted him to. Hell, she looked as though she wanted him to tell whoever was on the other end of that line she wasn't there, couldn't be reached, couldn't help if she were. But of course she didn't tell him that—not his Annie.

His Annie? But before he could do more than question that thought, she gave him the cheeky grin he had seen many times and which he only now began to suspect she used when she was hiding something from someone, maybe even herself, and reached for the telephone. "What?" she asked. "And finish ruining your reputation? I don't think so."

She snatched up the receiver before the ring could shriek again. "Hello?"

She frowned slightly as she listened, but her tension seemed to ease some. She held the receiver toward him. "Too late," she said. "You're already ruined. It's for you."

Now David frowned. Who knew he was here? He coughed out a laugh. Only about half the county. But he spoke cautiously. "Huerra."

"Huerra, how in the hell did you manage to wind up in the middle of one my investigations when you're supposed to be in a boat in the middle of Lake Allegro drowning worms?"

"Captain?" *Pete Tompkins?* Calling him here? Why? "What investigation?"

He heard Pete sigh. "I was going to call, hat in hand, and ask you to break your vacation long enough to introduce yourself to the local sheriff and then ask a couple of questions there in Allegro. But when I call, my mother tells me you are with the person I need you to question, and before I can dial again, the lab turns up your name written on a notepad we've taken in evidence. So maybe I'll just ask you. What did you have going with Jack Townley?"

"Oh—" He caught himself before the obscenity erupted from his mouth. Dragging the cord up and over Anne, he sat heavily in his chair and glanced around the room that only moments before had seemed so peaceful. "What happened?"

"God knows," Tompkins told him. "At least I hope he does, because sure as hell no one else does. The housekeeper said he was looking for a package in the mail, which came about ten this morning. He took it into his study and later made a series of phone calls. Just after noon, she heard him scream, found the door locked and called 911, but was so frightened she ran outside and was halfway down the block when the first officers arrived."

"Townley is dead?" Of course he was. Pete Tompkins worked homicide. Not burglary. Not robbery.

"Oh, yes. Oh, hell yes."

Dead. And not neatly. Not with that tone in the captain's voice. "How?"

"At first glance it looks like some sort of animal attack, but the windows were closed—not locked, but closed—and I don't think any animal is going to stop to shut a window, so I'm afraid we've got some sort of Freddy Krueger copycat loose in the city."

He felt Anne's eyes on him and glanced up. She couldn't possibly have heard Pete's words, but the color had blanched from her face. "Do you have a motive?"

"His safe was open, so robbery, maybe. That's what I wanted you to find out. The package was from a Dr. A. Locke. From what my mother said, I take it that was Dr. A. Locke who answered the telephone."

"Yeah."

"And you've been there with her all day?"

"Yeah."

"Any idea what was in the package?"

"Yeah."

"Jesus, Huerra, are you going to tell me what it was or are you going to make me drag it out of you one word at a time?"

David shook his head, but the action didn't clear

away the fog of questions he felt building. "It was a shell artifact," he said. "Engraved. About four inches in diameter. Is it missing?"

He heard the shuffle of papers. "I don't see anything like that on this list, or in the pictures. Is it valuable?"

"It could be. That's what we wanted Jack to tell us." He glanced at Anne again, but he knew what had to be done, even without her consent. "We took a tracing. I'll see that you get a copy. I don't suppose you found any notes?"

"Only the sheet of paper with your name on it, a list of telephone numbers we're in the process of checking, and one other word that looks like spiral, spires, spirit, with a question mark?"

"Spiro," David said on a slow exhalation.

"What does that mean?"

"Not what," David explained. "Where. It's the provenance. We just found out last night that Dr. Locke's great uncle was an antiquities dealer who had some dealings with the excavations at Spiro in the thirties. But keep that as quiet as you can. If your perp would kill for one shell, he might decide to come see if she has more."

"And does she?"

Anne had sunk back in her chair, her face chalk white, her eyes closed as slowly she dragged her head from side to side, denying—denying what?

"I guarantee you," he said, making a quick decision that might well damn him, "that shell was one of a kind."

"Let's hope so," Pete said. "Let's hope so."

Carefully David placed the receiver in the cradle and leaned back in his chair.

"Your friend is dead," Anne said, at last opening her eyes, revealing an anguish all out of proportion with learning of the death of a stranger.

He nodded.

"And someone stole the gorget?"

Again he nodded.

"Who?" she asked. "Who knew?"

"Good question, Doc," he said. The words and the cynicism just slipped out, and once released, hung in the air between them. "Who did know?"

She recoiled from the unspoken accusation he had been unable to check.

"Ah, hell, Annie," he said. "I didn't mean that the way it sounded."

"Didn't you?" she asked softly. "On some level don't you wonder who I told about the packages? Did I open them up and show Margaret? Did I boast about the treasure we'd found? Did I make sure Joe found out so I could gloat about it?"

He couldn't answer her, because he did wonder. All of the above. And he didn't want to doubt her, but for the moment, yes, he did.

She pushed back from the table and stood. She walked to the back door and tested the lock and then crossed the room.

"Where are you going?" Stupid question, Huerra, he told himself. He knew where she was going. But instead of the acerbic reply he expected from her in light of what he'd just said, she simply shook her head. "Someone has to check on him."

Well, hell. She was right, of course. But hearing her refer to that pile of bones and grave goods as *him*, as she always did, he realized, sent a chill down his back remarkably like the one he had felt the first time he saw her house.

He stood, scraping his chair back. "Wait a minute. You don't need to go up there by yourself."

She paused but didn't turn and didn't speak when he

caught up with her in the hallway. "Did you hear anything last night?" he asked.

She shook her head.

"See anything? Did anything unusual happen after I left?"

"No," she said.

And that was all that either of them said until they reached the closet. David stepped in first and looked around, and all his alarms went off. "Someone's been in here. Those boxes have been moved."

She followed him into the closet, knelt to examine the boxes he indicated and sighed. "I was in here, David."

"You—"

"Just hush," she said. "I started to check on him last night after you left. I came this far and then realized I didn't want to go in there with him. Not alone."

It was her house. It was her closet. It was her damned treasure. And if she wanted to check on it every fifteen minutes, it was her damned right to do so. So why did he have to work so hard to remember that? Why was he glad that she hadn't gone in without him? And why was he so reluctant now to go in, either with her or alone?

He turned away from the questions and mild rebuke he saw in her eyes, pushed the boxes away, and lifted the panel from the opening.

The light from the sitting room didn't penetrate the bends and curves of the passageway enough to do more than cast the glow of the opening across the dark room. David stepped through and more by memory than by sight located the pull cord for the ceiling fixture. He yanked on it, and the glare of the bare bulb flooded the room.

The warrior lay on his litter, surrounded by his grave goods. His copper armor gleamed softly, giving the appearance of a statue, or perhaps a sleeping man, until the stark whiteness of the bones visible beneath the armor, beneath the profusion of shells and pipes and pearls and pots destroyed that image. He appeared unchanged, undisturbed since he had been placed there, only God knew how many years before, except for the slight depression where Anne had removed the right femur—and except for one shell gorget that lay alone in a space on the cedar pole near where David had knelt two days before. He'd been careful then not to disturb anything more than absolutely necessary; he'd been careful to replace everything he'd removed. He'd left nothing on the pole or outside the confines of the litter.

David glanced at Anne. *Her house*, he reminded himself again. *Her closet. Her treasure.* Her lie? There was no reason she shouldn't have come in here if she wanted. There was also no reason she shouldn't have admitted a closer examination of what could make her an extremely wealthy woman. But she obviously thought there was. And there was no reason for him to feel as though she had betrayed him in some way much more elemental than simply hiding an innocent curiosity from him. But he did.

He bent to examine the gorget.

"No way," he whispered, kneeling, taking the gorget in his hand. Feeling again the slash of betrayal.

"What is it?" she asked from the foot of the litter. "We didn't leave anything there, did we?"

So innocent. David's fingers closed around the gorget. He forced himself to release them, to remember his strength and the fragility of the ornament. But it was there—damn! For a moment he had almost allowed himself to hope there were two identical gorgets. But there wouldn't be, not both bearing the small, peculiar nick he had noticed Wednesday.

"David?" she said again in the soft voice she always used in this room. "What's wrong?"

"What's wrong," he said, exerting the same tenuous control over his voice as he did the hand that gripped the gorget, "is that this is the shell we picked out to send to Jack Townley."

"No," she said. She knelt beside him and reached for the shell. He continued to hold it, but turned it so the light reflected from its engraved surface.

"Oh." The word came out on a soft hiss of breath and Anne sank onto her heels. She looked up at David, her eyes wide and questioning. Either she was truly surprised or they still taught advanced acting in med school. "We— How? When?" She shook her head again. "No. It can't be."

He pushed to his feet and looked down at her. He heard the chill in his voice, but there wasn't a whole hell of a lot he could do about that. Too often in interrogations he'd been forced into the role of "bad cop" because at some point it became impossible for him to disguise his disgust at the ease with which the slime he was interrogating slipped into the role of innocent victim, when the true victim was on a slab in the morgue. Lying did that to him, too. Especially unnecessary lying from someone he'd begun to believe he could trust.

"We have the tracings," he said. "Let's go take a look."

Anne was as silent returning downstairs as she had been coming up them. This time, David made no effort to break that silence.

She'd carefully folded the tissue paper and placed it out of sight—she'd said because of the visitors to the house—in what had to be the safest, or the place the least likely to raise questions about why she had a series of pre-Columbian tracings—with her copper, where she already had a tackle box full of similar designs.

Thursday morning he'd watched, smiling, while she'd stashed the tackle box in a stack of boxes and cartons in the room adjoining the kitchen. "Poe," she'd said grinning. "Wasn't he the one who said the best place to hide something was in plain view?"

Now he watched as she prowled through the stack of boxes looking for the right tackle box, and smiling was the last thing he felt like doing. Damn! Was it too much to ask that finally in his long, lonely, miserable life he could have someone he could trust?

Whoa! Where had that come from?

David walked to the table and reached for the chair he had abandoned only minutes before, but he didn't sit; he gripped the back of it, one-handed. Unlike the gorget, which he still held cautiously in his right hand, the chair wouldn't break. Maybe. He had someone to trust, he told himself as he felt the bite of wood against his palm and fingers. His brother. And his brother's family. And in the past he'd had the support and, yes, love, of his overworked parents. And, damn it, he wasn't that old; his life hadn't been that long. And if he'd been alone, it had been by choice. His choice. So why was he standing here moaning because Anne Locke had so obviously and needlessly lied to him?

Because he wanted Annie. He wanted to trust her. He wanted to love her. He wanted her in his life now, this weekend, the rest of the month he was to spend here, the rest of his life.

"Son of a bitch."

When the hell had that happened?

Anne swiveled around from where she was digging through boxes. "What?"

David shook his head. Then he sat. And pushed the plates and platters and bowls containing the remains of their dinner toward the other side of the table. And set the gorget on the table in front of him, next to the telephone that they had left there when they went upstairs. And forced himself to think about lies and betrayal. "Have you found them yet?"

"Yes."

He heard the less than gentle click as Anne closed a metal box, the soft fumbling sounds as she rose from her crouch on the floor, and then her steps. She stopped beside him. "Here they are," she said.

Any hope that he might be mistaken died when he placed the gorget on the tissue next to his initialed tracing, but still he turned it over and compared the reverse, and set it on the tracing to compare the nick.

"It's the same, isn't it?" she asked. "But how? How can that be?"

"What happened, Doc?" he asked without turning to look at her where she stood near his shoulder, giving every appearance of being as engrossed in the comparison as he. "Didn't you trust me enough to let this out of your control long enough to have it identified?"

"*What?*"

He trailed his fingers along the edge of the gorget when what he wanted to do was swivel in his chair, grab Annie by the shoulders and shake her until she admitted her deception, until she—until she what? Until she wrapped her arms around him and begged his forgiveness? It wasn't going to happen. Not in this lifetime. But if it did—just for the sake of speculation—what would he do?

He buried his face in his hands, raked at his eyes and his forehead, at the alien thoughts that had crept from some unknown well in his psyche. Pete was right. He had lost it. He sighed and then he did look at her.

"Except that sometime in the last two days it has been cleaned, this gorget is identical to the one we brought down Wednesday and packaged to send to Jack Townley. I can only think of two ways it could be here. Either sometime between noon and now someone sneaked into a house where we were both working, found the entry to the closet room, and returned an artifact worth thousands of dollars, and just as quietly left without either of us hearing a thing. Or . . ."

Her expression had gone all tight and closed, and her eyes, usually alive with humor, if not laughter, had narrowed and darkened. "Or what?" she asked.

"Or it never went to Texas."

She shook her head. "Of course it went. We wrapped it together. You carried it out to the car for me. I took it to town."

"That's right. You took it to town." And Bobby Preston had chosen that day to try to fly. David snatched that memory and held onto it. God. Maybe she hadn't lied. "And Margaret mailed it for you. What did she mail, Annie?"

She shook her head. "No. No, I'm not going to do this. Margaret is my friend."

"A friend who was in the house yesterday."

"And your friend, David? I'm sorry he's dead. Oh, God, I'm sorry he's dead. But did he get an empty box in the mail and not say anything? And how did he know to write the word Spiro by your name? No. There's another answer somewhere."

"Where?"

She reached across him and picked up the tracing, leaving the gorget on the table. "Upstairs."

He picked up the gorget to follow, but she stopped him with a sharp look at his hand. "Leave it," she said. "That way we won't have any doubt when we find another, or several others, that look just like it."

He'd turned off the light in the room when they'd

brought the gorget downstairs, but neither of them had stopped, or even thought, to close the panel. Now he stepped through it and began reaching for the light cord. The sound was softer than a whisper, barely audible over the sound of Anne's steps as she followed him into the room, of the combined sounds of their breathing as she, too, heard whatever it was. Anne lifted her hand to his arm, touching him for the first time since the telephone call that had started this search, and together they listened. A padding, back and forth, of something soft-footed but heavy, across the room, between the burial and the closet wall. And then a soft, guttural utterance—not spoken word but conveying some unknown message. Annie's fingers gripped his arm with an almost painful tightness at the faint but unmistakable sound of bones and copper and shells settling into place.

David thrust her behind him and yanked on the light cord.

The room was empty. No one and nothing greeted his quick visual inspection of the confined area. Nothing but the blank windows, intact over their backing of unfinished siding; the wallpaper, dingy in the shadows but still covering the walls in an unbroken pink floral pattern, except for the exposed studs and back side of the sheetrock of the unfinished closet wall; the ceiling, with nothing visible there but the bare lightbulb suspended from a tarnished metal plate and decades worth of cobwebs. No one but the warrior on his cedar litter, still in place, still surrounded by his earthly treasures. David spun around, searching behind him, but he knew there was only one way out of the room, the way that he and Annie had blocked.

Once again, Annie clutched his arm. He pulled her to his side and held her there. He didn't have to ask if she'd heard the noises. Her always fair complexion had gone even paler, as pale as when he had been talking with Pete about the murder, and her eyes, which minutes ago had seemed dark and lifeless, now held expression, but he wasn't sure that terror was an improvement. She drew in a deep breath, then another, as though by regulating her breathing, she could regulate her heartbeat, now racing in cadence with his. Not a bad idea, he thought, and tried it himself. It worked, finally, marginally.

When she began unwrapping her arms from around him and pulling away, he realized she had been holding him as tightly as he had held her. He didn't want to break that bond. There was safety there, and comfort, and, strangely, a belonging. Eventually, the feeling of belonging was what forced him to release her. How could he feel that for someone who only minutes before he had thoroughly and completely distrusted? How could he distrust someone who made him feel so—so at home, so welcome? So wanted?

"Annie?"

She jerked the rest of the way out of his arms and stood rubbing her hands over her forearms. "I'm all right," she said tightly. But she wasn't. Any fool could see that she had gone all brittle and fragile. "I'm all right," she repeated as she thrust her chin up a notch.

"That's good," he said, giving her this lie. "I'm sure as hell glad one of us is."

She looked wildly about the room before glancing down at the warrior and taking a half step toward him. She stood there in silence for a moment, and David wondered what thoughts raced through her as she fought the tears that glistened in her expressive eyes. He took a step toward her and the sound on the old pine floor echoed through the room. Anne twisted around to look at him, stopping him even as he recognized his need to touch her. "I'm all right," she said, turning back to the burial and dropping to her knees beside it and raking through the shells. "*I am.*"

"What are you doing?"

"I'm doing what we came up here to do. I'm looking for some more of those damned gorgets that look like the one we—*I*—sent to Texas. The one that got somebody killed."

"Annie, don't."

She turned at his softly spoken words and looked up at him. Her face twisted but the tears didn't escape. "I have to," she said, sinking back on her heels. "Don't you see. I have to."

"You sent it," he told her. "I believe you." And he did. At last. Too late? "It's all right. I believe you." He made another wary search of the room. Nothing. But damn it, something had been here. "Let's get out of here now. Let's go downstairs and talk about what just happened."

"No. Nothing happened. The wind blew or the house settled or we had an earthquake—"

"Annie." He dropped his hands onto her shoulders and tightened them until Anne sagged back against him. "Whatever it was, it has an explanation. Let's shut this room up and go—somewhere, anywhere, out of here—and try to figure it out."

Numbly, she nodded. He bent to help her to her feet. That was a switch. Since the day they'd met, she'd been the strong one, probably still was if he were completely truthful, because those sounds had affected him at a bone-deep level that went way beyond fear. But for now, it felt good to be doing *for* her, even if it were no more than getting her out of this room. What didn't feel good at all was knowing that anything could drain the enthusiasm from this vibrant woman the way whatever had made those sounds had. The way his suspicions had.

He felt her shudder and begin to rise, but she hesitated and looked once more toward the burial. She sucked in a shallow breath, shook her head, and reached toward the copper plates that had covered the skeleton's right thigh.

The armor that only minutes before had lain in a slight depression where the bone had once been. The armor that now lay level with that of the other leg.

The armor that once again covered a gleaming white bone.

David tightened his hands on Anne's shoulders, instinctively drawing her back from the body.

"This was here earlier, wasn't it?" she asked in a small voice. "Tell me it was. Tell me no one could have come into the house in the last few minutes and replaced it. Tell me!"

"It wasn't here, Annie." God, all the strength of his voice was gone, too. "I remember noticing the way the copper was displaced because it wasn't here."

"This isn't happening."

He knelt beside her and cautiously lifted the edge of the upper copper plate covering the femur. "This bone has been cleaned. Not much. Maybe just dusted. Like the gorget."

"It's Joe," she said. "Somehow. Some way. He's wired the house. He intercepted the shipments. But why? Damn it! Why?"

"Annie."

She jerked beneath his hands.

"No one has been in the house with us today. We can search, we *will* search, but there weren't any wires in the attic yesterday."

"Then what— How— It can't . . ."

He lifted her to her feet and turned her away from the body, toward him. She didn't help, but she didn't resist, either. "I don't know," he told her. "But I sure as hell want to find out. You were right, you know. Jack Townley didn't make those notes and those phone calls because he got an empty box from us."

She lifted her face to his as the memory of what had happened to Jack Townley, of what had brought them to the room, slammed into her. She lifted her hand to her mouth and swayed. "Karen," she whispered. "Oh, my God. Karen."

15

Downstairs, Anne fumbled through the kitchen drawer for her address book. *There's no reason to worry,* she kept telling herself, but her hands shook so badly she could barely turn the pages, barely see the number. David lifted the book from her and carried it to the table. There, he kicked out a chair for her and began dialing.

Anne couldn't sit. Did he think she could sit until she talked to her friend?

There's no reason to worry.

Why didn't Karen answer? There. Thank God. Someone picked up the receiver. *Her answering machine?*

Anne held the receiver with both hands. She didn't realize she was rocking back and forth until David scooted the chair behind her knees and pushed her onto it.

The message was blessedly brief. Anne waited for the beep and spoke as quietly, as calmly as she could, but she heard and hated the tremor in her voice.

Karen's voice interrupted Anne's garbled message. "Anne?" she asked with a shaky laugh.

"Karen? You're all right?"

"Yeah. You've heard already? My word, bad news

does travel fast. I thought you were so far in the boonies I'd have a chance to . . ." Karen's voice faded. "Sorry. It wasn't me. I don't know when they will release the name to the news media, but it was a lab assistant. Not me. And they haven't found the animal yet. If it was . . . an animal. But, hey. Thanks for calling. I'm still a little shaken. He had— He had some of my things—my driver's license—in his lab coat. The cops talked to me—it seemed like for hours. They didn't want to believe I didn't know him. Anne, he's probably the one who's been calling and, yes, stealing my things from the lab and from here, and I didn't even know him."

Karen's voice broke on a sob. Anne shivered. Cold, she was so cold and it had nothing to do with winter or high ceilings. She looked up at David, then gestured toward the telephone. He pulled a chair close and dropped his arm over her shoulder. She nodded, thanking him for the warmth and the comfort and tilted the telephone receiver so that he could listen in.

"Tell me what happened," she said softly.

"I wish I knew," Karen told her. "I wish to God I knew. Or maybe I don't. I saw him. I'm a pathologist. I work in a morgue. And I have never seen anything like that in my life."

"Karen."

"Yeah. Right. I— I don't know how to tell you this. But your bone's gone. I guess I'm glad for more than one reason that you called. I didn't know how you'd feel about my telling the police. I haven't yet. I didn't know it was gone until after they had released me to go home. I don't know if it's relevant. I don't know if he took it, or where it is. I can't give you any kind of report, except that, yes, it is old. More museum age than homicide, but I'd just gotten to the lab, just opened the package, when we had this damned impromptu staff meeting. And that went on and on and would probably still be going on if we hadn't heard the screams from the stairwell. Anyway, when I finally got back to my office, the box was in the cabinet where I'd put it, and all the packaging, but the bone was gone. I'm sorry, Anne—"

She saw David's eyes close, saw his lips thin, saw a nerve twitch in his jaw.

"Don't worry about it," Anne said. *No, Karen,* she thought, *you won't have to. There are two people right here who will do all the worrying for you.* She glanced at David. He nodded. "Do what you think best about the bone," she said. "It's no— It's no big secret. My uncle was an antiquities dealer. I was pretty sure it was something he had brought in, back in the thirties, but I wanted to be certain. You've confirmed that. Just— Are Rae and Mollie there? Or are they gone for the holidays?"

She heard what sounded like a sniff. "They're both due back any time now."

"You're sure? You don't need to be alone right now."

"I know," Karen told her. "My first reaction was to come home and hide, but I have a neighbor here with me now. I'm okay. Or I will be. I just don't know why this has upset me so much. After all, in my line of work—"

She heard the murmur of a man's voice in the background. Good. Karen might think she ought to be indestructible, but no one as softhearted as she was could face violent death on a personal level and not be affected. Anne knew from firsthand experience. "Hush," she told her friend. "See if your neighbor can find you some brandy. And for God's sake, call me if you need me. Heaven knows you were certainly there for me."

David replaced the receiver, but he left his arm over her

shoulder, and the two of them sat in stunned silence until Anne whimpered, "I almost killed her. I almost killed her. If he hadn't stolen the femur, Karen would be dead, too. Why? Why, David?" But, of course, he had no answer.

The sky outside had gone completely dark, dotted in the distance by the lights of Allegro that only a short time before had seemed so pleasant. The table remained cluttered with the remains of their dinner. The ceiling gleamed under its coat of paint. All the things that such a short time ago had brought her so much pleasure now seemed to mock her. What in God's name was happening?

And almost simultaneously the two of them noticed what was missing from the clutter on the table. David picked up the address book and moved it. He removed his arm from around her so that he could scoot bowls and plates to one side, but the gorget wasn't there. He rested his elbows on the table and buried his face in his hands. "I don't want to go back upstairs. I don't want to know if it's returned."

Feeling as though she were moving on automatic, the way she had too often in med school, Anne got up and checked the back door. It was still locked. She leaned against it. "We have to go," she said. "We left the panel open. We left the light on."

Upstairs, the copper plate had resettled over the warrior's right femur, and on the edge of one cedar pole, half on, half off, lay a four inch diameter shell gorget, marked with one unique nick, and easily identifiable as the one in the tracings.

They found no wires. No microphones. No hidden speakers. No electronic intrusion of any kind. With the aid of electric lighting where it was available, supplemented by two powerful flashlights, David and Anne searched the room where the grave goods lay, the closet, the adjoining sitting room with its chimney flue and plumbing run, the room in the north wing of the house, which must at least partially abut the hidden chamber, even the attic. They found dust. Lots of dust. And cobwebs. And, except in the attic where David and Wayne Samuels had worked the day before, no sign that anyone other than he and Anne had been anywhere near the walls, ceilings, and floors. Certainly no sign of any large animal.

And no one but the blind fool he had been only hours before could possibly believe that Anne Locke had any knowledge of what was happening, or how.

"There has to be an explanation," Anne said when they had completed their search and returned to the hidden room. "A logical, reasonable explanation."

Yes, there had to be. But God alone knew what it was. Anne stood at the foot of the litter, looking down at the warrior as though he could tell her what that answer was, and she hadn't yet noticed what David, standing just behind her, had seen the moment they reentered the room. The gorget no longer lay on the cedar pole.

They had left their flashlights in the sitting room, but David didn't need extra light to find the gorget. He knew where it would be—and it was—on the very top of a pile of beads and engraved shells near the skeleton's copper-covered right shoulder, if not exactly where he had first found it, then so close his eye couldn't tell the difference.

David lifted his hands to Anne's shoulders and pulled her against him. "Look," he said, nodding over her shoulder toward the floor.

She sucked in her breath when she, too, saw that the

shell had been moved. For a moment, she shrank against him. Then she straightened. "An explanation," she repeated. "All we have to do is find it."

Downstairs, David took a flashlight, his service revolver, and himself outside to search the perimeter of the house. Anne tried to go with him, but he stopped that foolishness by the simple expedient of glaring at her and pulling the door closed behind him. He found nothing. Of course, he found nothing. Life couldn't be that simple.

Anne spun around in alarm from where she stood at the kitchen sink when he opened the back door to return to the house.

"Nothing," he said. "I found nothing."

She didn't nod, smile, or ask any questions. "I'm putting the food away," she said, wrapping and scraping and reorganizing the remains of the holiday feast with quick, jerky motions. "What we really need on top of everything else is a case of ptomaine or salmonella."

David propped the flashlight on the table, tucked the revolver into the belt at his back, and began stacking and scraping their used dishes.

"You don't have to—"

"Yes, Annie," he said, silencing her protest and carrying the stack of dishes to the shallow sink. "I do."

They worked in silence. There were too many questions and too few answers for any conversation.

They had just finished drying the last dish when Anne heard the unmistakable sound of an engine coming up her steep driveway.

David's head jerked up and he cocked his head. Listening. "Someone's coming," he told her.

"Great," she said, sagging back against the counter. "That's just great."

"You don't get many drop-in visitors."

Anne choked out a laugh. "You noticed?"

Only emergencies. That thought sobered her. *Not now,* she thought. *Please God, not now. I don't think I can handle anything more tonight.*

Instead of coming on to the back of the house, the car stopped at the front, engine idling, where an overgrown and seldom used walk led to the front door. In the six months she had lived in the house, only three people had come to the front door: a salesman, and a pair of Mormon missionaries.

David walked to the back door and flipped on the light that illuminated the back porch and makeshift parking area, opening the door as he did so. After a moment, she heard the car resume its journey, then stop, then a door slam. She stepped to the back door beside David.

Blake Foresman. The sheriff. Oh, God, it was an emergency. Without knowing how they had gotten there, she found her hands clutching David's arm.

David glanced back at her. She couldn't call the expression on his face a frown, it was much too solemn for that, much too ingrained. But it softened slightly as he looked at her. He lifted his hand. For a moment she thought he might touch her cheek; with a shock she realized she was standing close enough to him for him to do so. Instead, though, after a lingering inspection of her face, he dropped his hand to hers in a light caress before he unlatched the screen and pushed it open.

"Blake," he said easily. "What brings you up here? Is there a problem?"

Blake wasn't in uniform. Anne grabbed that piece of information. He wore dark slacks, boots, a leather jacket, and a western hat, but he wasn't in uniform. "I don't know," he said as he stepped up onto the porch

and removed his hat. "Evening, Doc." That formality
concluded, he returned his attention to David. "I was
across town when I glanced this way. Thought I saw a
light bobbing and swaying around outside up here.
After what you told me this morning, I thought I'd better check it out. You folks have any trouble?"

What had David told him? Anne found she still held
David's arm. She released her grasp on him. David
glanced over his shoulder, giving her a look she knew he
meant to be reassuring, that he meant to tell her he
hadn't betrayed any of her secrets. And she believed
him. Just like that. She dredged up a smile and stepped
back slightly so that he could, too.

"Come in, Blake," she said. "I was just getting ready
to heat up some apple pie."

"Well, now," he said easily, smiling but wary as he
entered the house. "Does that mean yes, you did have
some trouble, or no, you didn't?"

David latched the screen behind the sheriff and
closed the back door. "I was outside with the flashlight
earlier."

"You hear something? Find anything?"

David shook his head. "Maybe to the first, no to the
second." He turned toward Anne. "Do you need some
help?"

"No," she told him as she reached for the coffeepot.
"This will only take a minute. Why don't the two of you
sit down?"

But they didn't sit, neither one of them, until she had
filled and plugged in the coffeepot and started toward
the refrigerator for the pie.

"Doc? Why don't you sit for a minute, too. There's
something I've got to ask you."

She'd suspected Blake was a more than competent
lawman; she'd heard it said and seen his quiet, calm

professionalism herself too many times to doubt her instincts. But until now he had never turned his professional demeanor toward her. "What is it?" she asked.

He pulled a chair out from the table and stood behind it, waiting. With a shrug, she sat. Only then did he pull out a chair for himself on the opposite side of the table. "Huerra?"

David glanced at him but reached for the chair beside Anne.

"Is your search outside the reason you're armed?" Blake asked.

David sighed and shook his head. "Damn," he said as he felt for the pistol at his back. "Let me just put this away."

Blake grinned. "Good idea."

David stashed the pistol in a drawer and took the seat beside Anne.

"So," Blake asked. "What did you hear?"

"I don't know for sure what it was," David told him. "Or even where it was. Whatever it was, it was big."

Which was certainly true. As far as it went. Anne shuddered at the memory of those footfalls. At the memory of Karen's description of the lab assistant.

Blake nodded. "And no prints outside?"

"None that I could find."

"We might ought to get Samuels up here to look tomorrow. He's a pretty good tracker."

"He didn't find anything last time," David said.

Blake studied him steadily across the width of the table. "Just the same," he said finally. "I want him to look.

"Now, Doc," he said, smiling grimly, "I've got to ask you about a bone."

So Karen had told. Well, there really wasn't anything else she could have done.

"The Chicago P.D. called me a little while ago. They'd run your name through their computer but they wanted to know what I knew about you since you'd moved back here, and what I knew about a bone you'd sent to one of the Cook County medical examiners, a bone that disappeared today in connection with a particularly nasty homicide."

"A right femur," Anne told him.

"Yes. According to what Dr. Ready told them, an old femur. A very old one. I was just wondering, Doc, where you got it, and why you didn't run it through my office."

Those were good questions. Questions she wasn't sure how to answer. There wasn't any way she wanted to take him upstairs and show him where she'd found the femur. And where it was now. And yet, he wasn't going to leave without an acceptable answer.

"I found it upstairs," she said, deciding to stay as close to the truth as she could. "In a closet. I don't know if you knew that Uncle Ralph was an antiquities dealer, that he was involved with buying and selling artifacts and, according to what my mom told me, involved somehow in the early excavations at Spiro. I was pretty sure the bone was old enough to be an archaeological find, something left over from his days in the business, so I didn't want to bother your office with it. But believe me, if Karen had told me any different, I would have called you in a heartbeat."

"Any idea why somebody would want to steal it?"

"It was just a bone, Blake," David said. "A centuries-old bone from a very tall, very dead man. It had no monetary value. But from what Dr. Ready said Wednesday and again tonight when we talked with her, things belonging to her have been taking missing for a while. It's possible that whoever is responsible for taking those items also took the femur."

That too was true. As far as it went.

"Yeah. That's kind of what me and the Chicago detective came up with, but I had to check it out. Have you two been here all day?"

David nodded. "Yes."

"Can anybody confirm that for you?"

Alibis? Surely Blake wasn't asking them for alibis. Surely no one would think they had anything to do with a murder in Chicago. *Unless they searched and found that damned bone.*

David smiled grimly. "I saw you a little before seven this morning. Pete Tompkins called me here about six this evening." He glanced up at the ceiling. The new ceiling. "You can ask Samuels what shape this room was in when he and his wife left here last night."

"Pete got in touch with you then?" Blake asked.

"You knew?"

Blake nodded. "I was having dinner with Gene and Gretta when he called. I don't suppose you want to tell me what that was all about?"

Anne couldn't help it. She stretched out her hand toward David. He took it and wrapped it in his. "A homicide," he said. "But then I suspect you already knew that."

"Yeah," Blake said. "I know Pete. I like Pete. And when he called tonight, I talked to Pete. Doc, you want to tell me what was in the box you sent to Townley?"

"I sent it, Blake," David said. "Anne just used her supplies to mail it. You see, the bone wasn't alone. There was an engraved shell artifact with it. I sent it to Townley to see if it might shed a little more light on when and where the bone came from."

"Any idea why somebody might want to steal it?"

"Yeah," David said. "If my suspicions are right, several thousand dollars, give or take a few thousand more."

Blake gave a low whistle. "Yep. That's motive enough for murder, all right." He glanced toward the counter. "I think I'll take a cup of that coffee after all, Doc."

Anne brought cups and the coffeepot to the table. Even though she suspected Blake's request was a delaying tactic rather than a desire for coffee, she poured and smiled and resumed her seat and gave him the time he seemed to want. Gave herself some time.

"Let's see if I've got this in order. Wednesday night, Samuels sees what he thinks are mountain lions prowling around this hillside. Would I be wrong in thinking you shipped those packages out Wednesday?"

"Wednesday afternoon," David told him.

Foresman nodded. Anne suspected he'd already known that. "And Friday, noon or so, after one of your packages arrives, a man is killed in his locked house in Dallas by some sort of wild animal, and a couple of hours after that, after another of your packages arrives in the M.E.'s office in Chicago, another man is killed in a county building secure stairwell by some sort of wild animal. And tonight, you're out searching the yard because you hear something that just might be another wild animal. I leave anything out?"

Anne closed her eyes. "No."

"Did *you* leave anything out?"

Just any mention of a fortune in grave goods, Anne thought. Just any mention of an armor-clad skeleton. Just any mention that the two items sent had returned to that skeleton. "Such as?"

Foresman leaned forward. "What I'm asking, Doc, is, did you send anything else out in Wednesday's mail? Am I going to get a call from some other jurisdiction wanting to know who you are, wanting to know what was in the package, telling me of still another murder?"

"No." David answered for her. "We sent only the two items."

"Things like this don't happen in my county," Blake said. "I don't like this. I don't like it at all."

Neither do I! Anne wanted to cry. *I came back here to be safe. I came back here to—* To hide. Oh, God, yes she had, even if she had never fully admitted it until now.

"I don't like it either, Blake," she heard David say. "That's why I'm staying here tonight."

"Good." Foresman stood, picked up his hat, and looked down at Anne. "Good. You keep her safe."

"I will." Now David stood. As he walked with the sheriff toward the door, Anne knew she should, too, but as she started to rise, David looked back at her. "Keep your seat, Annie."

She heard them. Just because they stood outside on the porch, did David think she wouldn't?

"I'll be on duty at eleven," Blake said. "I'll try to stay here in the south end of the county. If you need me, holler."

"I will," David told him. "And thanks."

"The two homicides have to be connected. I know that; you know that. Any idea who might be behind them?"

David gave a short laugh. "If you'd asked me right after Pete called, I probably would have come up with all sorts of theories, and even a couple of suspects. But the lab tech doesn't fit with any of them."

"Yeah."

Their footsteps sounded as they moved across the porch, but their words still carried into the house.

"It really isn't your problem, Blake. Both murders were outside your jurisdiction."

"Yeah, right. But it sure feels like my problem. So I

guess I'll keep an eye on this place as much as I can, maybe find out where Joe Hansom was today. And I'll stop by Wayne Samuels's place tonight before it gets too late and tell him you'd like to see him up here tomorrow morning."

David stayed on the porch until Blake turned his car around and drove down the hill. Then he closed and locked the door and leaned against it. "We're going to have to tell him, you know."

"Tell him *what*, David? What in God's name can we tell him?"

"If I knew that, Annie, I would have done it already."

Anne buried her face in her hands. "I'm sorry I got you messed up in this. All you wanted to do this month was fish and think."

"I'm not."

He crossed the room quietly until he stood behind her. He lifted his hands to her shoulders and with deft, sure strength began kneading her knotted muscles, easing the tension that had gripped her since Pete Tompkins's telephone call.

She moaned a little and surrendered herself to his touch. No, she wasn't sorry, either. Not really. She didn't know if she would have had to face the problems in her upstairs room if he hadn't been here. On one level, she almost suspected she wouldn't. But he was here, and she did have the problems, and she didn't know how she could face them without his help.

And she didn't know how he had so quickly become a part of her life, or why his touch was so impossibly familiar. So blessedly welcome.

Too welcome.

David was a cop. A big-city cop. And after his vacation was over, he'd go back to being a cop. In a world she could never return to, a world where violence and death were commonplace, where children were victims and attackers, where life was no longer valued, where blood and screams—

She pulled away from his touch. "You don't have to stay with me tonight."

He sighed but dropped his hands. "Sure I do. I just can't decide whether I need to stay downstairs, to protect you from anything breaking into the house, or upstairs, to protect you from anything breaking out."

"I'll be all right alone. I've lived here for months without anything happening."

"Got a road map?"

"David, I'm serious."

"So am I, Annie. I'm staying. Now, do you have a road map?"

"Why?"

He grinned, his little-boy-gone-bad grin, and she knew he wouldn't answer. At least not completely. "Because I thought that after Wayne gets here tomorrow, we might take a little day trip. Say, up to Spiro? Check things out. And then, depending on what we learn, we might try to find your crazy aunt."

David didn't sleep. Since Annie's bed apparently wasn't an option, he'd chosen the downstairs sitting room to camp out in. It was a little far from Annie's room, but with its uncovered French doors and double windows it was the most logical room to watch from. But damn it was cold. He didn't want to risk the exposure the light from a fire would bring to the room, so he wrapped himself in a blanket and lay back against the arm of the lumpy old sofa.

Anne Locke. What the hell was there about the

woman that made him feel as though she had been a part of his life forever? And was she completely immune to him? Occasionally he suspected she wasn't, like tonight when she moaned as he had worked the tension from her neck. Tonight, when she had pulled away from him as though he were the animal that had killed those people.

But she hadn't objected when he had taken over as host tonight, as though he had every right to: inviting Blake in, walking him out, answering the questions he had directed at Annie.

Well, what the hell was he supposed to have done? Let her go out on the porch alone to see who was coming? Flounder around wondering how to be honest and still not tell the sheriff what he really didn't want to know?

Hell, he didn't need this. Anne Locke was a forever kind of woman. He was a washed-up cop. She had a medical practice and a hundred-year-old home and roots in a small town. He had a career down the tubes, a rented condo, and a knowledge as old as he was that he could never live in a small town. She also had a not-so-small fortune in antiquities in an upstairs closet. He had, at the most, savings to hold him for a year, a police pension that wouldn't take effect for another five years, and a limp little 401K he'd been meaning to add more to but just hadn't got around to it.

So why did he feel as though he had just found a part of his life that had been missing forever? Why did he feel as though he belonged down the hall in that impossibly romantic bedroom with that impossible woman?

He looked up at the ceiling. "More lessons?" he asked. "Do you mind cluing me in as to what course we're studying this time?"

He got no answer, but then, he seldom did.

And if he was to get answers, what he really needed to know was what force, what power, had he and Anne unlocked when they knocked the hole in that closet wall.

Were they responsible for the deaths of two people?

And were they, and possibly anyone around them, in danger?

Damn! Maybe he shouldn't drag Samuels into this mess. Wayne had already been through enough hell for a dozen lifetimes.

The sound was faint, just a whisper of noise from the direction of Anne's room. David cocked his head and listened. Yes. There it was again. He threw off the blanket and rose, easing his way to the door, into the hall, toward the stairs.

It was Annie, going quietly, stealthily upstairs.

David frowned but lowered his revolver. What the hell was she doing?

He gave her a moment before following.

She'd closed the closet door, but a strip of light found its way beneath it and into the sitting room and told him all too clearly where she was.

Damn it! Didn't she realize she could be in danger?

Still, he didn't barge into the room. He eased the closet door open and just as cautiously sidestepped boxes and the panel until he stood in the opening.

She knelt on the floor at the foot of the litter, her dark red flannel nightgown pooled around her like so much blood. In one hand she held the small cedar box, open now, with its engraved mica lid in her lap. With the other, she touched the carved shell images. Tears ran unchecked down her cheeks.

The warrior was not aware of her. He'd never again be aware of anything as he lay there in solitary splendor. But David was aware of her, so aware it hurt, as she knelt grieving for a long-dead man.

He wanted to go to her, to yank her away from him, to tell her she was his, by God—

But something wasn't right.

"Annie?" he asked softly.

She didn't answer.

"Annie?"

Carefully he knelt beside her. When he reached for the box, she resisted only slightly before letting him take it. He placed the lid back on it and put it on the litter.

"Annie," he said again.

When she still didn't speak, he lowered his hands to her shoulders and turned her toward him. "Annie," he demanded. "Answer me."

She looked up at him, her eyes unfocused, then shuddered. At that moment, and only then, did she seem aware of him. Her face clouded with pain and then softened as she leaned forward and wrapped her arms around him, holding onto him for dear life. "You're all right," she said. "It was just a dream. You're all right."

Heaven. Or it could have been. But something still wasn't right. David held her away from him and looked down at her. "Yes. I am. But are you?"

"What— David?" Now he didn't have to hold her away. Anne pulled back and looked at him, questions and fear and the residue of pain all too obvious in her expression. She glanced around, and he knew that only then did she become aware of where she was. Of who he was. "How . . . "

He rose to his feet and lifted her to hers. She swayed slightly and he put his arm around her, to steady her, to anchor her to his side. She didn't fight it. Maybe she couldn't. Hell, he knew he couldn't.

"I followed you," he told her.

"But I— I never sleepwalk."

He closed his eyes and rested his forehead against her hair. "I wish you hadn't said that, Annie. I wish to God this wasn't something else that we're going to worry and wonder about."

"What did I do?"

He lifted his fingers to her cheeks and brushed across the dampness still streaking them.

"I cried? Why?"

"I don't know." He pulled her up against him hard. Damn it, he'd tried. He'd done everything he knew to avoid the hell this was probably going to cost him, but in the last five minutes, all the rules had changed. "I don't know much of anything anymore. But one thing I do know, I'm not letting you out of my sight or away from my side until this night is over."

16

1940

  Lucy was reading. It still wasn't easy, and it sure wasn't fun, but it was something she had to do if she was ever going to get out of school. And she had to do that. As much as she loved her mama, she had to get out of this house.

  That Saturday morning in early November had started out cool and wet, but about an hour ago the clouds had finally moved on to the east and the weather had pulled one of its autumn switch acts. Now it was warmer outside than it was in the house. That's why she had the windows open in the dining room where she had her books piled around her at the end of the long dark table.

  And that was probably why Papa had the doors to his study open onto the porch, just an angle away from where she sat, trying to concentrate on her homework so that she could leave when Walter came for her. Didn't they know that she could hear every word they said? Didn't they know Mama was in the house, only one more room away, in the kitchen? Didn't they care?

"It's a chance, Ralph," Aunt Marian said. Lucy had twisted around to look when she first heard their voices and knew that Marian stood in the doorway. "Maybe our last chance. My God, how can you stand being dependent on her family for every dime?"

"*Our* last chance, Marian?"

"Yes."

"And all I have to do is take the risk?"

"There is no risk. Can't you see that by now?"

"What I can see is that Jackson is dead, his son is dead. Billy Ray and that other digger are both dead. Every buyer I sent any part of it is dead— No. Adkins isn't dead. He's just a blithering idiot. And every other buyer has already heard about the damned curse on the stuff, a curse that attacks anyone who touches any part of that *marvelous* treasure of mine."

"Except us."

"What?"

"Except us. It hasn't harmed us."

"But we haven't—"

"Haven't what? We moved it into the house. I helped you pack the pieces you sold. We moved it into the attic."

"Yeah. And it moved itself right back."

"But we hadn't completely finished moving it when we stopped for the night. And that isn't the point, anyway. It's been almost five years. Don't you think if it was going to harm us, it would have done so by now?"

"Is that why you won't sleep in your bedroom any more, why you wanted it out of there, why you've locked the door on it and everything else you couldn't move into your sitting room?"

"Where I sleep isn't the issue either, Ralph. Or maybe it is."

"What do you mean by that?"

"Nothing. Just that I'm tired of living in poverty. I'm tired of being a hanger-on to a group of people I wouldn't acknowledge on the street and having those same people look down on me. You promised me more when I came here. You owe me more."

Lucy heard Papa's desk drawer slam. She closed her eyes, wishing she could close out what she was hearing, but she couldn't, because then she heard his voice, louder, as though he had moved to stand beside Aunt Marian. "And all I have to do is what, Marian?"

"I think you must take it. That seems to be the clue. We can touch it, probably because we have all of it; others can't. So all you have to do is take enough of that—treasure—to Henrik Johnson to convince him we have the real thing, to convince him he needs to buy it—all of it—and then it will be his problem and we can get out of here."

"Lucy."

Her mama's soft voice. Oh, no. She hadn't heard, had she?

Lucy opened her eyes. Walter and her mama stood at the door to the pantry. Mama beckoned to her with that same sad look on her face she had seen too many times. Lucy gratefully left her books and the sounds of her papa and Aunt Marian plotting to get rid of that poor, dead man upstairs, plotting to get rid of her mama and her. Plotting. Always plotting.

Walter was quiet when they went back into the kitchen, but he had a hard time hiding what he felt, and he was so mad now his freckles were standing out like paint against his ruddy complexion, and his blue eyes fairly sparked fire.

Mama had draped her apron over the edge of the sink. Now she folded it and placed it in the basket she kept in the kitchen for laundry. "I believe I will visit my father this afternoon," she said in her soft, slightly accented voice. "I will ask him to return me to this house at nine this evening. That would be a good time for you to return also, Lucy."

Lucy felt her mouth hanging open. She'd had to beg her mama for permission to go to the matinee at the picture show with Walter this afternoon, and now mama was telling her to stay out until bedtime? Walter tugged on her arm until she got her feet to moving, then opened the door for her and stood there, waiting for her to grab her jacket from its peg near the door and go on outside.

"Yes, ma'am, we'll be back by then," he promised, in a hurry, so that her mama wouldn't have time to tell them she'd changed her mind. But on the porch he stopped, and turned, and looked back into the kitchen, and Lucy looked, too. Her mama was just standing there in the middle of the kitchen, looking lost.

"You take care now, Mrs. Hansom," Walter said. And then, being Walter and, Lucy suspected, unable to just go off and leave someone hurting the way her mama must be, he took a step into the house. "Should we stay here with you until your father comes for you? Can we do anything for you?"

Her mama looked at him, still sad, still quiet. "No, son," she said. "Yes. Yes, there is. You take good care of my little girl for me."

"Yes, ma'am," he said solemnly. "I will do that."

And then her mama smiled. "I know that, Walter Briggs. I've known that for a long, long time."

They walked down the driveway. Even though she wanted to, even though she needed the physical connection with Walter, Lucy wasn't quite brave enough to reach for his hand. Not where Papa might look out the window and see them. Not when he might yell at her and make her come back to the house. Not when he might tell Walter to go away and never come back.

At the street, Walter turned to the left, out of sight of the house, and stopped at a dusty green truck. "Do you really want to go see that big monkey?"

Lucy dredged up a smile. All anyone had been talking about at school for the last week was that the movie *King Kong* was finally coming to the Criterion in Allegro, Oklahoma.

"A monster movie might be the only thing that could make me laugh today," she told him, "but I'm not sure Harvey Skinner would appreciate my laughing just when he's all set to protect Mary Sue Johnson from whatever might lunge off that screen after her."

Walter chuckled, and it sounded only a little forced. "I know what you mean. This will probably be the only time in his life Harvey can look like a hero without really risking anything. So," he said, patting the front fender of the truck, "would you mind going for a drive with me?"

"A drive?" Lucy looked at the truck. "You mean it? In this? Whose is it? Oh, Walter, you didn't buy a truck?"

"Not too likely," he said. "It's Abe McPherson's. I'm doing some work for him, helping him build a barn. He asked me if I'd pick up a load of posts at the sawmill and deliver them out there. I should have gone before I picked you up. I would have, if I hadn't hoped I could talk your mama into letting you go with me. We can still be back in time to go to the movie if you really want to."

Young Mr. Johnson helped Walter at the mill. He was called young Mr. Johnson because he was a Junior and it got real confusing when everyone out there was yelling for "Will." And he was young, only a few years older than

Walter, but old enough to be courting Miss Edmonds, the new high school teacher who had come to Allegro last year. He was a nice man, but then Lucy had known that forever, because she had cousins who lived on the next road over and she had visited in the Johnson house almost as much as she had visited in her cousins' houses.

But he was also a busy man that Saturday, and Lucy couldn't help but be glad, because that meant he didn't have a lot of time to tease her and Walter and ask how things were at home.

And Walter was busy. Thinking about something real hard. Something that he didn't even try to share until he had offloaded the last post, not letting her help even the least bit. She didn't mind, not really. She knew he'd get around to sharing whatever was bothering him with her soon. He always had. Just as she had always shared with him.

And besides, the homesite where Abe McPherson was building was beautiful, peaceful, sunshiny warm but alive with leaf color, set as it was on the top of a ridge, with mountains above and below and all around.

"Lucy," Walter said, finishing his job and dusting his hands on his trousers. "I've been thinking."

She couldn't help smiling. That was exactly the tone of voice he had used when he'd announced they ought to be blood brothers, exactly the tone he used for any important pronouncement he made.

"I could tell that, Walter," she said lightly.

He frowned at her, deep in concentration. "I figure you and I ought to go ahead and get married now."

Lucy leaned back against the tailgate. *Married now?* Whatever happened to *Lucy, will you marry me?* Had she missed something? Of course she would. Marry him, that was. She'd known that since the day she'd shown him the kitten in the loft and he'd gone back into the barn to see what Papa and Aunt Marian had done with the dead man. But he hadn't asked. He hadn't ever asked.

"Now?" she squeaked.

He nodded, sure of her. Sure of himself. "I love you. You love me. And I have to get you out of that house. I— I can get enough work to take care of us."

"And what about your schooling?"

"I— I'll get by. Lots of folks don't finish school."

"And the army?"

"I'll— I can still go, later.

"And your plans to learn a trade?"

"I'm a carpenter, Lucy. I've worked as one for years."

"And you're a darned good one, Walter, but every man in this county who can hold a hammer calls himself a carpenter. That doesn't leave a whole lot of work, even for someone as good as you."

"You love me," he said.

Yes. She did. "Only this morning, I was thinking how much I want to get out of that house. But not if it means giving up your future. And not if it means going off and leaving my mama alone there."

"Maybe if you left, she could, too," Walter said.

Mama? Leave her papa? Lucy shook her head. That would never happen. And if it did? "And all of us could just go off and leave him alone with Papa and Aunt Marian, with them selling off pieces of him and getting even more people killed?"

"Damn it, Lucy, they're going to sell him anyway, and we still can't do one damned thing about it. But I can get you out of there. Hell, I can even get your mama out of there. If I tell her how much you want to go."

She couldn't let him do that. Not for his sake. Not for the sake of the dead man in Marian's bedroom. Not for her mama's sake and not for her mama's pride. Lucy lifted her fingers to his mouth to silence him. He shook with frustration and that other, darker emotion that had come barging into their times together only after they had explored their friendship as children, that other, darker emotion that sang and sizzled through her blood, too, when they had their too-few precious moments alone.

He clasped her about the waist and lifted her to sit on the tailgate of the pickup, then stepped close, holding her tight. "Say yes, Lucy."

She shook her head. "Not to this, Walter. Not until we're out of school, that's only months. Not until after you've enlisted, and been accepted, and done your training."

"And if we go to war like it looks like we might have to?"

"Then I'll marry you before you leave. I promise you that."

"Say yes, Lucy," he said again, his voice harsh in the way it sometimes was when he felt things too strongly, when he wanted her too much.

"No," she said. "Not till later."

"Say yes, Lucy," he said, his voice hot against her throat.

She felt tears welling in her eyes. She knew he didn't think he'd be sacrificing anything by marrying her now, but she knew he would. And she knew she could never let him make that sacrifice.

"Only to loving you," she told him. "You know I do. You know I will."

"Say yes, Lucy," he groaned.

And there, beneath a clear, crisp November sky, with the remnants of autumn's bright leaves rustling in the trees around them, with the birds and the squirrels and the rabbits forgetting they were there and scurrying and scratching through those leaves that had already fallen, Lucy said yes to Walter, yes to everything except the legal bond that would ruin his plans, his future, his life.

They were on their way back to town, hurrying a little to get Lucy home by nine o'clock, when a sheriff's car, lights flashing, drew up alongside them and turned its spotlight on them. Lucy saw Walter glance at the speedometer. He hadn't been hurrying that much, he'd have been crazy to on this road. He frowned, but he pulled onto the shoulder and stopped.

The deputy stepped up to Walter's side of the truck and looked in. "Good," he said. Then, "Briggs." That was meant to be a greeting, Lucy knew, a kind of code between men that said all the things that women had to verbalize. But when he spoke again, she wished he'd had a code so he hadn't said what he did to her.

She'd seen him around, on duty and off, but she didn't know him. Obviously, though, he knew her.

"Lucy, honey," he told her, "you need to get on out to your grandpa's. Your mama needs you out there."

"What's the matter?" Walter asked.

The deputy motioned with his head, jerking it to one side. More code, Lucy recognized, telling Walter to get out of the truck, to step away so she couldn't hear what was said. But she had to hear it. She knew she did. "What's the matter, Deputy?" she asked.

He looked to Walter, but Walter nodded.

"It's your daddy, ma'am. There's been an accident."

Now Walter did step out of the truck. He patted Lucy's hand and walked back by the rear tire, and the deputy followed him.

"What happened?" Walter asked.

The deputy cleared his throat. "That switchback

north of town? His Buick didn't make it. We found him at the bottom."

"How bad?" Walter asked. But Lucy already knew the answer. Aunt Marian had wanted him to take part of the artifacts to the dealer, and Papa had been fool enough, or arrogant enough, or greedy enough to try. She didn't have to listen, but she did.

"I think he might have survived the crash," the deputy said. "He was outside the car. But some animal, bear maybe—something big—found him before a motorist saw the smoke from the burning car. I'm afraid he's dead. Real dead."

17

Annie was in his arms.

David absorbed that fact as he studied his surroundings in the early dawn light filtering through lace curtains on tall, narrow windows. He'd started his night in Annie's bed on top of the covers, telling himself he'd put at least that much distance between himself and temptation. But sometime during the night the room had grown colder and he had grown lonelier, and, less than half awake, he had tunneled under the comforter and electric blanket, wrapped his arms around Anne Locke and dragged her close.

She hadn't awakened—he remembered that much—just given a little sigh as she relaxed against him and slid deeper into sleep.

And she wasn't awake now, just snuggled trustingly against him as though seeking his warmth.

Trustingly.

Well, hell.

He felt his mouth twist in a wry grin. At least something in his life was going well. As an oath, that one had been downright mild. There had been a time in his life, not too long ago, when his thoughts, spoken or not, would have been a lot more colorful.

There had been a time in his life when he wouldn't have had the need to swear, because he wouldn't even have considered what he was now doing: freeing his arms from their protective embrace of the woman they held. Sliding out from under the covers. Feeling the chill of the floor seeping through the braided rug beneath his feet.

Annie moaned softly in her sleep and turned toward him, reaching but finding only empty bed. With another moan, she snuggled into the pillow he had just left.

No. He could not get back in that bed with her. He could not lie there with her as the world came to life, as she awoke. He wanted more from her, much more than she was apparently willing to give. And more than he was able to return. And if he ached, those feelings paled when he considered the ache and emptiness he'd feel if he did something to shatter Annie's trust in him, if he did something that would make her drive him away completely. But he did reach down and brush a wayward, tangled red curl from her cheek. And he could and did lift the comforter to cover her shoulder and the slender arm embracing the pillow he had so recently used.

He helped himself to Annie's shower and to a new toothbrush from the stash she kept on hand. Finding that the razor he had used a week before had not been tossed away, he tested it carefully, then used it again.

He didn't go upstairs.

He stopped with his hand on age-blackened varnish of the newel post and his foot on the bottom step, listening. Had he heard something? God, he hoped not. He had no idea what there was about that room that bothered him so. What there was about that skeleton— even before all the strange happenings began—that . . . haunted him. Yes. Haunted was exactly the word. He'd seen burial exhibits before, numerous times. Even an

Egyptian mummy in its blackened wrappings. But none of those had created more than a vague unease about the just use of a past culture's dead in public exhibits. Homicides, especially those when the body hadn't been discovered until only science could produce identification, were the only things that came close to evoking this reaction in him.

No. He wouldn't go upstairs. Not until he had to. God knew that would be soon enough.

He had the coffee made, the fires turned up, and the chill off the kitchen by the time he heard a pickup climb the driveway and brake to a stop outside.

He met Wayne Samuels at the kitchen door. Margaret waved from the truck but left without coming in.

"Anne's still asleep," he said, warning the other man to silence.

Samuels nodded, shrugged out of his jacket, hung it on a peg, and crossed to the coffeepot. "Rough night?"

Rough night, rough week, David thought. "Yeah. Coffee?"

"Always."

Samuels took his coffee hot and black. He leaned against the cabinet as he sipped it and glanced at the completed ceiling. "Not a bad job for a cop and a lady doctor," he admitted.

David studied Samuels. "Hell, if I'd known you were an expert," he said cordially, "I'd have invited you to help Thursday."

Samuels raised an eyebrow. "And risk having three angry women driving us out of the kitchen for spoiling their meal?"

David shrugged, and Samuels turned serious.

"You want to run out to the Tompkins place and grab some clothes? I can look out after your lady while you're gone."

"I don't think so," David said.

"I didn't either," Samuels admitted. "I know I wouldn't. What is it I'm supposed to be looking for?"

"I told Blake you probably wouldn't find anything this time, either."

"But I'll look anyway. So tell me why he thinks I need to look, and why, after a week you've suddenly decided the doc needs your protection at night."

How much could he tell this man without telling him everything? How much of the truth did he owe Samuels? Enough to keep him from getting killed.

"I don't suppose you and Blake will just go away and let Annie and me work this out by ourselves?"

Samuels gave a short bark of laughter. "Me, Blake, and Maggie," he corrected. "I told you she liked the doc. If it wasn't for Maggie, I never would have come Thursday, and Blake would still be trying to talk me into coming today."

"Right." David motioned toward the table. Samuels shook his head and remained at the counter. With a grimace, David leaned back against the sink. "Friday morning I told Blake what you thought you'd seen up here Wednesday night, and asked him about mountain lions— No, hell no. It goes back farther than that. Probably a lot farther. But for now, let's just go back to Wednesday.

"Anne and I found—a couple of things in the house, things that we now believe her Uncle Ralph brought in when he was dealing in artifacts from the Spiro mounds. Wednesday we sent them out, one to a collector I know in Dallas, another to a pathologist Anne knows in Chicago. Wednesday night you saw the cats. Yesterday, the collector was killed by some sort of wild animal. Also yesterday, a lab tech in Chicago was killed by some sort of wild animal. And last night we heard something, something big, pacing."

"Where?"

That was it? No reaction other than to ask where? As though this were an old story Samuels was hearing repeated?

David glanced at him. No. He saw no mockery, no ridicule, just a patient waiting.

So why not tell him? Why the hell not? "Upstairs."

Samuels scratched at the back of his neck. "And outside?"

"Maybe Wednesday," David admitted. "About the time we found the things."

"Wednesday night?"

"No. Earlier. One, two o'clock in the afternoon."

"You're right. I probably won't find anything. My uncle didn't when Marian Hansom took her dive down the stairs and blamed it on a couple of cats, and he was the best tracker ever born."

"That story again. Anne's mother mentioned it, but she also said Marian is 'crazy as a bessie bug,' whatever the hell one of those is."

"Yeah, she's that all right. Cats and curses. Uncle James said that was all she talked about. He looked for cats, outside, but found no sign of them. And, according to him, the curse sounded like an even bigger figment of her imagination."

"Anne's mother mentioned that, too. She said Marian claimed Ralph had infuriated some ancient god."

David expected Samuels's short bark of laughter. What he got was silence, and a reflective look.

"More than likely he infuriated some supplier or collector," Wayne said finally, "if what I've heard about his business dealings is anywhere near the truth. That would probably explain why his Buick went off the side of the mountain after leaving a quarter of a mile of real erratic skid marks."

"Murder?"

Samuels's mouth twisted in what could have been a smile, could have been a frown. "Maybe."

"Maybe. And nobody checked it out?"

"Hey, I'm telling tales I heard as a kid from someone who wasn't even there years before. But as I recall the story, no one thought old Ralph's death was any big loss to anybody. But it wouldn't explain why— Holy hell!"

"What?" David asked."

Samuels's mouth twisted again, and this time it was obviously into a bitter grin. "Why his body was mauled. Everybody thought it was probably a bear. But nobody checked."

"Your uncle?"

"Was logging at Pine Valley. Didn't come home until a couple of months later."

The two men exchanged troubled, silent questions.

"Look," David said, and knew he was going to have to say more. "I think we're safe. I can't tell you how I know this, but there seems to be a pattern in the attacks, at least the ones yesterday— I won't know about the others until I can talk to someone who remembers, and Annie and I planned to start doing that today. In fact, I had considered asking you to stick around while we're gone, not because of any supernatural threat but because I don't trust Joe not to send someone up to snoop around if he knows we're gone. But for God's sake, be careful."

"And Maggie? She's coming back for me later. Will she be in any danger?"

"No."

Annie's voice sounded from the doorway. Both men swiveled to look at her. She'd dressed warmly for their trip, and had her hair scalped back in that no-nonsense knot she wore it in when working. She looked rested, as though she had gotten a good night's sleep for the first time in a long time. Well, David was glad someone had. But she was pale. Too pale. How much had she heard?

"No," she repeated. "Neither of you will be in danger. Because you won't be here."

"Annie—"

"No, David. I won't put anyone else in jeopardy."

"But we can't leave the house unattended. You know what that could mean. And I won't leave you here alone."

She smiled at him. "If you would leave my friends here, if you're sure they will be safe, why shouldn't I be just as safe, alone, without you?"

"Because you won't stay out of the damned room."

Her smile drained from her. She closed her eyes as a wave of memory moved visibly over her features. "I won't, will I?" she said softly.

"Annie, damn it." In four long strides he was at her side, his arm around her shoulder. Supporting her? Or keeping her from running back to grieve at the feet of a long-dead man? "Here," he said, guiding her to the table. "Sit."

She popped up from the chair like a damned jack-in-the-box, thrusting her chin out. "Don't be silly. I'm all right. And I'm perfectly capable of—"

"Maybe you'd both better sit," Samuels said, stretching up from his slouch at the counter. "I've got work to do outside before the frost melts."

Wayne returned to the house just as David and Anne were leaving.

David didn't have to ask if he'd found anything; Samuels nodded at him as he shrugged out of his jacket.

"What?" David asked.

Wayne crossed the room and waited until David and Anne stepped back into the kitchen before turning and looking at David's boots. "You been out in back lately? Taken anyone with you?"

"I walked around the barn Wednesday, and I took Hank Foresman on a tour of the outbuildings a week ago when he showed up claiming to want work."

Samuels shook his head. "Hank wears Redwing work-boots. Whoever was out there hadn't been there when I checked out the place Thursday morning. His tracks cross the ones we left in the soft ground later that day. He was wearing a western boot, riding heel, about a size ten. It could have been Thursday night. It could have been last night. The ground didn't freeze solid till way after midnight this morning."

"It wasn't Thursday night; I checked out the place Friday morning. Hell, I was out there last night, looking for a damned cat. Where?"

"You name it. He scoped out the well house, the barn, most of the windows on the ground floor, came up on that porch outside the room where we watched the game Thursday, maybe tried the doors, maybe just looked."

David felt Anne's fingers clutch his arm. "All the windows?" she asked.

Samuels nodded.

"You'll stay?" David asked. "I'm not sure how long we'll be, I guess that depends on what we find and who we find to talk with, but it's got to take at least a couple of hours just to get up there and back."

"I'll stay. You take as long as you need. Maggie's coming back for me and we don't have anything else planned for the day. But you two be careful."

"Thanks. You, too."

They were on the porch before Samuels spoke again. "What room?"

Annie's hand jerked on his arm. David turned to look at the man.

"I don't intend to prowl your house, Doc. But if I hear something, I need to know which room I shouldn't go in."

Annie looked up at him, her eyes shadowed with the doubts and questions written in them. But damn it, they had to trust someone. And if they trusted Samuels enough to leave him here to guard this mystery, they owed him at least enough knowledge to, maybe, keep himself safe. Annie drew in a deep breath and nodded.

"Marian's sitting room," he said. "The one at the end of the first hall toward the back of the house. The one with the lavatory and parlor stove."

"The one that looks like it doesn't belong in this house?"

"Yeah," David told him. "That one."

They took the Blazer. David drove. Anne stared out into the fog that had descended into the cracks and crevices of the mountains, then down at it when the road climbed to follow the upper ridges. At this altitude, the hardwood trees had shed their leaves, and their bare limbs reached upward toward the pale early-morning winter light. Pleading, or prayer, she wondered as she studied those outstretched branches. Sometimes she wondered if there was a difference. Yes. Yes, there was. At least with prayer you had a hope of being answered.

She glanced at David. He didn't notice. All his attention seemed to be focused on something, probably the twists of the road as it wound along the ridges, dipping into patches of fog, rising out of them into the light.

He'd gone back into her house before they drove away, leaving her in the kitchen while he went into the interior for several minutes. He didn't tell her what he'd done, or what he carried in the small box he placed in the back of the Blazer. She didn't ask. She didn't want to know. Then they'd made a brief stop at his cabin, where he changed clothes and filled a small bag, before they headed north. He was once again crisply starched and pressed, as he had been that first day. And he looked so solemn. So unapproachable. Was this the man who had led her from the upstairs room last night, so fierce and yet so gentle, and who had held her through the night?

What had happened last night? What in God's name had happened?

She never sleepwalked. Not even as a child. But the dream had been so real. So real. And now she couldn't even remember what it had been about. But David had been in it. Oh, yes. David had definitely been in it.

And he had been in the one that followed, the one she remembered too clearly in every intimate detail, after he had returned her to her room. After he had plopped himself down outside the covers and anchored her in place with his arm. After he had burrowed his way under the blanket with her and dragged her against him. He hadn't awakened then, but she had, enough to hear him murmur her name, enough to feel him nuzzle at her throat and moan before dropping deeper into sleep.

The road wound its way down from the ridge into the valley surrounding Fairview just as the fog began to lift. Dim, thin light surrounded them, but it was growing brighter.

"You didn't have any breakfast this morning," David said, breaking the silence. "Do you want to stop? We can have fast food—the real thing."

She heard the teasing in his voice and felt herself relaxing marginally. He hadn't gone completely away from her after all. "Stop if you want. Coffee would be nice, but I'm really not hungry."

"I know what you mean." He stopped at a convenience store on the south edge of town. "Do you want to go in?"

She shook her head.

He came out a few minutes later with two large cups of coffee. He also had a couple of brochures and a bag of fresh doughnuts.

"They had a tourist information rack by the cash register," he told her, handing her the brochures. "These don't look as though they have a whole lot of information, but it's got to be more than we know."

"Spiro Mounds," Anne read aloud from the cover of the first brochure, which bore the picture of some sort of small statue of a kneeling male figure.

She opened the first brochure. "Did you read these?" she asked.

"No." David perched the cups in the slots of the plastic holder some previous owner had rigged on the dash and started the Blazer. "I just grabbed them. Why don't you fill me in as we drive?"

Anne nodded and opened the brochure. A drawing of a man, stretched forward probably in ceremonial dance, dominated the center. "Oh."

"What?" David asked sharply.

She held the brochure so that he could see. The man's legs and feet were bare except for bands of beads, much like bracelets on each ankle and just below his knees. But his upper body and arms were covered in a form-fitting pelt, which flowed into a mask completely covering his head. At least, she thought it was a mask. Four strands of beads circled his neck. Other beads circled his wrists. And his hands— Were they hands? Were those claws part of the costume for the dance? Or were they—

"Jaguar," David said. "Hell. Read."

Anne read. About the twelve mounds the park encompassed. About the civilization that had built them between A.D. 850 and 1450. About the site's importance in the commerce of the day, about its association with other mound sites throughout the southeast. About the ceremonies for the celebration of the seasons and the rituals centered on the death and burial of the elite.

There wasn't much, just enough to whet an appetite for information. But there were pictures. Pictures with no captions showing shells with the designs Anne had been seeing all of her life, pictures of a pleasant, tree-shaded, park-like setting with a series of hillocks.

Anne dropped the brochure to her lap and picked up the next one and turned it over, and then almost dropped it, too.

"Oh. Oh, no. No."

"Annie?"

"It's him," she said, clutching the brochure in both hands. "It's him."

David pulled to the shoulder of the road and set the emergency brake. "Let me see," he said. He reached for the folder. "Annie, let me see."

She gave him the folder, appalled by the protectiveness she felt for no more than a line drawing.

And it was just a line drawing, she realized as David looked at it, as she looked at it again. A face, dark eyes, strong chin, firm lips. The hair, the roach, the back of the head—these were not drawn, merely represented by a series of lines that could indicate shadow. A face. A part of a face. The long forelock drawn through two round beads. The visible earspool carrying the image of—of what?—an elephant? If so, an elephant as she had never seen one. And around the eye, a painted design pointing to the ear.

She traced that design with her fingers.

"It's called forked eye," David told her.

He returned the brochure and sank back against his seat. "It's a drawing. Just a drawing. Probably a composite the artist made up. I'll concede the similarity in the earspool, but there's not an ounce of copper showing. What makes you so sure this is our guy?"

"I don't— Yes. Yes, I do. The medallions. The ones in the cedar box."

"They're symbolic, Annie, and highly stylized. How can you see a resemblance between either of them and this drawing—"

"Because I looked at them, David, really looked, and you didn't. Just as you haven't really looked at this drawing. Why?"

He didn't answer. Instead, he held out his hand. She placed the brochure in it and watched him. He looked, but it was obvious he didn't want to. Why not? What could it cost him to look? But it was costing him something, that much was as evident as his forced examination of the drawing.

"Maybe," he said. He thrust the brochure at her and started the engine. "Maybe."

The state park containing the Spiro Mounds was miles from the little town of Spiro, miles off the state highway, almost on the Arkansas River, and within sight of one of the many lock and dam structures that had made the river once again navigable.

David circled the small, almost empty parking lot and

pulled the Blazer into a slot near the sidewalk leading to the front door.

The building was unobtrusive, built low to the ground and partially earth-bermed, with a concrete and square-post bower guarding the walk, while a concrete table and benches sat beneath a nearby tree. Anne waited quietly while David got out of the Blazer and walked toward the front of the truck. From this angle, she could see a group of low mounds off to the right, against a backdrop of trees as stark and winter-bare as the one that guarded the picnic table. She didn't want to get out. She didn't want to go any closer. But when David started toward her door, she opened it herself and stepped out.

He turned, and she saw that his attention, too, had been trapped by the stepping-stone mounds to the right.

"Those have to be the ones in the brochure," she said.

"Yes." He reached for her hand and clasped it. "Yes."

Why couldn't the place be closed? This was, after all, a holiday weekend. But no, they found the door unlocked, their path unimpeded.

The entryway faced a small counter of what appeared to be gift items and a rack of publications. A guest register lay open on the glass countertop. David picked up the pen but lay it down without signing. She looked at him but recognized the wisdom of remaining at least partially anonymous for the moment. She nodded and turned toward the open area to the right.

Clearly visible through the walls of windows that faced them, the mounds spread out across a well-tended lawn: the stepping-stone ones to the right, a large one almost directly in front of them that beneath its mantle of tan winter grass looked as though someone had taken a backhoe to the very top of it and had left it ravaged, others behind and to the left of that. To the right, below the cluster of mounds, was a primitive thatch-roofed house.

Only then did she notice the display cases of exhibits placed tastefully throughout the room. Only then did she turn and see the mural. She sucked in her breath. There, larger than life, the cat-man of the first brochure crouched in eternal dance among a group of other, symbolic dancers.

She felt David step closer to her and drop his hand on her shoulder. She raised her hand to his and fought the urge to shrink against him. This was a museum, nothing more. Those hills out there had been built hundreds of years before and had been ransacked decades ago. Did anything remain of the people who had built them?

A woman dressed in a pressed khaki uniform stood talking to a family near the doors leading out to the park. Two children, a boy perhaps ten and a girl about eleven, seemed to be the ones questioning the guide. David gave Anne's shoulder a squeeze and guided her into the display area.

Shells. Lots of shells and fragments. A small statue identified as a pipe. Ear spools. Small pieces of what was probably a cedar pole. A tattered remnant of lace. Fragments of a civilization long gone.

Three folio-sized books occupied pedestals placed in front of the waist-high window ledge. Anne walked to them, avoiding the view outside those windows. She scanned the books' captions until she found one containing drawings of the copper artifacts found during the excavations.

Slowly she leafed through the book. Hawks. Dancers. Gorgets. Human heads. Feathers.

She looked up at David in confusion. "There are no cats."

"Sshh." He nodded toward the guide and visitors.

"But where are the bodies?" the boy asked. "Skeletons? Bones? Mummies?"

His parents both gave self-conscious laughs.

"No bodies," the guide said pleasantly.

"Well, what kind of graveyard is this?"

"Daniel! Hush!" The mother took the boy's arm and began leading him toward the front door. "Thank you for your time—"

"Well, where are they?" the boy asked again, with a voice full of unthinking bloodlust.

In my closet, Anne thought. David rubbed his hand up and down her arm as a shudder worked its way through her.

The guide watched quietly until the family left, then shook her head and chuckled. She walked to where Anne stood with David beside the book of drawings.

The badge on the guide's uniform shirt identified her as Frances Collins. The slight, almond slant to her eyes, the café au lait tint to her flawless complexion, and the reddish cast to her straight, dark hair, identified her as a blend—a beautiful blend—of races: Choctaw, black and— What? Irish? Anne felt an instant affinity with her. And why not? If the woman was from this area, they probably had at least one ancestor in common. Wouldn't *that* thrill her mom's cousin Harriet?

"Hello. Can I help you with anything? Answer any questions?"

Lots of questions, Anne thought, if she only had the nerve to ask them.

David stepped forward and extended his hand. "Thank you, Ms. Collins. We're rank amateurs so we'll probably have lots of very basic questions."

"That's my job," she said cheerfully.

"I heard the boy ask about bodies," David said. "These were burial mounds?"

"Some of them." She pointed out the window to the stair-step mounds. "That's Craig Mound, the site of what we call the Great Mortuary, and, to the south, on that smaller mound, the crematory basin." She turned slightly and pointed toward the hillock from which the top had been gouged. "But Brown Mound also contained a significant number of burials."

"Crematory basin?" David asked. "Then the charming little boy who just left would have trouble finding a body, wouldn't he?"

Again the guide chuckled. "Not so much. While most of the burials were secondary burials . . . "

She broke off when she recognized Anne's puzzled glance.

"Secondary, in that the dead were buried once, then later exhumed, the bones cleaned and reinterred."

Anne nodded, an understanding of the term but not of the images it called forth.

"While most of them were secondary burials, a number of the higher ranking burials were primary, or just the one time, litter burials."

"With grave goods?" David asked.

"Yes. That's what makes the Spiro site such an important find." The woman frowned slightly. "And what almost destroyed it."

"Pothunters?" David asked.

"Oh, yes. Full-time, commercial ones."

"Who were they?" Anne asked. "The people who built these mounds?"

Ms. Collins cocked her head slightly, but accepted the change of subject. "They were a Mississippian culture, probably related by trade and religion with other

Mississippian centers, such as that at Cahokia in Illinois and Etowah in Georgia."

"And the Aztec?" David asked. "I see a similarity in some of the designs—the snakes, the speech symbol, the cats."

"You're not such a rank amateur after all, are you?" Ms. Collins said with a grin.

"About Spiro, yes, I really am," David admitted. "But I have done some reading about meso-American pre-history." Anne saw his bad-little-boy smile dart out and waited for whatever outrageous statement he would make to disarm this woman. When it came, it wasn't so outrageous after all. "Searching for my roots."

"Yes, well . . ." But it had disarmed. Frances Collins paused for a moment, smiled her understanding, and continued. "There's been an ongoing controversy about the meso-American connection for the past fifty years. Depending on who you read, and in what decade, either there was no connection whatsoever, or the Spiro people were engaged in trade with the southwest. What has become accepted is that the Spiro site evolved from one of several cultural centers in this area to the major cultural and trade center of the vast interior of this country. We've found evidence of trade with the Great Lakes, or Mexico, once again depending on your source and time frame, in the copper sheets used for engraving, to the Gulf of Mexico, probably the Florida peninsula, for the conch shells that were found in such profusion, and to the Rockies, although that was argued for a while, too, for various Bison products."

"Didn't a number of cultures use the conch shell?" David asked.

"Yes. In small pieces. And even entire, for storage containers, but we've yet to find the intact shells engraved as they have been here."

David walked to another of the large books, which had been left open to a drawing of a small statue that appeared to be a warrior or executioner decapitating the figure over which he crouched. "Young Daniel would have been right at home," he said. "Warlike, weren't they?"

"Maybe. But we found no evidence of any fortification of this site. They did control the river, which was the major trade route. And maybe their spiritual leaders were so strong, they grew out of the need for fortifications."

"What happened to them?" Anne asked.

Ms. Collins shook her head. "No one really knows. The best guess is a prolonged drought and the subsequent reduction in the supply of food to support the population in the villages surrounding Spiro, and perhaps a subsequent reduction in the faith necessary to support the hierarchy of the elite. In any event, by then this location was strictly ceremonial, with only a very few of the highest leaders living on the grounds.

"The villages shrank and finally disappeared as the remaining people became more nomadic, more 'hunter-gatherer' than farmer or craftsman. But we believe descendants of these people were still here at the time of European immigration—still are, as the Caddo or possibly the Wichita peoples."

"They weren't conquered and hauled away as happened in so many other places?" David asked.

"No. This world ended more with a whimper than a bang. However, an early rumor, started, I think, at the time the railroad was built through what was then the Choctaw Nation, held that a huge battle had been fought in the Redland Bottoms just west of here. That rumor persisted for years, still does among some of the locals, even though we've learned that what the railroaders uncovered was probably no more than the cemetery for one or more of the villages surrounding Spiro.

"Then they weren't all buried here?"

"No. At least not in the later days. I don't know what the cut-off rank was, because not all of the burials here were of equal rank, but it was probably pretty high. And there seems to be evidence to support that if one were that rank or above, his body, his grave goods, and maybe even his retainers were brought here for their final rest. Which might account for a number of the secondary burials."

"You're very knowledgeable about these people," Anne said.

Ms. Collins laughed. "I hope so. I grew up three miles away, hearing these stories from before I can remember, and I finished my master's degree in archaeology last spring." She grinned conspiratorially at David. "My own roots, you understand. I start work on my doctorate next fall, but I had to take a year off to be near my grandfather."

"Then you're the archaeologist in charge of this location?"

Ms. Collins' easy smile faded. "No. No way. I'm strictly interim. One year while my grandfather recovers and while the state finds someone qualified to take over here. Why don't we go out into the park? We have an interpretative walk."

Now it was Frances Collins who changed the subject. How interesting, Anne thought, but she followed the guide to the door leading outside, even managed to step one foot through it, when she realized she couldn't go any farther. Not even with David's arm around her shoulder. Not even with him close enough for her to feel his warmth. Not even with the questioning look

Frances Collins shot her as she stopped and refused to move forward.

"Go on," Anne said. "Please. It's— I— I'm sorry. I can't go out there."

Ms. Collins turned abruptly and ushered them back into the building. Taking Anne's arm, she led them through the displays, outside, and to the picnic table. "Sit," she said.

Anne did. Gratefully. While David watched, not puzzled but concerned.

"Annie?"

She felt his hand on the back of her neck. She wanted to speak, to assure him that she was all right, that she was *not* going to faint. What kind of wimp did he think she had become? But she seemed to have lost the strength necessary even to form words.

"It affects some people that way," Ms. Collins said. "Not many, but some. God, I wouldn't have this as a full-time job if my life depended on it."

18

When he was sure Anne wasn't going to keel over in a faint, David went back into the museum, to the vending machine he had seen down the one dark hall to the right, and slugged coins into it. He returned and handed Anne a can of Coke.

"Drink it," he said when she looked up questioningly. "You need the caffeine and the sugar."

"I thought I was the doctor in this road show," she said, but her smile was wan and her voice too weak to reassure him, in spite of her cheeky words, and she clutched the can like a lifeline.

Frances Collins leaned against the end of the table, not quite sitting, not quite hovering. He hadn't forgotten what she'd said, but only when he saw Annie's color returning to something approaching normal did he feel free to turn any attention to the guide.

"You say this happens often?"

"No," she said. "Not to this extent. Never to this extent. Are you all right now?"

Annie reached for his hand and squeezed it. Was she all right? He'd hoped getting her out of that house would get her away from the influence of whatever the hell they'd unlocked in that room. Obviously it hadn't.

"We need some answers," he said.

"Yes. I can see that. Would you like to go into my office?"

Annie glanced at the building. She'd go; he could see that in the determined lift of her shoulders. But she didn't want to.

"No," he said. The fog had lifted entirely. Winter sun warmed the air and the concrete table and benches. "It's pleasant out here, Ms. Collins."

"Frances," she told him, told both of them. "I have a feeling we've just progressed at least to first name status."

Anne managed a smile. "Probably farther than that," she said, extending her hand to the woman. "I'm Anne Locke."

They shook hands, and Frances turned to him.

"David Huerra," he told her, not at all sure they should be divulging any more than absolutely necessary, but recognizing in the sharing of their identities a trade of sorts. Information for information.

"That wasn't so bad, was it?" Frances asked. "Now, what is it you came to learn?"

"Were we that obvious?" Anne asked.

"Other than deliberately not signing the guest book? Other than not seeming surprised by the diversity of the exhibits even though you'd never been in before? Other than seeming to have a purpose in your search of them rather than the usual first-timers' meandering examination? Other than going directly to the book on copper and searching it as though looking for something specific? Well, no."

Frances counted off each point on her fingers and smiled as she said this, and, remarkably, David found himself smiling, too. "You'd make a good cop if you decide against archeology."

"Thanks, but I'm afraid I'm still operating on classroom time. Sorry. So. What do you want to know?"

He glanced at Annie. She nodded. Hell, why not? "Are you familiar enough with Spiro artifacts to be able to identify something for us?"

"Maybe. Most of them are pretty distinctive. There are some designs that overlap with other Mississippian locations, but there are some that are uniquely Spiro."

He'd folded the tracing and stuck it in his windbreaker pocket before they left Anne's house. Now he pulled it out and handed it to Frances Collins.

"Oh."

Her fingers caressed the penciled outlines with a reverence he had seen only a few times before. Jack Townley had almost had it. An ancient man he had met in Mexico City definitely had.

Anne sighed. "I guess that's our answer, isn't it?"

"Yes." David dropped his hand onto her shoulder and left it there, gripping her with a tension he recognized but couldn't seem to subdue. "What would something like that be worth today?"

"Depends." Frances laughed. "Doesn't everything? I heard of a broken one going for twenty-five thousand. But that was probably a rumor. And there are reproductions now being sold as original, points, fragments, things like that." She studied the sketch. "It's original?"

Anne nodded.

"And it wasn't ceremonially killed?"

"No." David answered her this time. None of it had been. Not one item accompanying the warrior had been damaged. Only the slight nick on this piece, and it could have been done before the burial. "Is that significant?"

"Yes. In that it probably denotes a really high-status

burial." She touched the drawing once more before returning it to him. "Conservatively, ten to fifteen thousand without documentation. Fifty to a hundred thousand with documentation."

He felt Anne tense beneath his hand. A fortune. A bleeding fortune. But hadn't they both already known that?

"Where are—" Anne smiled up at him before plunging onward. "You have only a few artifacts here. Where are the rest of them kept?"

"We have *no* originals here."

"What?"

Frances shook her head. "I guess you noticed this is not the most secure location in the world. We simply cannot afford to take the risk of losing another piece, and the insurance on the original of something like, well, like the basalt pipe you saw in the case is unbelievably expensive. The Resting Warrior pipe depicted in so much of the early literature is owned by the University of Arkansas. It's insured for a million and a half."

He felt the breath whoosh out of Annie.

"As for the rest of the artifacts, they're all over the world. During the commercial digging, before Oklahoma's antiquities laws were finally passed and took effect, there were buyers here at the site, literally snatching up everything the diggers brought out. It's been estimated that fully eighty percent of all high-status art in the U.S. was located in the mounds here at Spiro. There were more copper and conch items found here than at all the other North American sites combined. And now it's scattered. France, England, Germany, South America. Even China."

"But surely some of it was—was—"

Again Frances shook her head, but this time she found a smile for Annie. "Sure. Some of it. After the

W.P.A. and the University of Oklahoma took over the excavations. But by that time over four hundred burials, most of them high status, had already been disturbed. The commercial diggers had dug seven tunnels into Craig Mound—they called it the Great Temple Mound—and before they left, they dynamited all but one of their tunnels. Of course, by then, so much damage had already been done, the blasting probably didn't do that much additional damage. When the W.P.A. took over in June of '36 this place looked like a minefield. And much of the record that would have helped us understand a civilization as rich and powerful as the one that flourished here for—what? a thousand years or so, here and in the surrounding area—was gone. Scattered. Irretrievable."

Annie was getting ready to speak. He could sense it in the tension beneath his hand. Getting ready to say something that probably should never be said. "You recognized what was happening to Anne." If he was speaking, she couldn't. Not yet. "And you said you wouldn't have this job full time if your life depended on it."

Frances laughed softly. "I'd hoped you missed that. Now who's acting like a cop?"

David grinned at her, but he didn't relent. "Why, Frances?"

"Fair enough."

She'd said it easily, but now she seemed at a loss for words. With a glance at Anne—for reassurance that she wasn't going to be scoffed at?—she began.

"I told you I'm interim only. I'm not the archaeologist in charge. I refused to be the archaeologist in charge. Winston Harris, my immediate predecessor, youngish—mid-thirties—a classmate of mine in undergrad studies, had a heart attack after only three months on the job. But why should he have been immune?

Everyone in charge of this site has suffered some problem, mental, emotional, physical. Alcoholism, insanity, divorce, a bleeding ulcer—you name it, it's probably happened here.

"One not technically in charge, but closely connected, had his dissertation on Spiro and all his notes go up in a fire in his tent while on another excavation.

"Three members of the W.P.A. crews died in cave-ins on this site.

"And that doesn't even begin to touch the things that happened to some of those involved in the commercial dig; drowning facedown in a dry stream bed; being trapped in a cave-in while everyone else got out; crashing into a tree because the brake line was severed—forged, not cut or worn; painful, disfiguring cancer.

"And then there were those we only suspect were connected to the Spiro site. Collectors who were brutally murdered. One man who locked himself in a bank vault with a basket of Spiro pearls and was found dead the next morning—and the pearls were missing.

"I come out here sometimes at night, not because I want to, but because I can't seem to help myself. There's a heaviness here, after dark, that weighs down on me." She laughed self-consciously. "Even my stomach tingles. And concepts come so vividly—always, here—but more so at night.

"I can almost see . . .

"Some of this comes from growing up here, of hearing the rumors, even of seeing that damned huge feather cloak before the house where it was on display burned. But at night I can almost see that pair of big gold cats the old-timers talked about prowling the mounds.

"And I can almost— I *can* see the aura that seems to hover over the mounds."

She laughed again. "And of course we can't keep one blasted mechanical thing working for any length of time."

Annie had picked up on the word cats; hell, he had too. But not yet. He couldn't let her get into that yet. "Cloak, you said? Feather cloak?"

She nodded. "Six, eight feet long. At least a hundred and twenty pounds. It was supposed to have come out of the central chamber in Craig Mound, the chamber that most experts claim didn't really exist, at least not as more than a collapsed area between litter-borne burials, certainly not as a separate chamber. But Gramps said it did, said that when they broke into it, it whooshed like a sealed vacuum being opened, that big cedar poles making bins lined the walls, that there were boards painted with portraits that looked like Egyptians, and that there were maybe four burials there including the one with the cloak and the copper-covered giant that all the commercial diggers claim to have seen and no one knows what happened to. The experts say it probably didn't exist. My grandfather says it did."

"Who—" Now Annie spoke. "Who would wear a hundred and twenty pound feather cloak?"

"One heck of an important ruler. Maybe *the* priest, or *the* ruler. One thing for sure, he had to have had a fortune in grave goods with him, as well as a lot of faithful retainers and probably wives to follow him into the afterworld."

"Priest," David asked. "Not god?"

"No. Not god." Frances told them. "We think that these people had a naturalist religion that strove to control the forces of the spirits that inhabit animals, maybe even the elements. They probably worshipped to some degree, maybe only symbolically, the sun, moon, maybe the wind, rain, water, soil."

"And the giant?" Anne asked softly, intently. "Do you suppose he was one of the retainers of the priest?"

"No. I don't think so. From the way Gramps described him, he was—had to be—pretty powerful in his own right. He had to have been a high-status warrior who would have earned his own place in the hierarchy and would not accompany the priest in death. Instead he would be accompanied by his own attendants."

"And wives?" Annie asked.

"And wives," Frances said.

But he hadn't been. Or had he? How could they ever know now? How could Annie be so sure he had been alone?

"Can I talk with your grandfather?" Annie asked. "I need to talk with your grandfather."

For a moment Frances looked startled. "I'm sorry," she said finally. "He's had a stroke. That's why I'm home. To help my grandmother. He's recovering. But he still doesn't have his speech back. He may never have."

"No." Annie's voice softened and she reached for Frances's hand. "I'm the one who's sorry."

Frances shrugged off the dark mood that had momentarily claimed her. "You have more reason than just curiosity, don't you?"

Anne nodded. "Yes. You see my great uncle was probably at the digs at the same time your grandfather was. He was a dealer. He— He was responsible for removing a great deal of material from—from here."

Frances cocked her head to one side and stared at the drawing, now anchored to the table by Annie's Coke can. "And that's where that piece came from?"

Annie nodded. "That. And— And others. That I can't understand why he didn't get rid of because I think he died, if not in poverty then at least close to it except for the money his wife's family provided. Your grandfather might know him. And why . . . "

"I can ask. Communication isn't impossible, just horribly difficult. What was his name?"

"Hansom," Annie told her. "Ralph Hansom."

"Oh, shit." Frances had started to rise. Now she sat down abruptly. "The curse. The damned curse. He didn't get rid of it and now you can't."

Anne turned to look up at David. He stepped closer, pulling her back against him. But that wouldn't protect her. Would anything? "You've heard of him, then?"

Frances looked at him, shook her head, and laughed weakly. "Yeah. You might say that. You see, my grandfather wasn't particularly happy with what he had done here. This was during the depression, you remember, and this area had been depressed since before the Choctaw chose the losing side in the Civil War and had to free their slaves, then had to give them citizenship and a piece of the pie when the lands in the nation were allotted to individuals instead of being held in common title by the Choctaw Nation. Anyway, the commercial diggers were offering about the only jobs to be had. I heard Gramps say, more than once, that the items shipped out of the mounds were the major export for the county during that time.

"But, later, after his family was fed and clothed, he worried about his part in the grave-robbing. That's what he called it. The Choctaw had known these mounds were here for over a hundred years and not bothered them. And even though there had been some digging on the sly since—well, since God only knows when, probably since the first farmer managed to clear away the cane that covered most of these river-bottom lands by then and plowed up a conch shell or an ax, there wasn't any serious activity until 1933.

"And he helped. He took money to help desecrate a burial ground. At least that's how he looked at it after the fact. And that's how he told it to me while I was growing up. And when stories about curses and retribution crept in, so did your uncle's name.

"He bought something. Or stole it—Gramps was never very clear on that. And everyone who helped him died a brutal death. And everyone he tried to sell it to died a brutal death. And finally, he died a brutal death.

"Is that about what you'd heard?"

Annie closed her eyes and leaned against David, gathering strength. She reached into her jacket pocket and took out the folded brochure with the warrior's picture on the cover. "This image," she asked. "Where did it come from?"

Frances glanced at the cover; he could tell she didn't have to study it. "From an engraving on a copper plate we found in a burial when we made some trial excavations on the plaza. That's the area between Brown, the mound with the top gouged out of it—the commercial diggers did that, too—and Copple, the mound just barely visible at the back of these grounds. Actually, I'm not sure it was a burial. We trenched through a house mound. There was a great deal of material, so we decided to excavate it completely. We found three bodies, but they didn't fit any of the patterns of burial we know. It was almost as if they had died and the house had been allowed to fall in and cover them. One of them, a woman, was wearing this as a breastplate."

"Can I see it?" Anne asked. "No. I suppose what I mean is, where can I see it?"

"I wish I knew," Frances said. "It— You have to know that Spiro artifacts have a long history of just disappearing. From locked vaults, from archived collections. In recent days, these disappearances haven't been of major items, nothing like the Resting Warrior or Big Boy pipes, but little pieces—a little piece here, a little piece there. This breastplate is one of those pieces. Why?"

Anne reached for his hand. She was going to say it, and nothing he could say or do would stop her. He caught her hand in his and held tightly.

"Because we found the warrior he was modeled after. The one in the central chamber. The copper-clad giant that doesn't exist. And since we found him, two people have died brutal deaths."

They went back inside. Anne knew they would either have to do that, or leave, when a small but steady stream of visitors began arriving at the museum. Parked in Frances's cramped little office, surrounded by magazines, books, and articles about the Spiro people, about the artifacts, about the authorized excavations and the commercial digging, Anne sat with her eyes closed, listening as David paged through book after book. Looking for something. Looking for what? Answers? Did he honestly think he'd find answers to what faced them in those books?

He slammed one shut and scraped his chair as he stood and tried to pace in the crowded room. She opened her eyes and looked up. She'd seen him in many moods this past week, but never agitated like this.

"It's worth a fortune, Annie," he said from a temporary pause in his march at the corner of an overflowing bookcase. "We already suspected that, though, didn't we?"

She didn't answer; he didn't seem to need one.

"But not just in money," he went on. "Do you have any idea how much information can be gained from what your uncle hid in the dark fifty years ago?"

Frances opened the door and stepped into the room as David was speaking. She leaned against the door-jamb, silent, waiting.

"Him," Anne said, tired beyond belief. "He."

David shot her a sharp glance. "Why do I have the feeling I'm not going to like what you say?"

But maybe she wasn't too tired to smile. Just a little. "Probably because you won't. Probably because neither one of you will. He's not an *it*, David, or a *what*. He's a man who was buried with honor and dignity, then ripped from that grave. Aside from the fact that whatever is killing these people won't let us disturb him any more than he's already been disturbed, why on earth should we even want to? Why can't he be left alone? Why should he have to become some sort of encyclopedia? Is desecrating his grave for that purpose really any better than desecrating it for money"

"You don't want the money?"

"Oh, God, no."

He threw his head back and twisted his neck and shoulders, easing tight muscles, before sighing. "Don't you think we have an obligation to science, or history, or even to the people who once lived at this very site, to share what knowledge can be gained from this . . . from *his* burial?"

"I don't know, David. I just don't know."

He walked to where she sat and leaned against the edge of the desk, taking her hand in his. "What do you want, Annie? The decision is up to you. He's yours, you know."

What did she want? What had she wanted last night when she knelt at the warrior's feet, crying. What had she wanted when she held the cedar box and miniatures in her hand and grieved for something and someone she had no way of understanding?

One thing she did understand.

"No, he isn't mine," she said. "If I think that, I'm no different from my uncle. What do I want? I think what I want is for him to be at peace. After all these hundreds of years since he died, is that too much to ask?"

"And if we can do both?" Frances asked softly. "Would you be willing to let me try to find a way to do both?"

Anne turned to face the woman, feeling the strength in David's touch flowing into her as he continued to grasp her hand. "Can you?"

"I don't know. I can only try."

Anne looked up at David, but he offered no opinion, telling her by his silence that this decision was hers alone to make. But was it? Wasn't he as deeply involved in everything that was happening, had happened, as she? But he gave her the decision, and she made it. She nodded. "Yes," she said. "Try. God knows we have to do something."

Anne remained silent during the drive to the highway, There, David hesitated at the stop sign. She'd seemed rested that morning. Had that only been an illusion? Because now she had shrunk back into herself, had shrunk into the corner of the Blazer, shutting him out. Damn it! Why was she shutting him out?

"What is it?" she asked when he remained stopped at the sign long after traffic had cleared.

"You didn't have breakfast," he said. "Frances said Fort Smith is only a few miles to the east. Why don't we find us a really good lunch?"

She dragged her head back and forth against the headrest. "Please. Could we just go home?"

Yeah. They could do that. Hell yes, they could do

that. Why not? Leaving obviously hadn't done her one bit of good. Without speaking, he turned right and headed them toward the road that would eventually take them back to Allegro.

She slept. Not well. With little whimpers and a frown or a grimace of pain on her face. In the mountains just north of the Pitchlyn County line, he debated unsnapping her seat belt and pulling her closer, regardless of the built-in obstacle course of the bucket seats and small console, regardless of the slight risk to her safety. Until he saw emergency lights flashing ahead.

"Damnation." His hand froze on the seat belt release. Slight risk to her safety? In the mountains? On a road with more curves and bumps than a roller coaster?

She awoke as he slowed and eventually stopped in the line of traffic waiting to be directed around the clutter of cars and trucks a hundred yards downhill, but now out of sight behind a slight curve.

"What is it?" she asked.

"A wreck, I think," he told her. "Maybe a pretty bad one if the number of emergency vehicles is any indication."

She blanched. That was the only word to describe what happened. Already pale, already wan, her complexion took on the color of old, grayish parchment. And her eyes filled with a dread as old as the mountains that surrounded them. But when they reached the officer who was directing traffic, she leaned across David, to the window he had opened, and spoke clearly, with no sign of what he would have sworn was panic.

"I'm a doctor," she told the officer. "Can I be of help?"

"Thank God," the young deputy said. "Yes, ma'am, you sure can. Will you park over there, sir?"

David parked on the shoulder of the road, behind a sheriff's cruiser. "Are you up to this?" he asked her.

Anne just looked at him, without answering, but that one look was answer enough. She wasn't up to it. Not in any way, shape, form, or fashion—and *why* wasn't she? the thought nagged at him—but she was going to do it.

She almost spoke, almost reached for his hand, then she drew into herself, even as she seemed to draw on some inner source of strength, and opened the door instead.

"Annie, you don't have to do this."

She turned to look at him for only a second. "Don't I?" she asked. Then she stepped from the Blazer and walked toward the knot of people clustered on the narrow verge beside the pile of cars.

A baby was screaming. A young woman was sobbing and fighting against the restraint of an officer who held her away from the small boy on the shady shoulder of the highway. The boy wasn't crying. His eyes were closed, but his mouth was held in a tight grimace. His pant leg was split from groin to ankle, and a huge open gash exposed muscle on his thigh. A teenage boy knelt beside him, holding a bloody shirt as a makeshift compress against the wound. Once Anne saw the injured boy, she seemed to lose all awareness of anyone else. She shrugged out of her coat and draped it across the child's chest as she dropped to his side. "I'm a doctor," she said again.

"Oh, thank God." The teenager's words echoed the deputy's, and he scurried aside to give her room.

"My bag—" She looked up at David. "Would you—" She took the shirt and pressed it against the wound. "I didn't bring it. What am I going to do? I didn't bring it."

What was happening? This wasn't the Anne Locke he had spent the last week getting to know, the competent woman he had grown to respect. And it had nothing to do with Spiro or her uncle or skeletons in the closet.

"Annie."

His voice stopped her flow of words, thank God. "I have a couple of clean undershirts in my duffel. Will they work for a compress?"

She nodded and turned back to the boy on the ground. While she held pressure on the gaping wound with one hand, she tested the tourniquet on his thigh, sought and found a pulse in his throat, spoke soothingly to him as she lifted his eyelid to check his pupil, and shifted to move closer to him while she crooned words of encouragement and comfort. David watched her for a moment. Yes. This was Anne. Pale. Drawn. But the Anne he knew. And she would be all right.

But the boy wouldn't be, if he didn't hurry.

When he returned with the clean undershirts, Anne looked up at him long enough to smile and check to see how he had folded them before she nodded toward the boy's thigh where the makeshift pad had soaked through.

"Let me," he said. He dropped to his knees beside her and eased the clean pad of his shirt into place and held it there, freeing her to discard the other and hold the boy in both her arms. "Like this?" he asked.

She nodded and moved even closer to the boy, now lying on the rocky ground as she shared her body's warmth and her soft touch. "Yes. Thanks. His name is Wayne. He's ten. I was telling him we have a friend named Wayne who can track wild animals through the woods. Wayne, this is David. He's a police detective in Dallas. I'll bet that if you go to Dallas someday, he'll show you all through the police department and tell you about some of his really big cases. Won't you, David?"

She was crying. Crying like she had last night. Tears streaming unchecked down her cheeks as she held the boy and rocked slightly against him. The people around them were quiet, as though they suspected the doctor and her assistant were merely going though the motions, that the battle had already been lost. Even the baby had stopped screaming and the mother had stopped fighting to get to her son's side.

No, damn it! This boy wouldn't bleed to death while they waited for an ambulance, and he wouldn't surrender to the pain and give up. "I sure will, Wayne," David told him, with not a trace of his frustration evident in his voice. "One of the men I work with played college baseball, almost went pro before he decided he'd rather be a cop. He does a lot of work with the young people in Dallas, and he's been known to get an autographed ball every now and then. You come to see me, and I'll make sure he has one of those balls for you. Who's your favorite player?"

Wayne didn't answer. By then his grimace had faded. David shot a sharp glance at Anne.

"He's passed out," she told him. "But he's still alive."

The scream of the approaching ambulances broke the silence, but even after they screeched to a stop behind the pile-up, it seemed an eternity before one emergency med tech moved in to take David's place with the pressure compress, and another moved to take Anne's place to monitor vital signs.

Only then did David notice another ambulance crew working over another victim. Alive? Or dead? Suddenly he didn't want Annie to know that Wayne hadn't been the only patient. He helped her to her feet, took her ruined coat as their young helper handed it to him, and turned her toward the Blazer, away from the sight of that other crew.

"Where will you take him?" he asked the EMT who had replaced him.

"St. Ed's in Fort Smith," the man told him.

David nodded and hugged Anne to his side. "We'll check later. Let's go now, Anne. Let's let these people do their job."

She didn't resist. Didn't argue. Didn't insist on following the boy to the hospital. And for that he was grateful. Because she looked just about one step from having to be taken there herself.

He loaded her into the passenger seat of the Blazer before he prowled through his duffel and found a teeshirt to sacrifice to the cleanup detail, then used it to wipe the blood from her hands and arms.

"So much blood," she said, not helping him, not fighting him. "So much blood." She looked straight ahead, out the opened door, not at him, not at the wrecked cars, not at the blood on her hands and his. "And I wasn't any more help today than I was then."

19

They stopped at a service station a few miles down the road to wash.

"You folks hurt in that wreck up on Simpson Knob?" the underaged station attendant asked as he followed them to the door of the restroom.

"No." David turned the water on full blast and washed off a grimy bar of soap before he handed it to Annie.

The attendant looked at the evidence of the carnage. "With all the ambulances that went through, it must have been a bad one."

He was a boy, David reminded himself. Just a boy. With no more concept of what carnage and mayhem and death really meant than young Daniel at the museum. Annie didn't answer; he wasn't sure she was able to. He didn't want to.

"Yeah," he said, offering no information, and finally the boy left them to the soap and hot water.

Anne scrubbed for a long time before he took the soap from her and handed her a wad of paper towels. While he scrubbed she dried, then sat on the closed lid of the toilet, her hands clasped between her knees, and stared at something he couldn't see.

He led her back to the Blazer. After a moment's consideration, he left her there and went into the station. There wasn't a big selection, but he bought a half-dozen candy bars, a couple of bags of cashews, and two cans of Coke, and piled it all into a small box he found on the cluttered and grease-stained counter near the cash register. He handed her the box when he returned to the Blazer, but she just held it as he pulled out of the service drive and once again started toward home.

Annie's silence, her near-shock state, was worrying him, a lot.

He saw a sign pointing to a boat landing off somewhere to the right. For a moment he hesitated. Would it be better just to take her on home? No, hell no, it wouldn't. Not in the state she was in. God only knew whatever it was in that house would do to her in this weakened and sensitive condition. He took the turnoff and followed the winding road to a finger of a small Corps of Engineers lake.

The parking area where he braked to a stop led to a boat launch where the water of the lake was beginning to lash angrily at the concrete ramp. The parking area served a picnic site, shaded in summer but now merely surrounded by bare trees. There was no other vehicle, no other person, in sight. One more small favor he'd have to give thanks for.

But the wind had picked up, and the sun had apparently decided to go home for the day. There was no way Anne could be warm enough at one of the picnic tables without her coat, and there was no way he was asking her to put her body in that bloodstained reminder of what she had just had to do. And his windbreaker, stashed now in the back with her coat, was only marginally less stained.

He left the engine running and adjusted the heater.

Then he freed himself from his seat belt, popped the top on a can of Coke, and peeled back the wrapper from a chocolate bar. He propped the Coke in the holder on the dash and rested the candy bar across its top as he turned toward Annie, as he unfastened her seat belt, as he turned her to face him.

He handed her the candy bar and waited, not speaking, until she had taken a bite from it. She chewed and swallowed and looked at him. "I know what you're doing."

He found a smile for her. "I thought you might. Eat. A little sugar rush will be good for you about now. And I have some cashews to force-feed you some protein for when that rush crashes."

She took another bite of the candy. "Damn. I never thought there'd come a time in my life when I'd have to make myself eat chocolate."

Her words were right, but her voice still wasn't. Her color still wasn't. And the time wasn't right, but then the time might never be right for what he was about to ask. And he had to ask. He waited until she finished the candy bar and half the Coke.

"Annie, why did you study medicine?"

She closed her eyes and let her head fall back until it rested against the high back of the seat. "I don't know any more," she said. "Once— Once I thought I might be able to help. Once I thought I had to help, I had to learn to heal."

"Once." The word sounded hollow in the enclosed car. "But not now?"

"You saw how ineffective I was today. You saw how I fell apart."

"I saw how you did your best in adverse circumstances. I saw how you comforted and loved your patient—"

"My best? Yeah. Maybe that was my best. Maybe all I'm capable of doing anymore is holding somebody and crying while he bleeds—while he . . ." Her voice broke, and her face twisted in pain. "While he dies."

And that's when he knew that her reaction had some basis in her concern for the boy they had just left, but even more in the robbery in Chicago that she had barely survived and so many others had not.

"Annie. Oh, God, Annie." He twisted and maneuvered himself across the narrow console into her seat, lifting her onto his lap and wrapping her in an embrace meant to keep her demons at bay.

Maybe it did for a while.

The tension eased from her as finally she took the comfort he offered her and lay against his chest with her face hidden from him against his neck. He couldn't see her tears, but he could feel them. And he could hear the words, as broken as they were, she gasped against his collar.

"I can't do this anymore," she said. To herself? To him? To God? Who knew? "I just can't do it anymore."

And then her sobs came, all the more terrible because at first she tried to hold them back. And couldn't. All the more terrible because he realized they must be the first she had allowed herself since the robbery took place—when?—almost a year ago?

"I begged them," she said, and he knew she was reliving that moment. "One of my patients was thirteen, still just a child. He tried to be a hero and they killed him first. I begged them to let the others go. They thought it was funny. They told me to get down on my knees. I did. I'd do it again. But it didn't matter. They laughed. And then they panicked.

"I can't see a child bleed—I can't see blood—without seeing that room and all the people who had trusted me, who had counted on me, without being back in that room with those half-crazed, half-grown . . . "

"Annie, Annie, you're not there now." He rubbed his hand across her back, trying to soothe her, trying to bring her back from the hell she was trapped in. "I have you. I have you and you're safe. You're not there now. You don't ever have to go back there. You don't have to face it alone. You'll never have to face anything alone again. I'm with you."

She sniffed once and stopped fighting her tears, stopped fighting her sobs. He held her, this strong, confident woman who had been forced to her knees to beg. For others. He hadn't missed that in her tortured stream of words. Not for herself but for others. And he hadn't missed hearing his own words, either, even though he didn't understand where they had come from and why they felt as though they had been too long unsaid. *You'll never have to face anything alone again. I'm with you.*

Anne was still quiet and still emotionally drained when they reached Allegro, but then, so was he. He glanced at her before he turned into the drive leading up to her faded purple house.

"Let me take you someplace else."

She shook her head. "It's okay," she told him. "I'm okay. And going someplace else, for no matter how long, isn't going to make the warrior or the problem of what to do with him go away."

"No, but it might give you time to regain the strength you need to deal with those problems."

She gave a choked, humorless laugh and leaned her head against the back of the seat. "Do you really think anything is going to do that?"

She didn't seem really to want an answer. Maybe there wasn't one. He turned into the drive.

Wayne Samuels's truck was parked near the back porch. And so was the black Jimmy David had seen Blake Foresman driving the night before. Cautiously, he parked between the two vehicles and turned to tell Annie to wait while he checked to make sure they weren't walking in on a problem she didn't need to face. He might as well have saved his energy. She yanked the door open and stepped from the Blazer.

Margaret, Wayne, and Blake sat at the round table in the kitchen. All three looked up when they entered.

Margaret jumped up from the table. "Anne. My God—"

Blake Foresman scooted his chair back and rose to his feet. "Are you all right? Huerra? What happened?"

"A wreck," David said, and then he realized how they must look. "We weren't involved. We stopped to help."

Margaret closed her eyes briefly.

"Where?" Blake asked. "No one contacted me."

"I think the kid at the service station called it Simpson Knob."

Blake nodded. "A dangerous stretch. Thank God it's not in my county. How bad was it?"

"Not now, Blake," Margaret said as she walked to Anne's side. "Be a lawman later. Come on, Doc, you look like you could use a hot shower and a change of clothes."

Anne started to resist. David saw it in her eyes. But after one long, questioning glance at Blake, which he studiously ignored, she smiled at Margaret. "You're right about that."

"I'll come on back with you and tell you about the new paint the town has decided to bestow upon the clinic. It looks like we're going to have to find a gracious way to tell them to stuff their benevolence about ten feet below the town dump."

David waited until the two women had left the room before he leaned back against the cabinet.

"Okay," he said. "Anne didn't ask, but I will. What's going on, Blake? Why are you here?"

"Seems you and the Doc were spotted leaving town this morning," Blake told him. "So you had a visitor. One who didn't know that Wayne was here without a vehicle. One who didn't knock on the door but went to those French doors off the side porch and let himself in."

"I figured I'd call the sheriff while he was letting himself in," Wayne said, taking over the telling. "By the time I did that, he was in, so I moved around behind him and let him know, nice like, that he wasn't alone."

David could just imagine how *nice like* Wayne had been. "I'm glad it wasn't me you surprised. Where?"

Wayne waited a moment before answering. "The landing at the top of the stairs. It looked like he was trying to decide which hall to take."

"Damn! Who?"

"Joe," Blake told him.

"Joe Hansom? Himself? Not just someone he sent?" Blake nodded.

"Well, hell. I didn't think he was that dumb."

"Or that arrogant?" Blake asked.

David laughed. Nothing about this situation was funny. But, damn, it was either laugh or run his fist through a cabinet door. "So where is he? In custody?"

"No. I told him I ought to run him in. I think I put the fear of God in him, but with Joe you never can tell. I told him to get on home and stay there until I found out for sure if Anne wanted to press charges. Will she?"

"I don't know," David admitted. "I just don't know."

With Wayne and Margaret there for Anne, David

asked Blake to go with him out to the Tompkins place to get the rest of his things and check out of his cabin. Anne might not know it yet, but she had just taken in a boarder. And he figured that if his cabin was no longer available, she might not argue too much about him staying in her house. After all, where else in Allegro could he go on such short notice?

Blake didn't argue. Not about going out to the lake with him. Not about his plans. In fact, he offered his assistance if Anne should argue. Imagine that.

He waited while David showered and changed clothes and packed his few belongings, then flirted unmercifully with Gretta Tompkins when they went to the office for David to check out of the cabin. Blake also told Gretta that Anne had had a burglary, and that he'd asked David to help keep an eye on the place for him. Unofficially, and strictly on the q.t.

"Well, of course," Gretta said with an exaggerated huff of indignation. "If you don't know by now, Blake Foresman, that you can tell me something in confidence, then why on earth have I been feeding you pot roast for the last fifteen years? I did manage to raise a cop, you know."

"I know, darlin'," Blake told her. "But I also know how some of the other ladies—never you—in this town would take an innocent situation and twist it all out of proportion. I was hoping I could count on you to help us keep that from happening?"

Gretta grinned at him. "On the q.t., huh? Maybe connected with some big case he's working on?"

Blake bent and smacked a kiss on her cheek. "You got it, darlin'."

"Pete will have my badge for sure if I drag his mama into this mess," David said on their way back to town.

"You didn't drag her, I did." Blake chuckled. "And you see how hard it was to do. Don't worry. Gretta has helped before. She knows what to do and how to do it."

He negotiated a series of curves before he glanced over at David. "Is there any chance he's going to do that? Take your badge?"

"Maybe," David said. "Oh, hell, no. Probably not. I think he just threatened me with internal affairs so I'd take this damned vacation. But he might. And then again, I might just give it to him."

"You know you've got a place here if you want it."

David twisted his head to the left to look at the man, but Blake was concentrating on the road, not on him.

A place here? Was that an option? He hated small towns. He hated the way they sucked the life out of anyone trapped in them. But Anne didn't see them that way. She looked at Allegro as a haven, a safe place to escape from the danger of big-city crime.

Or maybe as a place to hide?

"Thanks," he said to the sheriff, knowing he had to make some response, and realizing the offer had been made without so much as a question about why his badge might be in danger. "Thanks for the vote of confidence."

"Yeah, you're welcome. I'd appreciate it if you'd return the favor."

"I trust you, Blake. You know that."

Maybe he knew; maybe he didn't. Blake Foresman didn't respond to that statement. "I did some checking on that other matter you asked about," he said instead.

"Other matter?"

"Lucy Hansom."

"Oh. Yeah." So much had happened that Anne's mother's comment about Lucy had completely slipped his mind, and he had no idea how Blake had gone from the subject of trust to an ancient missing person's report. "Did you find anything?"

"Not much. Not nearly enough for the disappearance of a young girl back in those days."

"She did disappear?"

"She and a boy—I guess a young man by then—by the name of Walter Briggs. They'd known each other most of their lives and some said they were planning on getting married. He came home on emergency leave from the army when his mama died just before Thanksgiving of '41, and they vanished. The army carried him as AWOL for years. Maybe still does. And maybe he did go AWOL. Maybe he decided the chances of going to war were looking worse every day so he took Lucy and they lit a shuck for parts unknown."

"And no one looked?"

"No." Blake said. "But that was right at the time Marian took her dive down the stairs and blamed a pair of big yellow cats that no one but her saw, at least no one who was willing to talk. She blamed them for Ralph Hansom's death, too. You did know that he died in a car wreck but his body was mauled? She also said that they'd killed Walter and Lucy, but she wouldn't say where. Or when.

"So we've got a fifty-year-old injury and one death, maybe three, blamed on cats. We've got a brand new death in Dallas and another one in Chicago. We've got you and Wayne Samuels talking about seeing or hearing big cats. We've got you and the doc running all over creation looking for God alone knows what, bringing her back looking like she's barely escaped from a war zone, and you so concerned about her safety you're willing to shred her reputation in this small town. We've got Joe Hansom, who's planning to run for a state senate seat, jeopardizing his chances by breaking and entering. And all of it seems to be tied to one godawful purple house. It'd be real nice if someone let me in on what's going on."

"Do you ever call on Anne for emergencies?" David asked.

Now Blake looked slightly startled at the change of direction. "Yeah. Some. Not often. If it's in the north end of the county, it's quicker just to go on into the Fairview Hospital. Why?"

"You ever notice anything . . . odd about her when you bring her someone from a wreck or a bar fight?"

"Odd? No. Not what I'd call odd. She does seem a little uptight. Not easygoing like she normally is. I thought it was— Hell, I don't know what I thought it was. Why?"

"Because she did escape from a war zone." Blake Foresman's earlier words were all too descriptive not to use. "You heard about the clinic robbery in Chicago?"

Blake nodded.

"Well, it seems that our Annie isn't quite over that. It seems that the sight of blood brings all of those memories back, real up close and personal. Today, she let down her guard enough to tell me."

"Well, hell." Blake was quiet for a moment. "You mean she's been carrying all that pain around all this time and we didn't know it?"

"Yeah. That's what I mean." He didn't have to say more. He knew from Blake's expression that the man would cut off his right arm rather than drag Anne back out for an emergency. Unless there was no other option.

"About the other," David said.

Blake canted his head to one side but kept his eyes on the road.

"I can't tell you. Not yet anyway. Give us a few more days. We'll either resolve the problem, or I promise you I'll fill you in."

"Fair enough. So long as no one else is in danger."

Was anyone else in danger? Was Joe alive only because Wayne had been there to keep him from finding the burial? And what if Frances found a way for them to get rid of the warrior and all his grave goods and the cats wouldn't let him go? Hell, if there were any truth to this curse, why weren't he and Annie dead already?

"*Is* anyone else in danger?" Blake asked.

"I can't be sure," David admitted, hoping he was right. "Probably not, if we're careful. If no one else gets involved."

"That's not good enough, Huerra."

No, it wasn't. Not for Blake. Not even for him. "I know. But it's the best I can do. That, and promise you that if there's any change, I'll fill you in immediately."

They'd reached the outskirts of Allegro. Blake growled out a sound that could have been agreement but probably was disgust.

"Where are we going?" David asked as Blake turned onto Main Street.

"Hardware store. Wayne asked me to pick up a new lock set for the French doors. It seems that Joe was not gentle with the existing one." He braked to a stop in front of the store and turned in his seat. "Tell me, is what you're guarding Anne against outside the house? Or inside?"

"I don't know that either." He looked at the brick facade of the hardware store in front of him, at the slightly shabby but still pleasant-looking downtown business district that stretched only three blocks in any direction. "You didn't ask why Pete was considering yanking my badge, but maybe you ought to know. I'd come dangerously close to being omniscient, at least in my own mind. The last case was just the icing, not the whole cake. I'd see the answer, clear as day, just don't confuse me with conflicting facts. But if the facts do conflict, well, hell, that's no problem. I know who did it; let's just beat those facts to fit and paint them to match."

"You're saying you manufactured evidence?"

"No. Good God no. Not yet anyway. Who knows what I might have done if I hadn't screwed up so bad on this last case."

He might as well spill it out. Blake might never know about Marla Hamilton and her country doctor daddy, but he would understand how unchecked prejudice could subvert an investigation.

"One of the suspects was—hell, he was a surgeon. He had it all, a Mercedes, a condo, a self assurance that came off more often than not as arrogance, and a woman he hadn't had before people around her began getting sliced up. Before long, I was convinced he wasn't just a suspect; he was the only suspect. But before I could prove he was guilty, two more people died, and the real perp almost killed my suspect and his lady.

"And who knows what might have happened if I hadn't realized my unfounded prejudices got so much in the way of being a good cop that I scared myself into knowing I had to change.

"No. What I'm saying is that in the week I've been here, I've gone from being a man who was convinced he knew everything worth knowing, to someone who's been confronted by the fact that he knows almost nothing. And the more I learn, the less I'm sure of anything except that if anything ever again hurts Anne Locke, it'll have to come through me first."

"You know that already. That quick?"

"Yeah," David said. Hell, maybe a small town wouldn't be so bad after all. Maybe this one wouldn't choke the life out of him the way the one where he grew up had. Maybe. Could he risk it? "That quick. And that sure."

Margaret had Anne working with her in the kitchen when they returned to the house, more to keep her busy, David suspected, than because she needed help with the meal preparations.

And they had told her about Joe. That much was evident when she looked at Blake and repeated the words David had used so often that week. "I don't know. I just don't know."

Blake declined her invitation to stay for a late lunch, but before he left he promised to stay in the area that night, when he again took the graveyard shift for an absent deputy.

When just the four of them remained in the kitchen, Wayne reached for the new lock set and turned to David. "Come on, city cop. Let's see if you know as much about locks as you do about ceilings."

Joe had not been gentle with the French doors or the lock. Wayne had already been at work, filling and gluing the damage to the bottom of the doors where the ineffectual stops had been splintered loose by the force of Joe's entry, and removing the old, mangled lock and knobs.

"Sure of himself, wasn't he?" David asked when he realized the amount of noise Joe must have made entering the house.

"Yeah."

"Any chance he wore a size ten western boot with a riding heel?"

"Yeah."

Well, that answered at least one question. "When did you know it was Joe?"

Wayne began pulling supplies from the bag. He examined each of them before placing them with deliberate care on a table he'd brought near to hold his tools. He then rubbed the back of his neck and stared out the doors toward the dining room windows.

David picked up the mangled lock and studied it, waiting for Wayne to work through whatever held him silent. Waiting for him to decide whether or not he'd answer.

"That's a hell of an alarm system the doc's got," Wayne said finally. "I was on my way out, fastest way possible, when I saw Joe coming through the woods toward the house and realized your oversized house kitties were probably just that-- an alarm system."

David dropped the lock to the table. "You heard them?"

"Oh, hell, yes. From somewhere upstairs, probably not too far from that room you warned me about."

So, it wasn't his imagination. If he'd ever had the slightest hope that it was, Wayne had just taken that away.

"Did Joe hear them?"

"Now that's the strangest thing. I'd have sworn anybody in a six-county radius could have heard them, but he didn't seem to. Not even after he was in the house, upstairs damn it, with them pacing and grumbling. I'd swear he didn't hear a thing until I stepped up behind him."

"Damn it, Samuels, you took a hell of a chance staying in the house. Why didn't you go ahead and get out when you first heard them?"

Wayne turned to the door and ran skilled fingers over his repair work. "Because after I saw the doc's cousin coming through the woods, and I got over the first panic, I realized something that's about as strange as anything I've ever known. I mean it, Huerra. Whatever they are, and wherever they were, your watch-kitties weren't fussing at me."

It wasn't difficult to talk Annie into moving her bedroom upstairs, at least for a while, especially since she'd learned that someone had been looking in windows the night before. The rooms upstairs had their share of problems too, but eventually they decided on those at the end of the front hall, as far away from Marian's sitting room as it was possible to get. David saw her settled into the room at the end, right over the study.

While the only place David wanted to be was beside her, he knew that the time probably wasn't right for that. She'd rallied some while Wayne and Margaret remained at the house, probably for their benefit, but she had to be feeling battered still from the effects of her little jaunt through memory lane. So he took the room next to hers and settled himself onto the narrow white bed, fully believing he'd spend a sleepless, restless night.

The rooms were stuffy from having been shut up for years, so he'd raised the windows in his and left them opened just enough to let some fresh air in, and he left the door open so that he could hear anything approaching. A slight breeze played through the room, not so cold as to be unbearable, merely touching him lightly before moving into the hall. He tugged the blanket around his shoulders and listened to the sounds of the night, to the whisper of the breeze, to the memory of other nights, other cool breezes, to the memory of laughter, sweet, childish, and loving, but he couldn't remember whose. They beguiled him into the sleep he'd thought would elude him that night.

20

The wind teased Lucy's hair, dragging it across her face as she stood with the small crowd of mourners at the graveside. She held herself very still, ignoring the chill the wind now carried. Her right hand was warm, caught tightly in Walter's, but that was just about all of her that was.

Walter was here. Thank God he'd made it in time for the funeral. There'd been some doubt, even with all the work Reverend Jones had done to get him his emergency leave. As it was, her mama had convinced Reverend Jones to delay the service almost an hour until Walter arrived. She didn't think Walter would ever forgive himself if he'd missed his mother's funeral. She knew he'd have a hard enough time forgiving himself for not knowing Mrs. Briggs was so sick, even though she had made them all promise not to tell him.

He stood straight and tall and proud beside her after the brief graveside service, while friends stopped to shake his hand, to clap a comforting hand on his shoulder, to tell him what a fine woman his mother had been. And he thanked these people, even smiled at some of them, but his eyes had a funny closed-off look, like he wasn't really listening, as if he wasn't really there.

She knew where he was. She'd gone the same place when her papa died, when people who hadn't been his friend in life tried to tell her they had been.

Walter had come there for her and had brought her back. She would do the same for him. But not now. Now was the time for grieving, for saying good-bye. Not for celebration. But it would be soon; so much had to be done in the three days he had been allotted.

But finally all of the mourners were gone. Only Reverend Jones, Lucy and her mama, Walter, and the two men who would close the grave remained. Reverend Jones clasped Walter's hand one more time before leaving, and Mama stepped up.

"Now you come to our house, Walter Briggs. Sara would have wanted that."

"Yes, ma'am," he answered. This time when he smiled, it was real. "I can't thank you for all you did for my mama, Mrs. Hansom."

"Hush, now. There's no talk of thanks between family. And you are family. Have been for a long time." She pressed a key into his hand. "This is to Marian's car. It's parked just outside the gates. Now you hurry on back to your house and change out of that good uniform, gather up your things, and come on home. Lucy? You'll be going with him?"

"Yes, Mama."

"Good. Bring him home now. Real soon."

Walter's house was small and plain and had always been kept scrupulously clean until Sara Briggs took sick a week after he'd left to go to basic training at Fort Sill. The ladies of the church had come in and cleaned it— after it looked like she wasn't going to get any better, and Mama had moved her into their second best upstairs bedroom—but it wasn't clean like Mrs. Briggs had always kept it. And it didn't have the good smells that had always come from her kitchen or the feeling of home that somehow she had always given it.

Walter looked around the empty house and knew. "How long has she been gone from here?"

"A month," Lucy told him. "Mama couldn't convince her to come any sooner."

"And you didn't tell me?"

"I tried, Walter. I begged her to let me. But she was so proud of you. She didn't want to do anything to upset you; she didn't want you trying to get out because of her, and she knew you would if you ever guessed how sick she was."

"Yes. I would have."

Lucy stood just inside the front door studying him. Maybe his mama shouldn't have kept her secret from him; maybe she owed him the right to love her. But he looked so handsome, so right, standing tall and strong in the army olive green. She knew he hadn't had the wool uniform specially tailored, but it looked like he had. Just like the Sam Browne belt, the smart-looking tan leggings and the brown shoes—shiny enough to catch a reflection even after all the miles he'd worn them coming home— looked like they had been made just for him.

Walter belonged in the army. She knew he'd talked about using it as no more than a job. But that had changed. She'd read it—yes *read* it—in his letters, beyond the words he'd written. And he would have left it for his mama. He'd leave it for her if she wasn't careful. But she wasn't in the same situation as Sara Briggs had been. She was healthy and young, and she had her mama and all her mama's family to help her while he was gone.

But if he looked right in his uniform, he didn't look right in this house. Not any more. He'd taken his cap off and folded it, and now he slapped the soft fabric against his thigh as he looked into what had been his mama's bedroom.

She reached behind her and twisted the key in the front door. Yes. It was time to bring him back.

She walked up to him and lifted her hands to his tie. He looked startled for a moment, but she was smiling, and soon he did too. "Careful," he warned her. "That thing has to be ironed."

"You've learned how to do that?" she asked in mock alarm. "My, my, the United States Army must really be something special."

She slid her arms around him. It felt so strange to find wool and leather beneath her touch where always before she had found cotton, or just Walter. But she hugged him, and she held him close, and she knew it the moment he let go of his smile and let go of just a little of the pride that held him aloof and away from his pain.

"Blood brothers, Walter," she reminded him. "We've shared our blood, and we've shared our love, and we can share this. I can help you with this, like you've helped me so many times. Let me. Please."

Then he was holding her, tight. Tighter than he ever had. So tight she could feel the shudders racking through him.

"Lucy. Oh, my God, Lucy. She was so sick, and I didn't even know."

"Sshh," she told him. "She didn't want you to know. She loved you so much, and she knew you loved her. She wanted to give you this, Walter. We had to let her. And you have to accept it the way she meant it, with love. Miss her, yes. I know you will, but she wouldn't want you feeling guilty because you weren't here."

He hugged her again, a quick, fierce hug, and she felt

him pulling his strength back around himself because he couldn't let himself be weak very long. Not even with her. "How did you get to be so wise?" he asked.

"I had help. A skinny little redheaded boy taught me that I wasn't dumb. He taught me that someone besides my mama really can love me. He taught me to love. And Walter, I do love you. So much that sometimes I can't believe it's all coming from just the one person inside me."

She felt tears on her cheeks. She'd already done her crying for Sara Briggs. But Walter hadn't. Maybe he couldn't. But she could do it for him.

He brushed at her tears with incredibly gentle callused fingers. "I love you, Lucy Hansom."

"I know that. I've known that since the day you pulled out that nasty-looking knife and asked me to cut my finger."

"And I want to marry you," he said in a voice thickened by the tears he would not shed. "Today, tomorrow. Before I leave I want you wearing my name. I want everybody knowing you belong to me."

Lucy felt a chuckle building right alongside the sob that forced its way out of her. "I don't think there's going to be any doubt about that. At least not for very long."

He put her away from him slightly, frowning down at her. "What are you talking about?"

"I told your mama. I hope you don't mind that I told her before I told you, but she needed to know. She was happy, Walter, real happy, knowing that you're going to have me to love you all the rest of your life. And that you're going to have our baby to love you, too."

He looked at her for a moment longer, stunned into silence, before his whole face seemed to glow. "You're sure?"

Yes. She'd known he'd be happy. She nodded and touched the wide band of leather that belted his long jacket. "Just as sure as I am that I can't figure out how to get you out of this sophisticated harness."

He whooped and picked her up and spun her around, laughing. "Lucy, honey . . ." He set her on her feet and stroked his hand down over her belly before he knelt and pressed his face against it. "Give me a minute," he said, and she heard his words all choked with the emotion he hadn't let himself show before. "Give me a minute," he repeated, "and I'll give you a lesson in a most improper way to get a soldier out of his uniform."

Marian seldom came to the kitchen for any purpose other than to gather her meal and carry it into the dining room. When Walter and Lucy arrived at the Hansom house, though, hours later, after laughing and loving, and crying some as they stripped the rental house of the last of the personalities of Walter and Sara Briggs, Marian waited for them in the kitchen.

She rose from a chair at the round table and raked her eyes up and down the cotton and denim work clothes Walter had changed into. She held out her hand. "My key," she said.

Lucy had wondered about Marian's generosity; it had seemed completely out of character, and apparently it was. Walter juggled the duffel bag and bag of his clothes he carried into one hand, and held out the key to the woman. She snatched it away.

"I've already told Ellie," she said. "Now I'll tell you so there will be no chance for misunderstanding. That is my car; not hers, certainly not yours. The next time your mother takes it upon herself to lend it to someone, I will see that the person driving it is arrested."

She didn't wait for a response, but she did make a terrific exit, even if that exit had to be through a pantry.

Walter set his duffel and bag on the floor and took the small box containing his mother's treasures from Lucy's hands. "My God, what kind of hold does that woman have on your family? I thought she was bad enough before your father died, worse still when I left two months ago, but this? Lucy, why does your mother put up with her?"

Lucy shook her head. She didn't want to think about Marian now. She didn't know why her mother put up with her. But she did. But for the most part Mama had ignored her after finally telling her that she wasn't her maid, and any cleaning up Marian wanted done, she'd have to do herself.

But she was getting stranger every day. Long before Papa died, Marian had locked the bedroom off her sitting room. She hadn't complained when Mama had asked Walter to close off the windows so no one would accidentally look in and see the man in copper. But lately she had taken to unlocking the door and going in and sitting on the floor by his side. Aunt Marian. On the floor. And—Mama didn't know this—picking up pieces of shell or copper and holding them close while she rocked back and forth.

Marian thought they were hers. Lucy knew that. Her papa had made provisions for Aunt Marian in his will, leaving her some of his business holdings. The only problem was, by the time he died, there were no business holdings.

Only the dead man.

And Mama had been real clear about him. He was in the house, so he was part of the house. *Her* house. Enough people had died already. Mama was not going to let Marian even try to get rid of him again.

And she was not going to run the risk of young Joseph or one of the cousins accidentally wandering into the room where he lay in final rest. She'd changed the lock once already, but Marian had managed to get it open, and it was downright creepy the way she'd go in there at all hours of the day and night and *talk* to him. Just like he could hear her. Just like he'd *want* to hear anything she had to say to him.

"I don't want to talk about Aunt Marian." Lucy walked to his side at the table and took the small box from his hands. She ran her hands over it reverently as she set it on the table. It contained so little: Sara Briggs's wedding picture, her silver thimble and hand-carved ivory crochet hook, a few school papers Walter had given her years before. The few dishes and quilts, which they had transported in Marian's car and which now sat in a trunk in the barn. These were all that remained of the things Sara had considered special—so little compared to the pile of grave goods that had been buried with the man upstairs. Yet Sara was at peace. Was he?

Mama made up the big downstairs bedroom for Walter, the one she hadn't slept in since Papa died. She hugged him when they told her they were going to be married before he went back to Fort Sill. Lucy saw a glint of tears in her eyes, but they were happy tears. Mama wouldn't let herself cry any other kind.

The church folks had come and gone by the time Lucy and Walter got back to the house, but they had left their offerings of food. Mama had them all set out on the dining room table and sideboard. Now she took a bottle of her grandma's muscadine wine from the back of the buffet and three delicate stemmed glasses from the bow-fronted china cabinet. She poured each of them a glassful and raised hers. "I've thought of you as family for years. Now I'm pleased to welcome you as an official member. May the two of you be as happy together the rest of your lives as you have been till now."

Walter hugged Lucy, and then he hugged her mama. "Thank you, Mrs. Hansom. I couldn't ask for better family. I just wish—"

Lucy watched Walter change what he'd wish for in mid-sentence.

"I just wish there was some way I could repay you for all the good things you did for my mother."

Mama would say thank you, but payment wasn't necessary. Lucy had heard her say that too many times to think she would ever change. But she did.

"Actually, there is something," she said. "I'd planned to wait a little while before asking you, but it seems we don't have all that much time after all. I have the supplies in the attic; I've had them for months now. Walter, while you're home on leave, I really would appreciate it if you'd build me a wall."

Marian hated the wall. She hated Walter for building it, Lucy for helping, and Mama for asking for it. She screeched out her hatred the next morning until Mama took her arm and shook her and said in a cold, tight voice Lucy had never heard before, "Marian, be quiet, or you and your son are out of my house, forever, and damn the consequences."

Marian got quiet, watching sullenly from her green-striped couch until Joseph wandered into the room. Mama was real quick to close the door then, shutting Lucy and Walter in the room with the skeleton while Walter worked on framing in what would soon look like the back wall of a closet.

Walter rested his hammer on a cross bracing. "She wants to be able to get to him," he whispered. "To sell him?"

Lucy shook her head. "I don't know anymore.

Maybe. Maybe just to be near to him. But with this in place she won't be able to do either. Ever again."

He leaned against one of the many studs already in place. "Lucy, with this wall in place, we won't be able to get to him, either. We won't be able to return him, even if we figure out how, unless—"

"Unless what, Walter?"

"Unless we move him before I finish the wall. Unless we hide him somewhere safe until we can figure out what to do with him. Unless we convince Marian and— damn, I hate this—unless we convince your mama he's still here, behind this wall."

"Mama wouldn't mind us moving him. She thinks he belongs—"

"Where, Lucy? Where does he belong?"

But of course she didn't have the answer for that. "Not here," she said. "Not in a closed-off, dark room behind Aunt Marian's clothes."

"No. And your mama knows that. But she wouldn't want us to move him. Not because we're greedy or malicious or even disrespectful. But because she'd be afraid something would happen to us. And it might."

"Papa moved him before. Nothing happened then. But he came back. He always comes back."

"Maybe because no one's ever moved *all* of him. Not since he was brought here. We could do that."

"Where, Walter?"

"I don't know. But I could find out. Abe McPherson's got a telephone. I could make some calls, ask around, maybe talk to the people from the University of Oklahoma or the Historical Society who've been digging up at Spiro."

Lucy glanced down at the man on the litter. The only light in the room came from a small bulb hanging from a broken fixture. He'd been buried with pride and ceremony. Surely he deserved a better tomb than this. And if anyone could find out, Walter could. They were old enough now, big enough now to do something other than hide and watch. And nothing would happen to them. Nothing could happen to them if all they meant was to bring him peace, could it?

21

She was warm. Deliciously warm. Warm and safe. Anne didn't want to wake up, didn't want to open her eyes, didn't want to leave the cocoon of soft mattress and hard muscle. She sighed and turned, snuggling closer to the source of the warmth and felt an arm shift and reshape its hold on her.

An arm? Hard muscle?

Anne blinked open her eyes to dim, early morning light. Good grief. How had she gotten to David's room? To David's bed?

He looked down at her and let his bad-boy grin peek out. "You walked again last night, Annie."

"Oh, boy." She tried to turn her face away, not wanting him to see the embarrassment in hers, not wanting to see ridicule or rejection or even stoic acceptance in his.

"I heard a noise about three o'clock, looked up, and there you were in the doorway."

"Oh, boy," she repeated.

Her gown had ridden up. Her leg brushed against his leg. His bare leg. In turning, she had placed her hand against his chest. His bare chest.

"I thought you might have heard something, but when I spoke to you, you didn't answer. You did look down the hall once, but then you came in here, lifted the covers and crawled in as though you'd been doing it all your life."

"I'm sorry," she muttered, easing her leg away from his and trying to lift her hand.

He caught her hand and held it still above his heart. "I'm not. I knew last night that if you were going to walk in your sleep, I'd rather have you coming to me than going to . . . to him."

She felt his life pulsing beneath her touch. Life. Vibrant, vital life. His pulse grew stronger as she stared up into his eyes, seeing none of those things she'd been afraid of seeing. It was the strangest thing, but she had the feeling his heart beat just for her, that it beat in unison with hers. That it always had. That it always would. And that at this moment, he knew it, too.

"Annie, what's happening to us?"

A glib response wouldn't do here. He knew about physical attraction; so did she. And while, yes, her body was responding to his nearness as his was unmistakably responding to hers, his voice carried too much wonder, too much frustration, and too much confusion to be asking about something so obvious.

He raised his hand to her cheek and trailed his fingers to her throat. There, her pulse leapt beneath *his* touch.

"It took me a while to sort out what I was feeling when I saw you kneeling at his feet Friday night—even longer to admit it to myself. I was jealous. Jealous of a man who's been dead seven hundred years, give or take a century or two. Jealous, when I've no more than kissed you. Jealous, when there's not a hope in hell we can ever mesh our lives and our homes and our careers.

"So when you came to my door last night, when you came to my bed, why did it seem no different than when you went to him?"

There was no answer, glib or otherwise, for that. She could only stare into his eyes, letting him see her own wonder, frustration, and confusion. And need.

"Annie. Oh, God, Annie." He hauled her against him and found her mouth with his. "I don't want this," he muttered when he dragged his mouth from hers. "We don't need this. Not now. There's too much—too much . . ."

"I know," she said. But her hands were as greedy as his; her mouth as needy. Her body as feverish. "I know."

Later, she would wonder how she could have been so rash, how she could have responded to David with no more than a thought that she thrust to the back of her mind about birth control or protection of any kind. But at that moment, all she could do was respond, as though she had been responding to him all her life, as though she had been responding to him the seven hundred years, give or take a century or two, that he had just mentioned, as though his touch and their sharing was as vital to her—to each of them, to *both* of them—as the blood that thundered through his heart and hers.

"Believe me," she murmured against his throat. "I know."

When Anne awoke again, she was alone. The covers were tucked neatly up around her, and her red flannel nightgown lay across the foot of the narrow bed. A slight breeze, more chill than cool, came through the partially opened window. As did light. Enough light to tell her it was past time to get this day started.

Later, dressed and more or less put together for their outing that morning, she went in search of David. She smelled coffee and bacon before she reached the stair-well. She hesitated a moment with her hand on the newel post. The warrior lay in the other direction. Should she check on him first?

And do what, Annie? Ask him if he wants breakfast, too? Her hand clenched on the post as in her mind she heard David's voice, clearly mocking. Or was it her own? She shook her head and squared her shoulders and marched herself down the hall.

Wayne and Margaret had already arrived to keep vigil for the day. Wayne rose from his chair in a quaint, faintly courtly gesture when she entered the room.

David turned from his position at the stove and let his eyes give her a warmer welcome than his almost casual, "Good morning. Coffee's ready. One egg or two?"

"Good morning." Was she blushing? Good lord, she didn't blush. She couldn't let herself, because if she did all her freckles stood up and begged for attention. Maybe not. Margaret was looking at her, but it was a speculative look, not a knowing one.

And just how was she supposed to greet David, any-way?

Just like nothing had happened. Just like he greeted her. That decided, she headed toward the coffeepot. "Only one egg, please."

He grinned at her. Turned as they were, no one else could see that grin. And no one else could see the way he searched her features, as if making sure she was all right, or the wicked wink he sent her way even though he didn't seem at all assured that she was. "Coming right up. I found some juice in your freezer. Hope you don't mind that I made myself at home."

Wayne and Margaret already had full cups of coffee, still steaming, so Anne realized they must have arrived only a few minutes ago, probably while she was in the shower. She smiled at them and walked to the table. Wayne held a chair for her and only sat down after she did. "I could get used to treatment like this," Anne said.

David turned back to the stove and cracked an egg on the edge of the skillet. "You look like you could use a lot of it, too."

Margaret chuckled. "It does no good to fight it, Anne," she said. "So you might as well enjoy being cosseted. After yesterday, you certainly deserve it."

After yesterday. For a moment the room spun around her. She had forgotten. How had she forgotten? "Did anybody— Is he— How is he?"

Margaret reached over and lay her hand on Anne's, stilling her. "Blake came by our place this morning before he went off duty." she said. "The boy is still in critical condition, but it looks like he's going to make it."

Anne slumped in her chair. "Thank God."

Wayne shook his head. "The way Blake tells it, it's thank God, and you two."

"No. All we did was give rudimentary first aid, the kind anybody can give. The kind those people on the scene were already giving."

Wayne just stared at her. "Rudimentary first aid? Is that what you call taking that boy's fear away? Giving him hope?" He shot a glance at David. "Promising him an autographed baseball?"

"Here. Eat." David put a plate in front of her. The flatware was already on the table, as were butter and blackberry jelly.

He draped a hand on her shoulder for a moment before dragging out his own chair and sinking onto it. He waited only until she had finished her egg and bacon and spread butter and jelly onto a toasted English muffin.

"We don't have to do this today, you know," he said. "We can wait. You can rest."

She carefully set the muffin back on her plate. There was cosseting, and then there was babying. "I'm fine."

"I know you think you are, but you've had a series of— You had a pretty rough day yesterday—"

"Wait until when?" she asked. "It isn't that far, but if we don't go today, it will be Wednesday, or maybe even Saturday before I can take the time to make the trip."

They went. Anne telephoned first, to make sure that Marian Hansom was really a patient in one of the nursing homes in Texarkana. She found her registered in the third one she called.

David drove. "Are you upset with me?" he asked when they were deep in the mountains.

Upset with him? What was he talking about? "No, of course not. Why should I be?"

"Maybe because . . . because I took advantage of you when you were especially vulnerable. Maybe because you regret what happened between us."

She turned her head to look at him. Good lord, he was serious. "You didn't take advantage of me," she told him. "I knew what I was doing, and I wanted to do it. Whatever gave you the idea I regretted anything that we shared?"

He reached across the chasm of the console separating them and lifted her hand in his. "We should have driven your truck. There's a lot to be said for good old-fashioned bench seats."

Anne returned the pressure of his hand, and when he placed hers on his thigh so he could grip the steering wheel, she laughed softly and left her hand where he had placed it.

"That's more like it," he told her. She peered at him and then down at her hand.

"That too," David said with a chuckle, "but what I was talking about was your laugh. I've missed it."

"David, it's only been . . . "

"I've missed it," he repeated.

Anne knew that she had seen Marian Hansom before. Her childhood memories included one of an old, querulous woman in a hospital bed, but where, she couldn't remember. Probably Ellie Hansom's house. Surely her mother had taken her there. She certainly remembered hearing about her. Even if she hadn't heard much, the conversations in the past few days would have filled in any number of gaps.

That had to be why the slender white-haired woman in the wheelchair was such a surprise. Anyone who had acted as ugly as Marian reportedly had, ought to be ugly, not regally beautiful.

The staff at the small, private facility must have told Marian someone had inquired about her, because she was expecting them. She wore a simple silk shirt and skirt. Her hair, thinner now than it would have been in her prime, gleamed like silver in soft finger waves, and her makeup also echoed a restrained version of the style that had been popular in Marian's youth. A delicate lace shawl draped across her shoulders, and a lightweight, woven coverlet lay across the arm of the chair, waiting should she become chilled.

Crazy Aunt Marian looked every bit the regal matriarch granting an audience. "You wanted to see me?"

David stood a half-step behind Anne and waited for her to speak.

"Yes," Anne said. "I'm Anne Locke. My grandmother was Ellie Hansom's cousin Rebecca."

Marian cocked her head back and studied Anne's

face and hair. "Did the Briggs family manage to insinuate itself into the Hansom family after all? But no, I forgot. You're Katherine's bastard."

Anne felt the blow physically. David gripped her arm, holding her steady.

"Bastard." It was as though Marian tasted the word once again before spitting it out. "That's what they called my Joseph, you know. You're also the one who bought the house. I don't suppose you're here out of family loyalty or love, so perhaps we'd better go somewhere private. You. Yes you, young man. You may push my chair."

David hesitated, but he stepped to the back of Marian's chair. A single glance at her over Marian's head told Anne just where he'd like to push that chair, but he kept his voice calm. "Where?"

Marian directed them to a small, plant-filled room. "No one ever comes in here. There's no television. But shut the door. No one knows my business unless I tell them."

She wheeled herself across the quarry tile floor to a grouping of chairs and waited for them to join her. "You will forgive me if I don't offer refreshments." She nodded toward the rattan chairs. "Well, sit. I don't relish holding this or any other discussion while I have to look up at anyone."

Anne took the chair closest to Marian; David, the other.

"Well, what is it? Why did you drive all the way down here?"

Anne glanced around the room. The plants surrounding the casual, tasteful grouping of furniture were lush and well cared for; the spotless tile floor glowed; the many windows surrounding them gleamed. Anne had visited many nursing homes since starting medical school; this was probably the most luxurious she had ever seen. It was also, undoubtedly, the most expensive.

"This is a lovely facility," she said.

Marian's eyes glittered and she let a small, satisfied smile crease her carefully made-up face. "My grandson takes quite good care of me."

Now that was an understatement. And could Joe really have the kind of money a facility like this charged? "He must love you very much."

Marian's smile faded. "What do you want?"

Anne leaned forward. "I want to know what you know about the man in the hidden room."

Marian sucked in a sharp breath as she drew back. She was quiet for so long Anne began to be alarmed, but just as she reached for the woman's arm, Marian laughed. Harshly. Violently. And Crazy Marian peeked out from behind the regal facade.

"You found him. You found him and you don't know what to do with him. Watch out, Anne Locke. Only I have the key. Only I have the right to him. And look what they did to me."

"Is he why Joe has been trying to buy the house from me? Why he's been sneaking around the outside of the house in the dark? Why yesterday he actually broke into the house?"

"He mustn't. He mustn't."

"Miss Hansom," David said. "It isn't a matter of what Joe must or must not do. He's done it. Did you send him?"

"You didn't tell him? You weren't fool enough to tell anybody?"

Anne sighed. "No. We didn't tell Joe. But why shouldn't we? You obviously have."

Now Marian smiled again. "But not where he is. Don't you see? I promised Joe a fortune, but only I know where he is."

Now Joe's actions toward his grandmother made more sense. Anne hated that she felt easier attributing him with greed rather than familial love, but that hat fit the man she had come to know a lot better.

"Joe mustn't know. The cats won't like that. They're very protective of him, you know. Even with me. Even with me.

"I loved him." Marian tilted her head to one side. In the shade of a leafy palm she looked almost young. "A long time ago, I loved him. And then he took that bitch to mate instead of me. We ruled the heart of this country from the Great Lakes to the Gulf. But we could have ruled the world. Together we would have ruled the world. I got even with him, though, and with her. She thought she was so smart with her herbs and her potions, but my source knew more than simply how to heal. He knew how to take life slowly, steadily. I would have killed her, too, but by then I couldn't get close enough. The cats wouldn't let me. The curse wouldn't let me. But they wouldn't stop me from killing those around her. They couldn't stop me from letting her die.

"And now he's mine. Forever and ever mine.

"All I wanted was the box. I took the things Lucy and that Briggs boy had stolen back to the room, and I picked up the box. I was going to take it with me while I drove to the country. It seemed fitting, you know, that I get rid of her picture, too. The picture should have been mine. And the box should have been mine. It will be mine once he realizes that I only did what I had to do. Once he tells the cats to leave me alone.

"They kill anyone who bothers him. You do know that, don't you?"

Anne nodded. *Crazy as a bessie bug?* Katherine didn't know the half of it.

"Is that what happened to Lucy Hansom and Walter Briggs?" David asked. "You said they had stolen some things from him."

Marian looked up at him. A shadow crossed her face, but she smiled. "You want to know what happened to them?" she asked shrewdly.

"I watched Walter build the wall. Ellie thought she was so smart to close off the room. She thought I wouldn't be able to get to him. I've come across lifetimes to reach him; why should one wall stop me?

"And it wouldn't have stopped that greedy daughter of hers either. I overheard Lucy and Walter planning to take him away before they closed the wall—take him away and not say anything to Ellie or to me, just let us think he was still back there.

"Didn't they realize I would know? Didn't they realize I couldn't let them do that?"

"What happened to them?" David asked.

Marian pulled back in her chair. "Why, the curse got them. I told everyone that. But they wouldn't listen to me."

David leaned forward. "You actually saw the cats kill Walter Briggs and Lucy Hansom? Where? And why didn't you go for help at that time?"

Marian dragged her head from side to side, slowly, deliberately. "Oh, no you don't. I know what you're trying to do, but I won't let you.

"I was in the hospital for weeks, you know. And Ellie went with me. She didn't want to, but her pride wouldn't let her go off and leave me alone, even if it meant missing the wedding. And she stayed with me. Weeks and weeks and weeks. When we came back to her house, there was no sign of them. She knew they were dead. She just didn't want to believe it. But she got even with me. She sent my Joseph away. She said she couldn't take care of him and me, too. And she made me watch as she finished the wall and locked the closet and left me so close to him and unable even to see him.

"Oh, yes. She got even."

She heard David's sigh. Somewhere in Marian's story ran a thread of truth, but where?

"Got even for what?" David asked. "Why did she keep you in her house when obviously there was no love between the two of you, Miss Hansom?"

"It's Mrs. Hansom," Marian said coldly. "And she kept me because she couldn't bear the thought of the scandal or the shame it would bring to Lucy and to her if anyone knew that I'd married Ralph before he ever met her, that he only married her because of her family's money, and that he promised me he'd leave as soon as he had acquired enough of the mineral interests, enough of the land, and later, enough of the artifacts that so enchanted him. But he didn't. No. The curse got him too. But if he'd listened to me . . . "

Anne sat bolt upright in her chair. All sorts of rumors had been whispered in the family, but never this. "You're saying that Ralph and Ellie weren't legally married?"

Marian smiled. "Is bigamy legal?"

"And this is what you held over her to stay in her house, with the man everyone thought was her husband?"

"No, no, dear. Blackmail is only good if it's used properly. It's what I held over Ralph. Ellie didn't know. Then."

David dropped his hand on Anne's shoulder, calming her, as he took over the questions. "But she obviously found out. How?"

"How? While building that damned wall she searched the room. My room. And she found my marriage license. She was stunned, but not surprised. She burned it. In my large crystal ashtray that had been empty for months because she refused to buy me cigarettes. She burned it and then she bought paint for the house. Purple. 'A fitting color for a brothel,' she said. 'Isn't that what they call a place where whores live?'

"I almost died when she got sick. Joseph was dead. My sweet Joseph that she turned against me died working on the dam for that lake. It wouldn't have happened if Ellie had let him stay. I would have seen that he got to college, that he didn't have to work like a slave for wages. But he was dead. And no one came to see me but his son, Joe. I'd talk to him; I always knew how much I could tell him and how much I couldn't. He's more like me than his father ever was, but that's all right. I understand that. I know how to use that."

Anne swallowed her distaste. "So he keeps you here in exchange for the promise of a fortune later."

Marian nodded, and her eyes glittered.

"After you die?"

Again, Marian nodded.

"Tell me," Anne asked. "If everyone who tries to claim this treasure dies, just how is Joe going to collect?"

"Now dear, why on earth will I ever have to worry about that?"

Anne stood. She'd been in this woman's presence too long. David reached for her hand but Anne stepped away from him. She glanced at him and knew he had more questions to ask, but she didn't care how much more Marian could or might tell them; she'd heard more than she wanted to hear. She had to leave. She didn't want him staying with this vicious old woman either, but he would. She knew he would. Just as she knew she wouldn't argue with him in front of Marian Hansom. She gave him a brief, tight smile and walked from the room, but in her heart she was running as fast as she could, as far away from Marian Hansom as possible.

David joined Anne a few minutes later at the Blazer. Without speaking, he took her in his arms and just held her.

"I'm going to paint the house," she said against his jacket.

He rubbed his hand over her back but remained silent.

"The first few days that are warm enough and clear enough, I'm going to have a crew up there. I thought she was just eccentric. I could live with that. But my God, what she must have gone through. Poor Aunt Ellie."

"You have to know that woman is capable of making up any story she wants to serve any purpose she might have."

"You think she was lying about being married to Ralph?"

"Annie, all she had to do to prove it was to write for a duplicate marriage license. And if she couldn't do it, she could have told Joe where to write and had him do it."

"Do you think she did? Tell Joe?

"I don't know. Would it be better for him politically to have an unmarried ancestor, or a bigamous one?"

"Poor Joe," she said, "what a quandary."

"That's better." David said, easing his hand to the nape of her neck and massaging the tension knotted there.

She sighed and relaxed into his touch before she opened her eyes to find him looking down at her with a gentleness she had felt so often coming from him. Felt, but not recognized. Needed, but not returned. "You're so good for me," she whispered.

"I try to be, Annie. I try."

"What are we going to do?"

And he knew without asking what she meant. Out of all of the problems facing them, he zeroed in on the one that should have been the easiest to solve. But wasn't. *What are we going to do about us?* What were they going to do about the attraction between them when his vacation was over, when he had to leave, and she couldn't. "I don't know, Annie."

"Kiss me?" She couldn't believe she'd said it. Kiss me. Here. In the parking lot in front of anyone who happened to look. But she had. And meant it. And wanted it regardless of who might be watching.

"And take away the taste of our visit with Marian?"

Was that why? As she looked into his eyes she knew that was a part of it. But only a part. "Yes," she said, knowing she had to be honest with him. She felt his arms tense around her, saw his eyes begin to take on a hardness alien to the David he had shown her, and knew she couldn't leave him with less than the complete answer. "Yes," she repeated. "That, too."

There was no question that night where either of them would sleep. While Anne readied for bed, David made one last sweep of the yard and the locks on the windows and doors. Then they went up the stairs together, to the room at the end of the front hall where she had begun the night before. It was cold, and Anne shivered in her long robe and flannel nightgown. David opened one window just a crack; Anne switched on the electric blanket she had brought upstairs, shed her robe, and crawled between frigid sheets.

David gave her one of his lethal grins as he scooted in beside her. "You don't really think you're going to need that blanket, do you?"

Anne swallowed once and looked at him. No. He

didn't really feel any humor; he was only trying to distract her from the path her thoughts had taken. And why? Unless his thoughts had gone there, too.

And why now had her thoughts chosen that path? She'd known from the beginning his time here was limited. Why, tonight, had that taken on such sinister overtones? But it had. When he moved closer to her, she raised her hands to his face. "You're going to leave me, aren't you? As soon as your time is finished here, you'll go back to Dallas, back to your life."

He pulled her close and bent his head to rub his cheek against her hair. "I don't know what I'm going to do, Annie, and that's the God's truth." His arms tightened fractionally. "Blake offered me a job."

Was that the answer? The answer to *what*? What was wrong with her tonight that made her see everything so fatalistically?

"Could you be happy as a county cop? Could you really live in a small town with all of its limitations and none of the city's advantages and not go stark raving crazy?"

"I don't know. What do you want me to say, Annie? That I love you? I don't know that, either. I only know that I've never felt this way about another woman. If I hadn't met you I wouldn't even have considered Blake's offer. If I hadn't met you I probably would already be back in Dallas, cursing my leave, prowling through all the alleys of my life trying to find out what I was going to do with the rest of it."

"Sshh," she whispered, stopping his flow of words with gentle fingers across his lips. Did she want him to say he loved her? Or would that cause more problems? "I only wanted you to know I understand. I— I wanted you to know that I . . . I don't expect more. I wanted you to know that I can't leave."

There. She'd said it. She'd warned him not to care too much. So why did it feel as though that wasn't what needed to be said? Why did she feel as though what she wanted was to beg him never to leave her again?

"I know, Annie," he said. "If I ever had any doubts about that, I lost the last one yesterday."

Well, damn it, she was crying, and her tears felt like ice on her cheeks. Why was she crying? She'd had to reassure him that she wasn't asking for forever, hadn't she? Because forever wasn't for them. Their meeting was a fluke, an accident, something that never should have happened, wasn't it?

Now he lifted his fingers to her face and traced her tears.

"Ah, damn it, Annie. We'll get through this. We'll find a home for your skeleton and scrape that damned purple paint off your house. You'll be happy here because this is where you need to be. And if you don't want to practice medicine, if you want to make jewelry, that's okay too. You're strong, sweetheart, strong enough to know yourself. Strong enough to do what's right for you."

She sniffed once and felt a sob bubble out. He was so good for her. So good to her.

"And if I want to be with you?"

With gentle pressure beneath her chin, he lifted her face toward his. "I'm here, Annie. With you. *Is* that what you want?"

She felt the soft brush of his breath against her forehead. Carefully, cautiously, she lifted her hand to his chest and felt his heart beating beneath her palm. For her. With her.

"Yes," she whispered. "That is exactly what I want."

22

Monday morning came all too soon. Anne rode to the clinic with Margaret, and they left David and Wayne discussing painters and the problems of stripping the purple paint from the house and replacing it in the erratic November weather, and probably Joe Hansom, although both men were careful not to mention his name as Anne was gathering up keys and bag and coat.

Any Monday at the clinic, but especially one after a four-and-a-half-day holiday, ought to have been hectic. It was hectic, for about an hour and a half, but primarily because a half-dozen patients without appointments were waiting for the doors to open, and Nellie didn't show up. Working together, Anne and Margaret pulled files and shuffled patients from the reception area to examination rooms, filled out billing slips, and grabbed the phone. Eventually, though, the small crowd thinned, the phone quieted, and Margaret signaled she would make coffee as Anne saw the final waiting patient.

Bobby Preston sat on the examination table, bouncing his dangling feet back and forth as he drummed out a vaguely military rhythm on the metal base of the table with his heels. His mother stood against the back wall, holding his jacket and looking harried.

Anne leaned against the closed door and manufactured a stern frown for this tiny terror. "Well, tiger, what have you done this time?"

He held out his arm and the towel wrapped around it. "Darned old stitches just came out."

Anne glanced at his mother and lifted her hand to her mouth to try to hold back a chuckle. It wouldn't do to let Bobby think she was laughing at him; at eight, he had an abundance of male pride. Toni Preston understood that all too well. She had clasped her own hand across her mouth, and her eyes wore an expression of equal parts chagrin, frustration, and love for this male creature who seemed bent on driving her crazy. Anne exchanged a brief, surreptitious smile with her before she advanced on the boy.

"I guess I'd better see what damage those stitches did. Just came out, you say? All by themselves?"

"Well . . . almost."

Anne lifted the towel and studied her once neat row of sutures. "And the bandage? Did it come off by itself, too?"

Bobby gave another bang to the table with his heel and looked away from her, staring steadily at the bright red thumbtack she had stuck into the wall for her younger patients to focus on while she looked into their eyes. "I kind of . . ." His words got lost in a maze of mumble. Anne waited. When she remained silent, he grimaced at her. "I kind of sold it."

Anne choked. Toni Preston was having a similar reaction. "You . . . You *kind of* sold it? A bloody bandage?"

"Yeah." His face split in a gap-toothed grin. "I cut it up in a bunch of pieces. I got more for it than for just a look at my stitches."

Anne couldn't help it. She reached out and ruffled his hair. "Oh, Bobby. Bobby, Bobby, Bobby, what am I going to do with you?"

"Sew me back up?"

She nodded. "You've got that right. I hope you got enough out of your venture into capitalism to make this worthwhile, because it's going to hurt."

He nodded too, solemnly. "That's what Mom said. She promised me ice cream if I don't say any bad words." He stuck out his jaw. "So go ahead, Doc. I can take it."

Margaret slipped into the room as Anne finished replacing Bobby's bandage and pulled his sleeve into place over it. "Don't sell this one, Bobby," she warned. "And don't let these stitches escape. There's a limit to how many times I can stick a needle through your hide and still have enough skin to hold the thread."

He giggled at that, and Toni stepped forward to drape his jacket over his shoulder. "Don't worry, Dr. Locke. His father has already explained just what will happen if he sells anything else without getting permission first."

Anne chuckled again, and bent to give Bobby a quick hug. "See you in a week, tiger. And not a day before. Got that?"

He shrugged out of her hug but grinned at her. "Got it."

Anne started to follow the Prestons to the front desk to take care of the checkout procedure, but Margaret stopped her. "Exam room two," she said softly. "I'll take care of Toni."

Another patient? Anne hadn't heard anyone else come in. But then, she hadn't been paying a whole lot of attention to anything except an eight-year-old heart stealer.

No chart waited in the slot outside the closed door of

exam room two. Anne frowned. This wasn't like Margaret. Still frowning, she opened the door.

Nellie sat on the chair at the small built-in desk. Huddled there. With her face turned toward the wall, and her shoulders hunched.

"Nellie?"

The young woman turned slowly. When Anne saw her face, she crossed the few steps and knelt in front of her. "Oh, God, Nellie. What happened to you?"

"I'm sorry. I shouldn't have come here. I didn't know where else to go."

"Oh, honey." Carefully, not knowing the extent of Nellie's injuries, Anne took the young woman in her arms.

Nellie held herself erect within Anne's loose embrace. "I thought I was free of him," she said in the emotionless voice of one who had endured too many violent emotions. "I thought at last I could make a life for myself and for Lilly."

"A man did this to you?" Anne asked in shock. But she wasn't really surprised, was she? David's words of Thanksgiving day played through her mind. "Someone you know did this?"

Nellie's only answer was a stifled sob.

"Is Lilly all right? Where is she?"

"I couldn't risk taking her to her regular sitter. I called Gretta Tompkins and asked if she could keep her today. I didn't tell her why. I didn't get out of the car when I took her out there. I told her—I told Lilly not to say anything. I can't put my baby through this. What am I going to do?"

Anne drew back and brushed Nellie's hair away from her battered face. "First, I'm going to examine you and treat what needs to be treated, and then we're going to call Blake and have him put that bastard where he belongs. Behind bars."

"No!"

The sheer panic in Nellie's voice rocked Anne back on her heels. "No?" she asked softly. She heard the exam-room door open and looked up to see Margaret slip inside and lean against the closed door. "Nellie, you can't let him get away with this."

"No." Nellie grabbed her arm. "You don't understand. He'll take Lilly away from me. He promised me that."

Anne glanced up at Margaret. "He can't do that, honey."

"Yes. Yes, he can. He got me evicted. I don't have a home. I can't work—"

"Sshh." Anne rose to her feet and held out her hand for Nellie. "It will be all right," she promised. "Somehow we'll make it all right. Now let's get you put back together."

Anne's tiny office contained a couch, which had as its only redeeming factor a sublime comfort. After assuring herself that Nellie's injuries were painful but not threatening, Anne gave the young woman acetaminophen and a mild muscle relaxant and insisted she lie down. Now Nellie slept a tortured sleep, covered by a light afghan that one of the grandmothers Anne treated had given her as a welcoming gift.

Margaret had finally found the time to make coffee. Anne joined her near the coffeepot in the supply room at the back of the building and held her mug in both hands, aware of the chill in the unfinished room. Aware of the chill in her.

"I want to hurt someone," she said. "I never thought I'd say that, but I think I would take great pleasure in hurting whoever it was who did this to Nellie."

"Yes." Margaret didn't say more. She didn't have to.

"She says she's been evicted. She needs a place to go. I have the room . . . "

"That's not a good idea, Anne."

"I know. I can't jeopardize her or Lilly by bringing them into that house until we—" She broke off abruptly. Margaret didn't know; no matter how much it seemed as though she was as deeply involved with the man in the closet as Anne, she wasn't.

"Yes," Margaret said again.

"Do you know who it is?" she asked, suspicious of Margaret's easy acquiescence. And then another doubt struck her. "We can keep her safe, can't we? We can protect her?"

Margaret stared up at the ceiling. "We have room for them; we can see that no one harms them."

"But Wayne— Excuse me, Margaret, but I got a clear impression that Wayne is extremely careful about who he allows near him. How will he feel about you inviting two almost strangers into your house?"

Margaret gave her a twisted smile. "Wayne knows suffering, and he knows refuge. He's really much better than when he first came home. Besides, he's a real sucker for a little kid, and Lilly's already captured a piece of his heart. It will be all right. It will be more than all right. It just might be what he needs to finish bringing him back into the world."

The town fathers' generosity hadn't extended so far as to provide carpet for the unseen portions of the clinic, so the sound of a man's booted footsteps echoed through the hallway. Anne glanced in alarm at Margaret, forgetting immediately that she hadn't completely answered her questions. Margaret calmly reached across the counter and picked up a new, unopened bottle of ketchup by its neck and held it up loosely, warily, more or less like a baseball bat.

"Anne? Annie? Are you back here?"

Both women relaxed when they recognized David's voice. Margaret smiled sheepishly and looked at the bottle in her hand.

"Yes. Back here," Anne called out before cocking an eyebrow at Margaret. Stately looking Margaret. "Neat trick," she said. "I'll have to remember that."

Margaret shrugged. "A long-necked beer bottle makes a fine weapon. At least it did back in the days of my misspent youth. There is a resemblance."

Anne had both hands over her mouth to stifle her laughter, and Margaret was still looking with dazed confusion at the ketchup bottle she gripped by the neck when David rounded the corner.

He glanced first at Anne and then at Margaret. Anne saw the moment he considered the bottle as a weapon and then dismissed that idea. Margaret. No way. Or was there? "Is everything all right back here?"

And suddenly it wasn't funny anymore. Anne shook her head. "Someone beat up Nellie."

"Son of a bitch! How is she? Is Lilly okay? What did Blake say? Has he caught the bastard?"

Margaret quite carefully replaced the bottle on the counter. "Lilly is fine, or at least safe with Gretta Tompkins. Nellie won't let us call in the police."

"Why the hell—"

"Sshh," Anne whispered. "Nellie's asleep in my office."

"Was it the same guy?"

Margaret cocked her head at David in a silent question.

"David told me Thanksgiving day he thought Nellie had been abused," Anne told her before answering David. "I don't know. Probably. She said she thought she was free of him."

"Damn!"

Which echoed Anne's sentiments exactly. "What brought you down here? Something wonderful, I hope, like telling me to pick out paint colors."

"Oh. Oh, hell."

No. Not wonderful. She braced herself.

"Frances called. She's set up a meeting."

Anne slumped against the cabinet. "Oh, hell." That, too, echoed her sentiments. "When?"

"Today. This afternoon."

"This afternoon? I can't take the time right now—"

Margaret looked from David to Anne. "Does this have something to do with that room upstairs and the reason why Wayne has been patrolling your house but barely tolerates my being there?"

"Yes." Anne's voice was almost gone. "Yes."

"Then you can take the time. You only have two firm appointments this afternoon. Neither one of them is critical. I'll call and reschedule."

"Why today, David?" Anne asked. "Why not tonight? Or Wednesday afternoon?"

"She said this was the only time the museum rep could make it."

"And you believe her?"

"Yes. It's the rep I'm not too sure about."

"So what do we have to do?"

"Excuse me," Margaret said. "Do you really want me hearing this?"

At their stunned silence, she grimaced. "Thought so. Go. Talk about it in private. But do one thing first. I'll keep Nellie with me, but I took a look out the back door a while ago. Her car is there, and unless I miss my guess, she managed to get back in her house long enough to grab what's really important to her. The car doesn't need to stay in sight, here, or anyplace else, until we're sure she's safe. Take it back to your place and stash it. Okay? Then go do what you have to do, and if it's half as dangerous as Wayne's actions make me believe, then for God's sake, be careful."

Anne drove Nellie's Escort to her house. David followed closely. When she reached the top of her driveway, she glanced around. Even behind the house, the car could be spotted if someone were really looking for it. She hesitated only a moment before she drove to the old barn at the back of the drive and stopped in front of its doors.

David walked to the side of the car, and she cranked the window open. "Inside?" he asked.

She wondered at the reluctance she heard in his voice. "Isn't the building sound enough?" she asked.

"Yeah," he said. "Yeah. I guess it is that."

He unbarred the doors and opened them, and Anne drove through them into the shadowed interior. She'd forgotten how grim it was inside, had almost forgotten the hole in the roof. She stepped out of Nellie's car and locked it before giving in to a curiosity that approached reluctant fascination to look around.

Fallen leaves. Pieces of discarded furniture. An open, abandoned trunk. An ancient, dead car.

Almost without realizing what she was doing, she circled Nellie's Ford and headed to the other Ford that sat neglected and lonely, lord, so lonely, beneath the overhanging loft.

"Annie?"

David had waited at the doors. Now he entered the barn and put his arm over her shoulder, stopping her forward progress.

"That car?" Anne asked. "I wonder how long it's been here."

"It hasn't been tagged since 1941."

"'41? When Marian fell? Do you suppose it was hers?"

"Maybe. That might explain it. It was a pretty spiffy model when it came out back in '35. Would it have been in Ellie to let it sit here and rot, maybe remind Marian every once in a while that it was out here?"

"Or like Mom said, for Marian to refuse to allow her to sell it?"

She felt a shudder work through him. He was wearing a windbreaker, but in here, out of the weak sun, the air seemed colder than outside. Much colder. "Let's go in the house," she said on a shudder of her own. "I want to hear what Frances said."

"Yeah. Good idea. Go on in and I'll get these doors closed."

Anne hesitated on the back porch and looked back at David as he worked at putting the bar back across the now closed doors. Firmly putting it back. But when he joined her on the porch and they went into the warmth of the kitchen he said nothing about his puzzling actions.

Wayne nodded at her and left them alone in the kitchen.

David put his hands on her shoulders. "The rep wants to see a picture of the burial, and a few of the actual pieces."

It took a moment for his words to register. "A few of the pieces? The whole idea was to find someplace where it wouldn't have to be separated, ever, and their representative wants to see *a few* of the pieces?"

"Yes. That's what he wants. Actually, he was more specific than that. He wants samples of shell, pottery, copper, and the skeleton itself."

She couldn't do it. She couldn't go in that room and tear loose a bone for someone to poke and pry at. But somehow, worry for her safety and David's seemed a more valid argument than her reluctance to play ghoul. "And just how are we supposed to get them there without getting ourselves killed?"

"We don't have to go, Annie. We can bring him here. For that matter, you can call Joe, tell him where his grandmother's treasure is and let him have it and the responsibility for it today. Right now. But I thought you wanted to find a way, a safe and reasonable way for him to be at peace and yet of value to the scientific community. And it seems to me that Frances's call might be that way. Or it might not. The only way we're going to find out is to meet with this man. Away from here, in case he's not able to meet your requirements. And the only way he's going to be sure of what we have is if we take him samples."

"And how do we do that? How in God's name do we do that?"

"I think I know."

She stepped back, just looking at him. He dropped his hands from her shoulders and let her go.

"Why didn't something happen to us when we brought the pieces downstairs, or to you or Margaret when you took them to be mailed, or for that matter to an unsuspecting mail carrier?"

"All right," she said slowly. "Why?"

"I think it must have something to do with the dirt that's so prevalent up there. I'm not sure what, but something. We didn't clean the pieces. But when they came back, they had been cleaned. Maybe the dirt— I know it's crazy, but what the hell about this whole thing isn't? Maybe the dirt acts as some sort of connective tissue. As long as it's there, with the piece, some . . . supernatural force tells the cats it's okay. Or maybe just doesn't tell them it isn't."

"So as long as we leave an amount of dirt on each piece, we should be safe?"

"Yeah."

"And if you're wrong?"

"I'll go alone. But I'm not wrong."

He'd go alone? Did he really think she'd let him do that? Take the risk of being trapped in a closed car on a mountain road with—with . . . Oh, no. If nothing else, she'd go just so she could throw everything out the window if they were threatened. But she'd argue that later. "How can you be so sure you're not wrong?"

He looked at her in stark despair. "Because I'm a stupid, arrogant, ignorant son of a bitch, Anne. Because in spite of what had already happened, I didn't realize the danger I was putting you in. I've already proved this theory."

"What?"

"Yeah. Saturday. I took a gorget with us when we went to Spiro."

23

Anne sat stiffly erect in the split and sprung passenger seat of the Blazer. In her lap she held a sturdy, square box with its flaps securely closed. Inside, in a nest of crumpled paper for protection of the items, and a generous layer of dirt for protection of a different kind, they had placed an engraved, intact conch shell, a delicate pottery cup no taller than three inches, a small rock crystal pipe bowl in the shape of a jaguar, an engraved copper plate from the warrior's right shoulder, and one of his earspools showing the image of what she could only describe as an abstract elephant.

The museum representative had requested a bone, but Anne had flatly refused to separate any of the skeleton. Instead, she had moved the copper covering the right femur and knelt by that bone with a yardstick as David took a picture with the Polaroid camera he had picked up at the drugstore in town before he came to the clinic for her. That photograph and three others, each taken carefully to show the burial in its best light but mask its surroundings, were now tucked securely into the pocket of her jacket.

She slipped her hand into her pocket and touched them.

Were they doing the right thing?

David glanced at her as she shifted in her seat. Without speaking, he reached across the narrow console and took her hand. He clasped it tightly and pressed it against his thigh. Beneath the starched crisp denim, he was warm, so warm, living flesh and muscle, with life's blood pulsing through him. When he died, as he must, as they all must . . .

Her fingers dug into his thigh as that thought lodged in her heart. Of course he would die. Of course she would. That was a given, a part of the journey.

"What is it?" he asked.

"I was—" She turned slightly in the seat to look at him. The box grew heavy against her thighs. The pictures in her pocket burned her fingers. He would leave her. She'd known that since the first day. They'd talked about it last night. She just hadn't thought of that leaving in terms of death. She shivered, and he gripped her hand, lending her warmth.

"I was just wondering if, oh, say a thousand or so years in the future, someone will be digging up our bones and analyzing the innerspring mattresses and custom coffins we'll probably be buried in to try to determine what we ate and worshiped, how we lived, how we died."

"And if they do?"

"I guess it will mean that the civilization we know now didn't survive."

"Yeah. Probably. But it won't matter to us, Annie. Not by then. Just as it can't matter to your warrior. We'll be dead. Just like he's dead. And the spirit that animates us will be long gone from the empty shell that housed it. Just like it is from his."

His voice took on a new intensity. Who was he trying to convince? Her? Or himself?

"He's bones, Annie. Just bones. And because his burial survived, the memory of a way that is as dead as he is has a chance for survival. I don't know what this is that's protecting the shell that remains, but that's all it is. A shell. The life, the essence that was him, is gone. The civilization that honored him in burial is gone. All that remains is a small collection of *things*. Things that if shared can give the memory of that civilization a semblance of life. But not your warrior, Annie. Not as he truly was. He will never live again."

No. He wouldn't. She turned her hand in David's and interlaced their fingers. It was foolish, probably even dangerous; he couldn't drive that way for long. But right now, she needed the connection.

The museum and park were closed on Monday and Tuesday. Frances had explained that to them. She had also suggested that the closed museum would give them the privacy and the anonymity they insisted upon for their meeting.

Two cars waited in the parking lot. One, an elderly pickup of indeterminate years, probably belonged to Frances or to her grandparents. The other, a big Mercedes sedan with Oklahoma tags but a prefix Anne didn't recognize, had to belong to the museum rep. David parked in a slot well away from both vehicles and sat frowning at the Mercedes for several seconds after he had turned off the key to the Blazer.

"Is there a problem?" Anne asked at his continued silence.

He shook himself and turned to her. He lifted his hand and brushed a stray curl back from her cheek. "Probably not," he said. "Are you ready?"

Was she? Somehow, Anne didn't think so. But she

had to be. She gave David a quick nod and an equally quick smile.

His fingers lingered on her cheek. "It will be okay," he promised. "Somehow. Some way." And she wanted to believe him. Oh, how she wanted that.

Frances opened the outer door only moments after David's knock. She glanced at the box Anne carried but didn't reach to take it. "I've set up a table in the room where we normally project the slide show. He's waiting." She closed and locked the door behind them. "I— He just got here a few minutes ago. He's . . . He's . . . Dr. Tilman apparently was not able to come. This man is not who I expected."

"Do his credentials check out?" David asked.

"Yes. Oh, yes. There's no doubt he's who he says he is. I've seen him at a distance a number of times. But I took the liberty of telling him that I had to wait for you to contact me because I didn't know how to contact you."

"You don't trust him?"

"I don't know. Dr. Tilman, yes. I'd trust him with my life and everything I own. But there's something—" She grinned ruefully. "I get paranoid periodically, and downright offensive when people look right at me and don't see me. I could be wrong. I have been before."

David nodded and draped his arm around Anne, and they walked into the exhibit hall. In front of the windows, Anne paused for a moment, looking out at the mounds. Timeless. Quiet. But somehow, underlying the sense of peace the park tried to portray, she sensed something ominous waiting. Just waiting.

"Annie?"

She glanced up at David. He too was looking out over the park, toward Craig Mound and its stair-step companions. She straightened within the loose embrace of his arm. "I'm ready."

The man seated at a table in the adjacent room looked as though he would be at home in the car in the parking lot. He rose gracefully when they entered the room and closed the folio of pottery artifacts that had been placed on the table. Although Anne hadn't had much money of her own, she had been exposed to it, lots of it, during her years in Chicago. Anthony had come from a monied background and during their courtship, brief though it had been, had insisted on dragging her to charity fund-raisers and intimate gatherings, either truly small ones or those with only a few hundred or so of the host's closest friends.

She took quick inventory of the man who had insisted on seeing them so quickly. Thousand-dollar suit, five-thousand-dollar watch, hand-tailored silk shirt, custom-designed tie, special-order-only Italian shoes, two-hundred-dollar haircut, subtle more-precious-than-gold aftershave or cologne.

And he took a quick and equally thorough inventory of them. Anne had wanted to change into what in Chicago she had laughingly called her going-to-the-bank clothes, the kind that told the man whom you were begging for money, for yourself or your clinic or your favorite charity, that you really didn't need it. She'd thought that perhaps that would give them better footing in their negotiations.

"Why do we need a better footing?" David had asked. "Annie, you have what he wants. That's all the bargaining power you can possibly need. Besides, you might not see the real him if you go dressed for success."

So they had worn jeans, casual sweaters, and casual shoes. David, of course, was as starched and pressed as he always was except when dressed for physical labor. And she—well, the jeans were only six months old, and they were clean, and still, mostly, blue. But everything she and David wore could have been purchased in any small town in the state for a lot less money than the museum rep's shoes. And he knew it.

She watched the appraisal and the faint, barely perceptible dismissal that flicked through his eyes when he finished. The faint, but more perceptible distaste he revealed when he let his eyes be drawn back to the healing bruise on David's slightly Hispanic features. And she knew what Frances had meant. This man had looked right at them, but he didn't see them, only stereotypes. Stereotypes beneath him, way beneath him.

She set the box on a cleared space on the table between them and rested her right hand on it as she reached up to cover David's hand on her shoulder with her left.

Frances stepped into the room with them and closed the door. She glanced at Anne's defensive posture but nodded toward the rep. "This is Stephen Carlton," she said. "He represents the Carlton Foundation, which has endowed an Oklahoma prehistory room at the Winchester Museum in Tulsa."

Carlton stepped forward, hand extended. "And you are?"

David returned a smile as false as the one the man offered them. "Anonymous."

The man dropped his hand but held on to his smile. "Yes, well, I think we've gone beyond that now that we've met. I understand you have Spiro artifacts for which you wish to find a home."

"The right home," Anne corrected gently. "An appropriate home. One that can give us certain guarantees."

"I think you'll find the Winchester more than adequate. We're a small facility, but well endowed and well staffed. Your artifacts will have a more than appropriate display area, and more than adequate climate-controlled storage for those items which, for some reason or other, are not included in the public viewing."

Point one. Anne felt David's fingers flex beneath hers. "No," she said, just as gently as she had spoken before.

Carlton glanced at her. "No? No to what?"

She rubbed her hand over David's, drawing strength from him. "I'm not at all sure I want the artifacts on public display. The only reason I'm even considering placing them anywhere is because of their value in leading us to understanding the culture that once thrived here. But whether or not they are ever placed on public display isn't really the issue. Whatever we decide about that, I must have your assurance—written, legal, binding—that the artifacts will never be separated."

"Separated from what?"

"From each other. The collection must be kept intact."

"I can assure you that we would never sell or donate any part of the collection without your permission."

"No. Please listen to me, Mr. Carlton. The collection must be stored in the same location, in the same room, together, touching, at all times."

He glanced at her and then at the box. "With demands like that I certainly hope you have more than the contents of that box."

Almost feeling as though she were abandoning it, Anne slid her hand from the top of the box and into her jacket pocket. She retrieved one of the Polaroid snapshots and handed it to Stephen Carlton.

He glanced down at it, and his brows drew together. "This is a hoax, right? Ms. Collins, if I can prove you're party to this, I'll have your job."

Anne took the other snapshots from her pocket and handed them to Frances. The woman looked at them, visibly stunned. "Oh, my sweet lord," she whispered. Her hands trembled when David took the photographs from her and placed them on the table. He shared a long questioning glance with Anne. Did she want to go on with this? No. Would she go on with it?

Now her fingers trembled as she worked them under the flaps of the box and opened it. "Frances?" she asked. "Will you help me?"

Frances walked to her side and looked down into the box as Anne lifted the large conch shell from its nest. She turned to hand it to Frances, but while the woman touched it with loving, wondering hands, she refused to take it. "Oh, no. No, I don't think so. Not in this lifetime."

Carlton had no such compunctions. He reached across the table for the box. "I wouldn't do that if I were you," David warned softly. "The lady will take them out of the box and put them on the table."

And Anne did. The conch shell, the copper plate, the delicate cup, the rock crystal jaguar, the earspool.

Unable to restrain himself any longer, Carlton snatched up the earspool. "A long-nosed god?"

Beside Anne, Frances nodded confirmation.

Carlton pulled a spotless linen handkerchief from his pocket and began to rub the earspool. "There aren't—what? more than two of these known to have survived from this site?"

With an alarmed glance at David, Anne reached out her hand. "Don't!"

He glared up at her, annoyed, angered, or maybe just so surprised that she had dared to order him that he failed to hide his condescension. "I certainly know how to clean an artifact without injuring it."

"That isn't the issue," David said coldly. "She said don't, and unless you reach an agreement with her, she has every right to direct the care and handling of her property."

Anne noticed that he had said unless, not until, and she was very much afraid that until was getting farther and farther away.

She chuffed out a sigh and began lifting items back into their nested box. Carlton took the conch as she reached for it and turned it to look inside the bowl of the shell. They had filled it with grave dirt. Now he upended it. "Is it stained from the black drink?" he asked as he began shaking the soil onto the tabletop.

The growl started low and grew until it swirled through the room. Frances stiffened beside her, her hand stilled in its gentle tracing of the crystal jaguar Anne had already returned to the box.

"Put it down!" David ordered.

Carlton frowned at him and continued dumping soil and rubbing at the bowl with his fingers as the growl surrounded them, growing in intensity. Unbelievably, the man seemed totally unaware of it.

David reached across the table and yanked the shell from Carlton's hands.

"My God, why did you do that? You could have broken it, jerking it away like that."

But the growling faded to a low grumble.

Anne took the man's linen handkerchief from the table where he had dropped it and began sweeping the spilled soil across the table to her waiting hand. And when David placed the conch shell in the box, she scattered the soil over and into it and over the other items.

"I believe we have our answer," she said as she closed the box.

"Yes." David picked up the photos.

"I'll need those for our Board of Trustees," Carlton said, reaching as though to take them.

"No." Calmly, competently, David stacked the four photos together and then, with no apparent effort, ripped the pile in half, and in half again. He tucked the pieces in his windbreaker pocket and picked up the box. "Thank you, Frances. We appreciate your efforts."

She shook her head, let out a closely held breath, and placed her hand over her heart. "I can't say it's been a pleasure, but it's certainly been an experience. I'm sorry it didn't work out."

"Something will," Anne told her. "Something will have to."

"What the hell are you people talking about? Is everybody in this godforsaken corner of the world crazy?"

"He hasn't a clue, has he?" Frances asked.

Anne shook her head. She didn't understand; she might never understand. "I don't think so."

David took Frances's hand and held it in a moment of silent thanks. "Can you give us five minutes, maybe ten? It will be safer if he can't follow or trace us."

"The key's in the lock. If you'll leave it outside, I'll call someone to come and let us out."

Anne gave the woman a quick hug, which Frances returned. "Go," she said. "I'll be fine."

They went, hurrying out of the small room. As the door closed behind them, she heard Carlton's voice raised in protest, and Frances's voice, slurred now in the soft dialect of the area, the dialect she knew Carlton had expected simply because she looked the way she did.

"No, you wait just a minute," Frances said. Her words sounded clearly through the closed door as Anne followed David toward the locked front door, and while her accent was soft, her words were anything but. "You came down here under false pretenses. You have single-handedly destroyed any chance of the Winchester or probably any other museum gaining an invaluable collection. You have insulted possible donors. You have insulted me, and you have threatened my job . . ."

David thrust the box into Anne's hands as they reached the front door. He twisted the key from the lock, pulled the door closed behind them, and quickly locked it. Together, without speaking, they sprinted for the Blazer, but at the Mercedes, David stopped. The car wasn't locked. He opened the driver's door and tugged on a lever just inside, then opened the hood and fumbled in there. He grinned at her as he eased the hood closed. "That'll stop him."

"What?"

"Just a couple of loose wires. Want to bet our buddy has absolutely no knowledge of how this baby works?"

Anne felt a laugh building. God. Was it just a laugh? Or was it hysteria threatening to break free?

"Want to bet no one closer than Fort Smith knows how to work on a Mercedes?" she asked.

"No way," he told her as he took her elbow and hurried her to the Blazer. "I'm relatively sure that Frances will help you win that bet, hands down."

They met few cars on the road to the highway, and although Anne kept her eyes focused on the side mirror and the road they had traveled, she saw no big Mercedes roaring up behind them.

"He didn't hear them," she said. "My God, they were all around us, and he didn't hear them."

"Wayne said Joe didn't hear them either."

Anne twisted in the seat. "Wayne heard them? In the house?"

"Yes. The day Joe broke in. He said the cats warned him."

"Oh, lord." Anne hugged the box to her. "What are we going to do, David? What on earth are we going to do?"

"Something," he promised. "Something."

At the highway, he turned left.

"Where are we going?"

"Into Fort Smith. If somebody is following, if somebody was posted along the road, we'll lose them in city traffic."

Her pulse rate had returned to almost normal. The traffic along the state highway grew heavier, but no one appeared to be paying any attention to the battered Blazer. Eventually the two-lane highway became a divided interstate. A sign directed them to an off-ramp, and they took it and the well-traveled road toward town.

"You can let go of your death grip on that box now," he told her.

She glanced down. Her knuckles were white where they clutched the edges of the box. Her fingers didn't want to straighten. She laughed self-consciously and laced them together, stretching them, coaxing circulation back into them.

"Why don't you stick that behind the seat? I think we've been assured we're safe."

"I guess we have at that." She twisted within the confines of the seatbelt and tucked the box behind David's seat, and then, because the day had taken one of the November weather's quirky turns into a late, late Indian summer and the sunlight streaming into the Blazer had become uncomfortably warm, she shrugged out of her jacket and dropped it on top of the box.

"Better?" he asked.

She stretched and eased tight muscles and reached to touch his shoulder. "Yes."

They reached the downtown area, a blocks-long stretch of red brick buildings, some of them appearing a hundred years old or more, many of them charming, a few in sad need of repair. They drove the length of it, from the huge, closed hotel and a vibrant, old church at one end, to the high, arching bridge that spanned the width of the Arkansas River at the other.

David turned off the main street and drove past the courthouse and federal buildings, eventually winding past the entrance to the military cemetery and the restored buildings that remained from the fort that had given the city its name.

But this was not a sightseeing trip. Anne sensed that in David's constant vigilance of oncoming traffic as well as of the vehicles behind them. She looked out at the stately white-trimmed red brick building across the wide lawn and wondered if one day they might return as tourists. It didn't seem likely.

David returned to the main street, traveled a few blocks, and pulled into an angled parking space at the curb.

"What?" she asked.

"I think we made our getaway without being followed." He nodded toward the building in front of them. "And I know I'm hungry."

And so was she. But there was the box on the floor behind his seat.

"Leave it," he said. "It's covered by your jacket, and I'll lock the Blazer. We're on a busy street, parked at a busy sidewalk."

She nodded and got out of the car and waited for him at the parking meter. He stuffed a quarter in the slot and grinned at her. "Your hair's all falling down," he said.

She swiped an anxious hand to her hair.

"It looks great," he said, giving her one of his killer smiles. "Leave it?"

She chuckled. "I think I'll have to. I only brought identification and a little mad money with me."

"Good."

"Good? You're on the streets with someone who has to look like a mad woman and you say good?"

He took her arm and pulled her close into a loose hug. "Yeah."

What they found in the storefront restaurant wasn't the fast food she suspected David was addicted to, but it was the best burger Anne had ever eaten. Thick, juicy, on a homemade roll, served with huge wedges of roasted potato, and coffee to die for.

They were seated at a dark pine booth against bare brick walls and gleaming hardwood floors. At the front of the room, against the storefront glass, a profusion of plants grew, but none were allowed to encroach past a certain point. And near the antique cash register stood what looked to be an authentic gravity-flow, glass-bulbed gas pump, with the top cleaned and fitted as an aquarium.

Anne loved it.

She loved the stream of nonsense conversation David kept flowing.

She loved him.

Damn.

Well, she'd gotten through worse; she'd get through this. And she'd enjoy the time she had with him.

She would.

Anne was sated with good food and their conversation when they left the restaurant, almost content but with her senses humming with awareness of him. He'd taken her arm, and they were chuckling softly over some bit of nonsense when they reached the Blazer.

David tensed. "Damn it all to hell!"

Anne had idly glanced toward a mother and three small children making an awkward, ambling journey down the sidewalk. At David's fierce oath, she turned toward the Blazer. The driver's side window had a gaping hole in it, surrounded by spidery veins in the shattered but still connected safety glass.

David reached for the door handle but jerked his hand back. Instead, he stepped to the door and looked into the Blazer, stepped back and glanced into the back.

"It's gone, isn't it?"

"Yes, and so is your jacket."

"Well, great. Just great. What do we do now?"

"Oh, Annie." He shook his head. "I don't want to do this. If this were my car, I'd be tempted to just get the hell out of Dodge. But it isn't. I've got to report it."

"And what do we tell the police officer?"

"As much of the truth as we can."

"A lady's jacket and an empty box." The officer repeated David's words and shook his head. "Damn, Huerra. Welcome to Arkansas."

"Actually, it's a gentler welcome that the one he got to Oklahoma," Anne said. "There, one of our natives knocked his car into the rear end of a log truck. With him in it."

"This is a heck of a way to spend a vacation. Are you sure you wouldn't rather be back on duty? No offense, Dr. Locke."

Anne laughed softly. Officer Stanton had been a pleasant surprise. Well into middle age and comfortable with who he was and the work he did, he'd gone about taking their report with a minimum of discomfort. And she didn't feel too badly about lying to him. If the box were found, it would be empty. "None taken."

"Okay," he said, closing his pad holder on the brief report. "Tell the dealership in Fairview this will be ready for their insurance company tomorrow, day after at the latest. I'm really sorry—"

A harsh scream ripped through whatever Stanton would have said, and repeated, echoing its cry of terror and pain. The three of them turned. It had come from a nearby alley, probably magnified and tunneled toward the street by high brick walls.

"What the—" But Stanton was already turning, tossing his pad holder down, reaching for his service revolver, running.

David put his hand on Anne's arm. "Stay here. I'll go."

Stay. Oh, yes. Definitely. There was no way she wanted to know what caused that cry, no way she wanted to see the result of that pain. There was no way she could help, she knew that already. She could only follow David as he ran toward danger and death.

"The hell I will . . . "

And they were all running, fighting to get through the small crowd of people that had already clogged the opening to the alley.

"Let me through," Stanton ordered. "Come on, move it, folks, let us through."

And remarkably, they did.

The screams had stopped. The snarling had stopped. The growls had stopped.

The body lay in an alcove off the alley. Stanton approached it cautiously. David grabbed Anne's arm and hauled her to a stop. "Let me go," she told him.

"You don't want that."

No, she didn't, but that didn't, couldn't, make any difference. Maybe she wasn't too late. Maybe she could . . . something. "I have to help if I can," she said as she jerked her arm from his grasp.

"Annie! Wait!"

But she didn't. She couldn't. She reached the alcove just as Officer Stanton turned from the crumpled mass in the doorway and staggered toward her. He caught her in his arms but not before she saw what was left of—of a man?

She gagged and whirled away from the body. David grabbed her and held her face against his chest.

"Get her out of here," Stanton ordered. "There isn't anything she can do. See if you can keep the lookers back, and call for help. Homicide, Animal Control, God, I don't know. I'll stay here and . . ." He looked around the alley. It was empty. Anne could have told him that. As empty as the cardboard box at the entrance to the alcove. But Stanton wouldn't believe her. He stood there, an incredibly brave man protecting a dead man and a crime scene from something so far beyond his experience he could only imagine the danger, while he urged David to get her to safety.

David did. She stopped at the end of the alley. "Go for help. I'll keep them from going back there."

"And just how do you plan to do that, Annie. You don't know what ghouls some people can be."

"Simple." She reached out and touched the sleeve of a man who crowded against them. "I don't think you want to go back there, sir. There's a real serious gas leak. I think it's going to blow at any minute."

David grabbed her to him and just held her as the shudders racked him. "Don't go back there. Don't put yourself in danger. Promise me."

She nodded abruptly. She'd used her supply of words and her bravado. Only then did she remember what Karen had said about the killing in her lab.

David used the radio in Stanton's police cruiser. His first words were guaranteed to get the maximum help in the minimum time and cut through the bullshit of bureaucracy demanding to know who he was and why he was on a restricted radio. "Officer needs assistance."

For a small department, an amazing number of official vehicles swarmed the scene. David had his shield in his hand and his hands in plain sight when the first car arrived. "Block the alley," he said. "Keep those civilians out. Stanton's in there guarding the crime scene."

He hadn't a hope in hell that would work, at least not without a lot of explanation on his part. But it did. The officer ran his car up on the sidewalk and closed off the alley entrance. But he yelled down the alley. "Stanton? You okay back there?"

A siren coming up the alley from the other end cut off Stanton's reply, but not until at least one reinforcement had heard his voice.

Annie. Where was Annie? A man in a suit forced his way through the throng to David's side and shoved a badge in his face. "What's happened here?"

There she was. Pale. God, she looked like she might pass out at any moment. But she was coming to him. If she could reach him through the press of officers surrounding him.

He took a step toward her, only to be stopped by a hand on his arm. He glared at the hand; he glared at the man who put it there. "Let her through."

The man nodded and the crowd surrounding him parted. Annie stumbled and he caught her. She sobbed once and leaned into his strength. He looked over Annie's head at the man obviously in command.

"Officer Stanton was taking a burglary report from us," he said. "He has our names and addresses. He had finished the report and was leaving when we heard a scream from the alley. I'm a police officer from Dallas. Anne is a doctor. We accompanied him into the alley approximately fifty yards to an alcove and a doorway where we found a body. We saw no one. He asked for our assistance while he guarded the scene. Anne blocked the alley and I used his radio."

"Is that how you remember it, ma'am?" the man asked Anne.

She nodded.

"And you didn't stay to see if you could give medical aid?"

Anne raised her head and looked at her interrogator, and David thought he would never forget the sick revulsion in her eyes. "Go look at him," she said. "Go look at him and then come back and ask me that question."

24

No one reported hearing growls or snarls, not Stanton, not any of those who had been drawn to the alley by the screams. Certainly not David or Annie. The Fort Smith police let them go. There was, after all, nothing more to be said or done by them, and that department had all it could handle.

The Blazer's heater had all it could handle, too, fighting the increasingly cooler outside air of late afternoon as it whistled and roared through the shattered window.

David had taken off his windbreaker and draped it around Anne's shoulders, but it wasn't enough.

He stopped in Fairview. The Chevy dealer was remarkably unconcerned about the damage to the loaner, maybe because David's car still sat, untouched, in the back lot. "You're hell on cars, Huerra," was all he'd said, and cheerfully at that, before he'd lent him still another vehicle, a modified Suburban.

Blake had not been available when he called the sheriff's office, but the dispatcher promised to find him and relay the message that David needed to talk to him. It was time to live up to his promise to the sheriff, and he wasn't looking forward to it.

And he wasn't looking forward to taking Annie back to that house. But he had to.

He'd seen her look like this once before. Damn it. Only two days before. At the fork in the highway just outside Allegro, he pulled to a widened place on the side of the road and stopped.

This truck had bench seats.

He unsnapped his seat belt and hers and dragged her to his side.

She was cold. Still cold. Little shivers shook her. And she wasn't with him. Where was she? In Chicago pleading futilely for the lives of those who had trusted her? At the top of Simpson Knob, physically holding life and blood in a small boy? Or in an alley in Fort Smith witnessing a sight that rivaled any nightmare he had seen in fifteen years as a cop?

He rubbed his hands up and down her arms, across her back, and finally just wrapped her as close to him as he could and held her. "It will be all right, Annie girl. We'll make it all right. We can do it. Somehow."

He felt her drag in a tortured breath and rock against him. "It isn't supposed to happen here. I came here because this kind of thing isn't supposed to happen here. No violence. No blood. No crime. Harriet Nelson or June Cleaver in every kitchen. Who was he, David? Someone sent by that awful man from the museum? Someone sent by Joe? Or just a thief who picked the wrong car? And what difference does it make who he was? This place is supposed to be safe. Damn it! Bad things don't happen in little towns like this. That's why I'm here; that's why I have to stay. It's the big cities where greed and death rule not—"

"Annie, Annie, it can happen anywhere. Some places are safer than others, but no place is completely safe."

"No, you don't understand. I won't let it happen

here; I can't let it happen here. I need someplace in the world, someplace in this whole big world where I won't be afraid."

He felt his throat tighten, felt the pressure of not being able to promise her that he would always keep her safe. Because he couldn't promise her that.

"You're safe here, Annie," he said around the constriction in his throat. "And now. Right here and right now you don't have to be afraid. Start with that, darlin'. Build on that. You can do it."

"And when you leave? What do I do then?"

She was sure, so sure he would leave her. Was she right? Could he survive in this corner of the world where she had chosen to hide? Could she?

Anne seldom saw a sunset. The hill behind her house cut off any view of one from her home. Her home. Only a week before those words had brought her great pride. Now— Now she suppressed a shudder as David turned the Suburban into her driveway and downshifted for the climb. Twilight already hid the yard and lower windows, and from the kitchen a light gleamed.

Margaret's truck sat parked in the turnaround. Of course. The clinic would be closed by now, and she and Wayne wouldn't leave the house unguarded.

God. Did any human have to guard the house?

David parked and took the key from the ignition. He, too, looked up at the house, at the back wall bare of windows, at the overgrown hillside behind them, at the closed and barred doors of the sagging barn.

"I should have run with you that first day," he said softly. "I should have said, 'I'm not going in that house, and there's no way in hell I'm letting you go back in without me.' I should have stuffed you back in that brown truck of yours and hauled us both out of this county."

She fumbled for his hand and held on.

"We're not in any danger from what's in there," he said. "I'm pretty sure of that. But I'm not so sure we're safe from anyone who decides to come looking. I'm sorry, Annie."

"Why are you sorry? If it weren't for my crazy, greedy family, there'd be no problem."

"Now that I'm not so sure of."

A shadow separated from the side of the house and moved forward, just before the bright beam of a flashlight trapped them in its glare. Anne could have sworn her heart stopped, then started again at double speed.

"Damn. It's okay, Annie. It's okay." David opened the truck door, and when the interior light came on, the flashlight went off. "Sorry, Wayne. I should have realized you wouldn't recognize the truck."

Anne watched as Wayne stopped and examined both of them in the dim light. "You two okay?"

"Yes." David slid from the seat, still holding Anne's hand. He bent toward her, looking at her face, her eyes, focusing for a moment on her lips. His own quirked ruefully, and he gave her another of his wicked grins. "We'll neck later," he whispered. "This will be a great truck for it. Much better than the Blazer."

With a sob or a chuckle, she wasn't sure which, Anne slid from the truck. With a little effort, she convinced her knees to support her, and she convinced her legs to work as she walked with David up onto the porch and into the warmth of her kitchen.

Wayne came in with them. Margaret entered the room from the hallway, and the two of them shared a silent communication before Wayne shrugged out of his coat and hung it on a peg. "Don't suppose you'd want to tell us what happened to the Blazer, or to Anne, or just in general what in the hell is going on, would you?"

"Wayne." Margaret's soft voice both chastised and invited his silence.

"No, hell, no, Maggie. If it were just me, I would keep my mouth shut. But you're here, and that poor, hurt little girl and her baby, and this is the second trip out of three in as many days that he's brought Anne back looking like death warmed over. It's time to ask questions."

David looked down at Anne. He was going to tell— she knew that—with or without her permission. And he was right to do so. Slowly she nodded.

"And it's time for answers." Still looking at her, David spoke to Wayne and Margaret. "Just as soon as Blake gets here."

David met Blake on the back porch when he arrived.

"Tell me that homicide in Fort Smith doesn't have anything to do with the problems coming from this house," the sheriff said without preamble.

"I can't do that, Blake."

Blake slumped slightly. He scrubbed at the back of his neck. "Well, hell."

David opened the screen and stepped back. "Come inside."

Nellie had joined them in the kitchen for a few minutes. She'd even been persuaded to drink a cup of soup. But the two men and undercurrents she had no way of understanding obviously made her uneasy, even though she tried to hide it. Margaret fixed her a cup of hot tea, gave her more analgesics, and convinced her to rest in the downstairs bedroom.

Gretta Tompkins, perhaps understanding the need

for an early bedtime, had kept Lilly up and active all afternoon. So after a quick supper for her, even though it was not late, it wasn't difficult for them persuade the little girl to take a nap with her mama.

That left Wayne and Margaret, David and Anne, and Blake, seated at the round table in the kitchen.

Still pale, still wearing his windbreaker, Anne had her hands stuffed in its pockets. An unpleasant, expectant hush had settled over the room. She looked up at David. "Where do I start?"

"I'll do it." Somehow it seemed the least he could do for her. "If you'll let me."

"Oh, please."

Now, all he had to do was figure out how to explain the unexplainable. But maybe that wouldn't be completely impossible. Wayne met his glance from across the table and gave him an almost imperceptible but nonetheless encouraging nod.

He supposed he'd have to start at the beginning. And where else would that be but with the man upstairs? His gesture at the museum, tearing up the photographs, had been more for security than for dramatic emphasis; in the wrong hands those pictures could be dangerous. He'd meant to shred them further and dispose of the pieces, but he hadn't yet.

"Annie," he said softly. "Give me the pictures. In the jacket pocket," he added when she just looked at him, confused.

She remembered. Nodding, she withdrew her hand from the pocket and handed him the pieces of photographic paper.

The puzzle wasn't difficult; he'd only torn them twice—four parts to each of four distinctive portraits. With only a moment's study he pieced them together and lay them in the center of the table, clearly visible by the three people—friends, good friends, trustworthy friends—across from them.

Wayne gave a low whistle and looked up, understanding. "Ralph Hansom's treasure."

"Yes."

"Is that what got him killed?"

"Probably."

Blake looked up from the photo he had been tracing the perimeter of in fascinated disbelief. "You're saying he was murdered?"

"No." David hurried to stop that misconception. "I believe his car went off the mountain with him in it, and that no other person was involved."

"Then what—" Wayne stopped, finding the answer to his own question. "The cats? Inside with him?"

David nodded. "I think so."

"Cats," Blake said. "Like these cats you've been hearing, seeing, tracking?"

"Not like them, Blake," David told him. "The same ones."

"Wait a minute. That was almost fifty years ago. Are you telling me that you've been tracking geriatric mountain lions?" He gave a short laugh. "Or maybe their ghosts?"

Wayne leaned back in his chair and reached for Maggie's hand. "Maybe," he said. "That would explain why Uncle James didn't see them."

"Wait a minute," Blake said, looking from Wayne to David. "Hold on. Stop."

Wayne stopped.

David stopped. He recognized the need Blake felt to deny the unbelievable. He'd done it himself. He recognized Blake's need to orient himself with something familiar and real. He'd done that, too. But Blake had now had his moment to do that; it was time to move on.

"In the last three days, we've spoken to Frances Collins, the interim director at the Spiro Mounds Park, and to Marian Hansom, Joe's grandmother, as well as to you, Blake, looking for answers to questions we didn't even know how to ask. Each answer we got led us deeper into confusion, but there were some things that kept recurring. Cats. And curses. And death."

Blake shifted in his chair, but he gave David his full attention.

"In 1935, Ralph Hansom apparently either stole this burial," David told them, indicating the photographs, "or hired someone to steal it. Everyone who helped him, everyone he tried to sell it to, died a brutal death.

"Frances's grandfather was a digger at the site. She heard this from him. She says the old-timers talk about big golden cats prowling the mounds. She didn't tie the deaths she told us about to the cats. She did tie them to the curse.

"Marian Hansom blames everything on the curse: Ralph's death, her poverty, her injury." He glanced pointedly at Blake. "The deaths of Lucy Hansom and Walter Briggs. She also admitted that the reason Joe is supporting her is because she has told him about the fortune this represents, but not where it is."

Wayne and Blake knew the next part of the story; he doubted that Margaret did. "We found the burial on Wednesday. That was the first time we heard what could have been a large cat. We sent a shell to a collector in Dallas. He was murdered. We sent a femur to a friend of Anne's in Chicago. It was stolen from her. The thief was murdered. Both by large animals."

Margaret gasped and clutched Wayne's hand. "These are the cats he's heard?"

"Yes, Margaret, I believe they are."

He turned to Blake. "The day Joe broke in, the cats

warned Wayne. He heard them, before and after the break-in. Joe didn't.

"We asked Frances to help us find a way to let archaeologists and historians benefit from the knowledge this burial can reveal and yet protect anyone who might come in contact with it in the future.

"We met today with a representative from a private museum in Tulsa. We took him these four pictures and five items from the grave goods. All Anne asked in exchange for turning this collection over to him was a legally binding promise that it would be kept secure and together. He gave lip service, but it was apparent he didn't intend to do that. It was also apparent that the cats didn't like his treatment of the artifacts."

"You heard them?" Blake asked.

David nodded. "I heard them. Anne heard them. And Frances Collins heard them. God, Wayne, I know now what you mean about the volume. We were in a windowless room, maybe fifteen by thirty. They were all around us. And Stephen Carlton didn't hear a thing."

"So I was right." Wayne grimaced. "They weren't fussing at me, were they?"

"Oh, they were fussing, all right. They only stopped when we forcibly took the last artifact from him and packed it away with the others. I don't know what would have happened to us if we hadn't done that."

"And Fort Smith?" Blake asked. "How did they get from the Mounds park to Fort Smith?"

"We went into the city to make sure no one from the museum followed us home," David said. "I would have sworn I wasn't followed. We stopped to eat. While we were in the restaurant someone broke into the car and stole the box of artifacts."

"The man who was killed in the alley?"

"Yes, Blake. I saw the empty box just outside the doorway where he had been trapped."

Anne laid her hand on his, seeking his attention. "We have to call Frances," she said. "We left her locked in the museum with that awful man. We have to make sure she's all right."

"Huerra, damn it!" Blake rose with a roar. "What the hell kind of path are you cutting through this part of the country?"

"With her permission, Blake." Annie said quickly. "She told us to. She kept him locked in with her so that we could leave. Please. Please . . ."

David turned his hand and laced his fingers with hers.

She returned the pressure. Whatever she had been about to beg for, she didn't. "Would you please see if you can get in touch with her? She lives with her grandparents, but I don't know their names."

Blake dragged his chair around, scooted it back up to the table, and rested his hands on the back of it. "Sorry, Doc. Sure. Sure. I'll have my dispatcher call the sheriff's office up there. They'll know. But first—" Now he was the one giving a pointed look—at David. "You said the box was empty. Any idea what happened to the items that were in it?"

He felt Annie's fingers jerk within his. He drew her hand up and clasped it in both of his, rubbing it. Warming it. "They ought to be back by now, don't you think?"

"Yes."

Oh, hell. If the first part of this story had been hard for Blake to believe, how much more difficult would be the rest of it?

"Have I been upstairs since we came in this afternoon, Wayne?"

"No."

"Has Annie?" he asked, knowing that not even his Annie would be safe from suspicion.

"Thanks," David said when Wayne dragged his head to one side in a negative gesture. "Remember that, please. Make the call, Blake," he suggested. "Then we do have to go upstairs. All of us."

Blake called his office and requested the information, then hauled the telephone back over to the table and set it in front of his chair. It rang in only minutes—minutes that had dragged because of the silence around the table. Blake noted a number, said a few terse words to the caller, then scooted telephone and the scrap of paper with the number on it across the table.

David considered giving the telephone to Annie to make the call. Considered it for about the space of two heartbeats. She had rallied, but not that much, and not that well. He dialed the number.

Frances answered on the second ring.

"Are you all right?" he asked. "Annie wanted to be sure you survived confinement with Carlton."

"Yes," Frances said over the mumble of a television in the background. "But I'm not sure he did. He was looking awfully ragged by the time Gramma got there to unlock the door."

He patted Annie's hand and mouthed the words, "She's all right."

"I'm sorry we had to do that," he told the woman on the phone.

"Those are the magic words, aren't they, David? Had to. I'm sorry I got you nice folks involved with him."

"Will there be any repercussions for you?"

"No, I . . . " Her voice faded as the sounds from the television grew louder. "Wait a minute. What? What Gramps? Oh, my lord."

"What is it, Frances?" he asked sharply.

"What it is, is the Fort Smith news," she said eventually, and he knew what story she must be seeing, but not how much was being told. Their names shouldn't be mentioned. There wasn't any reason for them to be dragged into the news story. But the mangled body was news. Big news.

"Yeah," he said without her having to ask. "Someone broke into the car and stole the box of artifacts."

"Oh, shit."

He listened to the faint hiss of the line and the rumble of the television newscaster.

"How is Anne?"

How was Anne? He glanced at her. About at the end of her endurance? Holding on by a thread and sheer determination? "Better," he told her, praying it was true.

"I'm coming down there," Frances said abruptly. "Something's got to be done. Carlton's going to try to find you. God only knows what he'd do if he got his hands on the burial. Do you suppose he was responsible— Never mind. We can talk about that when I get there. Maybe— Maybe together we can come up with something."

"Can you—" Hell, why not? "Can you make sure you're not followed?"

For reply, she only gave a wicked laugh. "Give me finding directions for where you are."

Maybe his paranoia was working overtime. Maybe it was time for his paranoia to start doing just that. If Blake had found her telephone number so easily, who else might have? "No," he said. "Call when you get to town. Then we'll either give you directions or come and lead you here."

Anne looked in on her other guests before they went upstairs. Lilly lay curled against her mother with her thumb securely in her mouth. Nellie slept heavily, her battered face cushioned against a down pillow, unaware that Anne watched. Unaware of anything, not even dreams at this level of sleep. Good. That was what she needed. Sleep to let her body heal. Sleep to give her a chance to recapture her strength.

Was that what she herself was doing, Anne wondered as she pulled the door shut against any noise they might make going upstairs. Retreating from the shock and the pain to recover? Or had she finally reached the limit of what she could endure? She wasn't sure.

Neither was David. He thought she didn't know; he was careful not to be too obvious as he hovered over her. She knew. What she didn't know was how to bring herself out of this cushioned fog that had enveloped her.

"How is she?" David asked at her side.

"Asleep."

"Good."

The two of them led the way upstairs. Anne might have resisted the way David held her arm if she hadn't glanced back and seen that Wayne had taken the same protective posture with Margaret.

The door was closed, as they had left it. David pushed it open and flipped the switch for the overhead light. They'd left the small stove lighted, burning low.

Marian had lived in this room for how long? Years and years and years as a bitter, vindictive, and greedy woman. The hate that fueled her, the madness that governed her, ought to have permeated even the boards beneath their feet.

But it hadn't. The room was warm. Warm and as inviting as its shabby sophistication would allow.

Margaret looked with interest at the art deco sofa and parlor stove. Wayne glanced at the off-center light fixture and then at the closet wall.

"That's what raised Anne's suspicions," David told him.

"A false wall?" Wayne asked.

"Yes, but not where we thought."

David opened the closet and then discovered he either had to let go of her arm or drag her into the closet with him. He patted her arm—he'd done a lot of that since they left the museum—but he let go of it and walked into the closet. She heard the sounds of him wrestling the panel away and stepped back, indicating that Blake should follow him into the closet.

He did. Wayne followed him. Margaret remained by her side. "Should we go back downstairs?" she asked.

Only that morning, Anne had thought that it seemed as though Margaret had been involved forever. Now that feeling doubled. How strange. "No," she said.

The three men stood at the foot of the skeleton. Anne and Margaret stepped to one side, standing together. And he was a skeleton, Anne told herself. No longer a warrior. No longer a man. Bones. Just bones, as David had said, with the spirit that animated him long gone.

But why did the loss seem so recent? Why did the separation seem so new? She felt Margaret's arm come around her waist in silent support and looked up to see moisture glistening in her friend's eyes.

And why did it seem as though she had stood just here, before, with this woman, sharing her support as she grieved for this man?

Blake broke the spell. "Wait a minute. You said you sent the femur, the *right* femur, to Chicago."

Anne slipped from Margaret's side and went to kneel beside the litter. "Yes," she said. She shifted the copper slightly. "This one." She didn't look at Blake's face; she knew she'd see blatant skepticism there. "And this gorget is the one we sent to Dallas." All of the other items except the crystal jaguar had already settled into place. It still rested on the edge of the litter. One by one she touched them. "And these were in the box that was stolen from the car in Fort Smith." Now she turned to look at Blake. "We told the police officer the box was empty, because we knew it would be when they found it."

Blake was dragging his head from side to side. "I trust your word, Anne Locke, but I'm having a whole lot of trouble with this."

"Frances is coming," David told him. "She can identify the pieces that we showed Carlton."

"There's another way," Anne said. "Pick out a piece, Blake. One that you can easily recognize."

"Annie—"

"It's all right, David. We've done it. And maybe this is the only way Blake will truly understand."

Blake approached the foot of the litter warily and went down on one knee. Just as warily he reached toward the heaped up treasures. When she saw that he picked up the cedar box containing the miniatures, Anne wanted to call back her words, wanted at least to cry out, *Not that one. Anything else, but not that.*

She didn't have to. A low rumbling came from her left, not really threatening—not yet—just making its presence known. Blake tossed down the box and backed carefully away from the litter.

"That's it?" he asked softly. "That's the sound you heard?"

"Not quite," David stepped between Blake and the warrior. "I don't think it was really pissed off at you, just moderately upset. You read it that way, Wayne?"

Wayne had already thrust himself between Margaret and the sound. "Yeah. That about describes it. Why don't we take the women downstairs."

The crystal jaguar had not moved. Anne scooped a

little loose dirt from the floor of the litter and sprinkled it on and in the pipe bowl. "How about this piece, Blake? Would you be able to recognize it?"

"Anything. Anything, Anne. Don't you think you should move away from there?"

Should she? Anne looked at the litter, at all that remained of the man who had amassed such wealth and power. Someone who for some reason unknown by them, and in spite of what was now believed about the religion of his time, had gone to his grave and his after-life alone. And he was still alone. Anne knew that as certainly as she knew he had been torn from his grave.

"Annie."

David had moved to stand beside her. Now he held his hand for her to help her to her feet. He was right. She knew he was right. Only bones and a lingering memory. And he was worried about her. Concern tightened his features and darkened his eyes. And maybe he was right about that, too, because no matter how much David meant to her, a part of her wanted to stay right where she was. With a man who had been dead for seven hundred years.

But of course she wouldn't do that.

She shifted the crystal jaguar into her left hand and took David's hand with her right as she rose to her feet. Such a fierce frown he had. Such a possessive grip. Did he realize that? She gave him a smile to ease his frown. He closed his eyes briefly, and when he opened them both his frown and his grip eased.

They left the light on in the room. David and Blake settled the panel into place and closed the closet door. They waited in the hall while David closed the door to the room behind them. "We can't lock it," he said. "We haven't found a key or changed the lock. But I think we can find a way to convince you."

25

Anne watched how each person dealt with the story David had told.

Maybe she hadn't wimped out, after all. Maybe her way was just as valid as any other for dealing with an unbearable situation.

Blake had wanted to leave the rock crystal jaguar in plain sight so that he could watch it constantly. Because neither she nor David knew exactly how the transfer worked, they'd argued against that as potentially dangerous. Instead, Blake had pulled his car in front of the porch steps, in full view of the window in the kitchen door. After David lightly dusted the ancient pipe, Blake had locked it in the glove compartment and then had locked all of the car's doors. He'd also gone with Wayne and David to check the locks on all the doors and windows on the ground floor of the house.

Now he paced, and all too often he walked to the back door and looked out as though he half expected to find the door ripped from his Jimmy.

Although he tried not to be too obvious, David watched Anne.

Margaret faced the time by digging into Anne's pantry and freezer and putting together a meal.

Anne spent the time knitting herself back together. Thread by thread, by thread.

The only one who seemed unbothered by the wait was Wayne, and Anne suspected he had learned places inside himself where he could go and no one would ever know.

When Frances telephoned, everyone in the room seemed to breathe a sigh of relief. They'd been on hold, waiting for something. Now they knew what.

Blake wouldn't leave. Wayne drove into town to lead her back to the house. And Margaret began setting the meal on the table.

They heard the cars climbing the drive, and each moved in an action determined by God alone knew who. It reminded Anne of a funeral gathering, each person going through the motions of a normal life when everything normal had been shattered by death.

Wayne opened the door and ushered Frances in. She stopped just inside the door and looked around the kitchen as she shed her coat. "Wow," she said. "This is going to be great. Is it as huge as it looks in the dark?" But when Wayne took her coat from her, she turned and noticed Blake and her smile faded. "Sheriff? Is there a problem?"

"No." Anne handed her a cup of coffee. "Blake's here because we asked him, and I hope as a friend."

"We're all friends," Margaret said from her place at the stove.

And they were. More than that. Anne's eyes sought out David. Some much more than that. He held the chair for Frances, a courtly gesture he seemed to have picked up from Wayne, or maybe not. Maybe it had already been ingrained in him. How truly strange,

Anne thought. A week before she had known only two of these people, and those two in a professional capacity.

Now they would forever be a part of her life.

Even when they left her.

Damn! She had to get out of this morbid mood. Not everybody was destined to leave her. Why did she keep coming back to that thought? No. No, no, no. Before it had been David, only David, she'd known would go. Now it was *all* of them. Ridiculous. In all the emotional knitting she'd been doing, she must have dropped a stitch.

"Did you have any problems getting here?" David asked.

"No more than any other person who's been spoiled by flatland river bottoms," she said.

Blake still prowled. Now he glanced at Frances. "Ms. Collins?"

She turned questioningly toward him.

"Could you recognize the artifacts that David and Anne brought to the park today?"

"Well, yes. Of course. They were unique in design. Have they been recovered?"

Margaret closed the oven door with a determined thump. "Oh, go on and check, Blake Foresman. No one's going to want dinner until this is resolved anyway."

Blake turned toward Anne. "Do you suppose . . . "

"I don't know," she told him.

David went with him. Frances looked puzzled but resisted asking any questions. At least for the moment. Anne was sure the woman would have plenty of them later.

When the men returned Anne knew from Blake's ashen face that the jaguar had disappeared from his truck.

David moved to her side. Blake stopped inside the door and just stood there. Anne remembered all too well those first moments when she and David knew that the warrior's grave goods returned to him. She remembered the suspicion that David, and even she, had felt before believing the unbelievable.

"Go," she told David. "Take him upstairs and get it over with."

Now more than ever the gathering took on a funereal air. She hadn't been able to go to Anthony's funeral; she'd still been in the hospital. But she remembered her grandmother's, with all the family coming home. Singly or in groups, all of them had gone to the funeral home to view the body—the shell—that had been her grandmother. Anne had slipped away by herself to say good-bye to her grandmother. She hadn't wanted to share what little time she had to say good-bye to her with others. As strange as it seemed, she felt the same way now.

Did the others?

"Will you come with us?" David asked her.

"No." She glanced at the woman sitting quietly, if not completely patiently, at the table. "Frances, would you like to see the burial?"

Frances clutched her hands together in front of her on the table. "I don't know. I find I'm having a surprising amount of trouble with this." She laughed shakily. "It's a hell of a note for a woman who has worked most of her life trying to get an advanced degree in archaeology, but since you showed me those photos earlier, he's become a person to me, not just a study, and I'm having a real hard time with the fact that someone, thief or scientist, it doesn't really matter to me right now, ripped him out of his grave."

"I know," Anne told her. "But maybe that's a good reason for you to see him."

"Besides," Blake said, still a little subdued, "I'd like you to confirm something for me."

Frances went upstairs with the men.

"Are you all right?" Margaret asked when the two of them were alone in the kitchen.

"I'm getting there," Anne told her. And she truly believed she was.

The others were all quiet when they returned to the kitchen. Frances smiled uncertainly at Anne. "I'm still not comfortable with the questions I've had to ask myself today, Anne Locke, but I will forever thank you for sharing that treasure with me."

Blake lapsed into silence, only occasionally rousing himself to mutter the three syllable *hell* that was the one sure sign he was disturbed.

Wayne walked over to Margaret and without warning hugged her tight to his chest. "I love you, woman. I don't think I've told you that in a long time. Too long."

Margaret's eyes filled. No tears fell, but her voice quivered slightly. "I know that, Wayne Samuels. I've always known that."

And David—David who, more than she, had been able to come and go from the room without seeming to be affected by the man who lay there—David seemed strangely subdued.

Of course Frances identified the items that she had seen at the park. Of course the crystal jaguar had returned from Blake's locked truck.

And of course, with the close of the meal they ate simply because they had to, and because Margaret put it on the table in front of them, the questions began. Tentatively. Touching first on what was real, normal, and known, before moving into speculation. Crazy Marian. Joe and his greed. Ralph and his greed. Frances's grandfather's part in the commercial digs.

The deaths of diggers and dealers. The disappearance of Lucy and Walter. The three brutal deaths that had taken place in the last four days.

Anne listened, not sharing, allowing David to speak for them. Thinking about the man upstairs. Thinking about the world he must have known. Thinking about the world that had dragged him back.

Thinking about David, as he glanced up sharply at something that was said. As he frowned later at something else. As he reached for her hand and held it against his thigh, massaging her fingers almost unconsciously as one portion of his fertile mind worked on some problem while another engaged in the conversation now flowing around the table.

Did he know he touched her as though she had been a part of his life forever?

During the meal and discussion, Blake had regained his voice and his vocabulary. "So what we're saying is, if we don't protect that not-so-small fortune Anne found, the cats are going to do it for us?"

Anne shuddered at his choice of words.

"That about sums it up, Blake," David told him.

"Well, hell." The sheriff in Blake took over. "Let's see who knows about this. Marian Hansom. Now she's a wild card in any deck. Who knows what she's liable to say or to whom? Joe Hansom, who apparently wants it bad enough to spend a fortune on care for a grandmother he must know is using him, bad enough to risk his political campaign and future as a free man to break into this house at least once already. Stephen Carlton, who might not know who you two are now but probably has the resources to find out." He did a quick head count. "The six of us. Anybody else? Nellie? The little girl?"

David shook his head. "No. I don't think so. Wayne?"

"Not from us. She came in with Maggie after the clinic closed and except for the little bit of time she was in the kitchen earlier, she's shut herself up in that front bedroom, sleeping."

"That's another thing," Blake said. "Somebody want to tell me what happened to her?"

"Not now, Blake," Margaret said. "I think she should, and Anne thinks she should, but Nellie is scared to death to get you involved—"

"Well, hell, that's reason enough—"

"And as soon as I can convince her of that, I will call you," Margaret promised.

"The problem is, what to do with a monetary and scientific fortune," Wayne said. "A deadly fortune."

"Yep. That about says it," David admitted. He turned to Frances. "Tell me, now that you've seen it, now that you've heard what can happen, do you think there's a snowball's chance that *any* museum would honor a requirement not to separate the burial?"

"I want to say yes," Frances said slowly. "But there's been so much competition over the years, so much rivalry, and so many items that have simply disappeared, that I'm afraid I can't."

"Marian doesn't want Joe to get his hands on it before she dies," Blake offered. "There's always a possibility she'd keep her mouth shut about its location. Could we maybe build a vault around it and just leave it here? At least until you folks found someone you could trust to turn it over to?"

"I'll go along with whatever Anne decides," Wayne said, "but Blake, do you really think that would be a wise course of action?"

"Hell, no, I don't think it's wise. I want it out of my county. I just don't know how to get it gone without risking more lives."

"Annie." David lifted her hand from his thigh. She missed the warmth and nearness until he clasped it in both of his. "Even though I agree with Blake on this, I'll go along with whatever you want done. But we have to hear from you. What do *you* want to do?"

She looked around the table at the small coterie of caring people gathered there. What did she want? She wanted the impossible. She wanted him at peace. "I just want to put him back."

She saw sympathy in their eyes. And compassion. And regret for what couldn't be.

Frances propped her elbows on the table and clasped her hands under her chin. And looked at Anne. Really looked at her. And opened her mouth on a silent word. And lifted her head. "Well, why not?"

"What?" That was the last thing Anne had expected anyone to say.

Apparently it was the last thing any of them expected anyone to say. Her question was only one of five.

Frances held up her hands, asking for silence. "Wait a minute. Let me think. Oh, God, let me think." She caught her hands to her mouth and rocked back and forth in silence for what seemed like forever as Anne waited, scarcely daring to breathe. *Could they do this? Could they restore him to the grave that had been stolen from him?*

"Okay." Frances pulled her hands from her mouth and stopped her rocking. "Craig Mound is sterile soil. What that means is that it was dug out and dynamited by the pothunters, and sliced away in thin vertical layers by the W.P.A. and the university, until there was nothing left on the original location. Nothing. Down to a depth low enough that the excavators were sure was below the level of any possible archaeological find. Then the dirt was sifted and sieved until the tiniest fragments were found and removed and catalogued. And then the soil was replaced and shaped to the measurements and specifications and photographs that were available at the time.

"There's no reason for anyone ever to dig in that mound again. Except . . ."

Anne realized she had been holding her breath. She released it, but she didn't release her grip on David's hand. "Except for what, Frances?"

"Except for a rumor that crops up every few years about constructing a viewing chamber in Craig. But you know how state government works. And since the oil bust, finances are really tight. We can't even get authorization for more excavation—Brown hasn't been completed, Copple barely started, the Plaza only sampled—so the chances of something like a viewing chamber are almost nonexistent. Almost, I have to say. But if we're careful, we can put him away from where any possible chamber should be located."

Now they all looked at Anne. *Whatever she wanted to do.* The decision was hers. David endured the pressure of her fingers on his, even gave hers a slight squeeze in encouragement.

Yes. This seemed right. She leaned against David's shoulder and let the rightness wash over her. "Yes," she said. "Yes. Let's do it."

"When?" David asked.

"The park's closed tomorrow," Frances said.

"The sooner the better," Blake added.

Margaret glanced at Anne. "Then the clinic is closed tomorrow, too. I'll need a few minutes in the morning to reschedule the appointments."

As quickly as that, it was decided.

Wayne and Margaret opted to stay there the rest of the night rather than wake up Nellie and Lilly and move them for what could be no more than a few hours.

Anne invited Frances to stay, but she insisted she had

to get back to her grandparents, and that she needed time in the morning at the park before they arrived. Agreeing on when and telling them where they should meet the following day, she said good night. "Just hope the blasted tractor won't decide that tomorrow is a good day for it to go on strike," she said on her way out the door, and Anne knew she was only half joking. "It does that with disgusting regularity."

Blake left with Frances, promising to escort her safely at least as far as the county line.

Anne showed Margaret and Wayne to an upstairs room and found linens for them, but when she offered to help make the bed, Margaret shooed her away. "Go on," she said. "You have to be dead on your feet."

And she was. Almost. Until she was ready for bed. Until David and Wayne were making one last check around the outside of the house. Until she accepted that there was something she had to do.

Removing the panel had become almost easy over the last few days. Now Anne slipped it aside and entered the room. She considered not even turning on the light, but she wanted to see him one last time. She pulled the cord, flooding the room with light from the bare bulb, and looked around the shabby chamber where a once powerful ruler had lain hidden for half a century. As tombs went, it wasn't much.

She knelt at his feet and lifted the small cedar box containing the miniatures. Nothing growled at her when she picked it up. Why? Because she realized how special it must have been to him and to the woman pictured? She didn't open it. She didn't need to; the images were engraved on her memory. Instead, she touched it reverently and placed it where she had first seen it, where it had returned after Blake had tossed it down. Near that fragile, vulnerable left foot.

She felt tears on her cheeks and let them fall freely.

"Are we doing the right thing?" she asked.

But of course he didn't answer. He would never again answer anyone.

"Annie. Oh, Annie." She heard a wealth of anguish in David's voice as he dropped his hands to her shoulders and pulled her back against his thighs.

"I'm just saying good-bye," she told him. "I need to do that."

He didn't argue with her. Perhaps he had his own need to say good-bye, perhaps he only felt he had to guard her. He kept his hands on her shoulders, standing over her, until something within her told her it was time to let go. She looked up at him, and he helped her to her feet. Only then did he touch her in any other way. He lifted his hands to her face and traced the path of her tears. "He's dead, Annie. He's been dead for a long, long time."

"Yes," she said. "I know." And she knew something else. The reason for the anguish in David's voice and in his eyes as he looked down at her. This man loved her. Whether he admitted it or not.

"I learned something today," she told him.

She knew why he touched her face, because she felt the same need to touch him, to affirm that he was real, that he was here, with her. She lifted her hands and traced his cheekbones, the fading bruise, the fine line of his nose, his cleanly sculpted lips. She saw the pulse beating in his temple and touched her fingers to it, feeling its echoing beat in her own heart.

"You may not want to hear this," she warned, "but I don't think I can fail to tell you."

He tensed beneath her touch, but she wouldn't let him pull away from her. Sighing, she leaned forward, feeling the beat of his heart beneath her cheek, feeling the strength of muscle beneath her arms as she held him to her.

"I learned I love you, David Huerra. Whether you stay in Allegro or return to Dallas, whether you want me for a lifetime or only for a month, I love you."

She heard what sounded suspiciously like a groan before he tightened his arms around her, pulling her impossibly close. "Oh, God, Annie, I was going out of my mind thinking about you in here grieving for your warrior—"

"I was, David," she told him. "I believe there's a part of me that always will, and *please* don't ask me to explain that because I don't think I can. But there's another part of me, the part that lives and feels and wants and dreams, that is so glad you came into my life."

"Annie—" His breath whispered on her cheek before he turned with her, reaching one-handed for the light cord. "Let's get out of here."

Loving was a celebration, Anne realized when they returned to their room and David took her in his arms. A celebration of living, of the spirits of each of the lovers. Or was there no separation of spirit? Because David's touch, his caress, his need, blended so completely with her touch, her caress, her need, that she was no longer sure where Anne stopped and David began. *If* Annie stopped and David began.

Morning dawned gray and cold, probably little, if any, above freezing. David eased into the morning warily, watching his breath condense in the frigid, unheated room.

Annie had burrowed under the covers and lay as close to him as she could get without crawling inside of him. He could just see the top of her head beneath the edge of the blankets, but he could feel her warmth along the length of him, the soft cushion of her breast against his side, her leg wrapped over his, her foot seeking his calf for warmth. He could feel the beat of the pulse in her arm where it rested across his ribs and feel the puff of her slow, steady breath against his throat.

Annie loved him. Anne Locke loved him, David Huerra, beat-up, washed-up cop.

What the hell was he supposed to do about that?

26

A *few harsh, dry snowflakes* dusted the tops of the vehicles in the driveway when Anne made her way to the kitchen to begin preparations for breakfast, but by the time Blake arrived and Wayne and Margaret returned, they had melted, though the day still promised to remain a grim and chilly gray.

Lilly bounced into the kitchen as the conspirators ate a hasty meal, followed by Nellie, whose bruises were even more prominent, and who walked as though each step had to be taken with painful deliberation.

Nellie. Oh, lord, Nellie. How could she have forgotten about her? Anne rose to go to the young woman, but Nellie spotted Blake at the table and stopped with a sharp gasp. "Sheriff?"

Blake rose. Anne saw the moment he realized the extent of the beating Nellie had taken, but to his credit, he hid that response from Nellie. "Morning, Nellie. You're just in time for breakfast. Come on over and have some orange juice, honey."

Nellie cast a wounded, betrayed glance at Anne, but with Lilly bubbling through her good morning greetings

to Wayne and David, she had little choice but to continue into the room.

David stood and held a chair for her, and by the time
Nellie reached it, she was too weak to do more than collapse gratefully onto it.

David's eyes met hers over Nellie's head. Anne recognized his silent message. Nellie needed more medical
help than a few aspirin and bed rest. She needed someone to take the responsibility of caring for her child
while she healed; she needed someone to tend to her
meals and her medication, and to see that her physical
needs were met. She needed warmth and caring and
loving.

And soon, very soon, all of those who could have
given her that care and love would be leaving this house
for several hours.

Nellie was also a wild card in their hasty and secret
plans.

Could they trust her? Should they trust her? Or
would confiding in her only give her a burden she
wasn't equipped to carry?

Having completed her flirting, Lilly climbed into
Margaret's lap and demanded juice. Wayne laughed.
"Well, I guess that tells us who she thinks is really
important."

"Not so." Margaret glanced up at her husband with a
smile so full of love it hurt Anne to watch. "We saw who
she went to first."

Already standing, David brought glasses, plates, and
flatware from the cabinet to the table.

Nellie cringed from him. Without seeming to notice,
David poured juice in her glass, passed her the toast,
and spooned scrambled eggs onto her plate. Only then
did he return to his chair by Anne's side.

Nellie looked at the food on her plate, at her

daughter happily seated on Margaret's lap, and the people around the table who welcomed her into their midst and asked no questions. Her eyes filled. With a moan she stumbled to her feet. "I— I'm— Excuse me."

Anne watched as Nellie made her way from the room. No, damn it! The girl didn't need to be alone. And she was just a girl, even if she did have a four-year-old daughter. A girl who had to be in as much emotional pain as she was in physical pain. And if Anne understood anything, it was emotional pain. She tossed her napkin to the table as she stood. "Excuse me," she said. But without waiting for response she followed Nellie.

Nellie sat on the edge of the bed. Her tears streamed unchecked; her fragile shoulders shook. "You think I should talk to Blake, don't you?"

Anne sat beside her and carefully pulled Nellie against her, cradling her, for the moment, against the pain of the world. "Yes, I do. But that isn't why he's here."

"It isn't?"

"No."

"I'm such a coward. My daddy always told me that. I thought— I thought when I saw all of you there that you were going to make me tell."

"But you came on into the room. And you sat there, even though you were obviously terrified. That doesn't sound very cowardly to me."

"But I—"

Anne held her shoulders and she leaned away and looked at Nellie's ravaged face. "Blake is here, and Margaret and Wayne, too, because something pretty serious happened yesterday. To . . . To David and to me. Something we need their help to deal with."

"Do you want me to leave?"

This child thought she was a coward? Good lord, did

she know how much strength it would have taken for Anne to have asked that question?

"No. But we're going to leave you. I don't think you should be alone. What I think we should do is take you to Gretta for the day."

"And let her see . . ."

"And let her take care of you and Lilly. The other option is to leave you here alone. Lilly is wonderful, but she's an active four year old, and while I think you'll be safe here, I don't think you're strong enough to care for her right now. Not by yourself."

"Can I think about it a little while? Is there time for me to do that?"

"Yes. Yes, of course there's time. Why don't you lie back down. We'll send Lilly to you after breakfast, and you can give me your answer then."

The five of them crowded into the hidden room. David knew they had to begin. Frances would already have begun excavation. The longer they postponed this, the harder it would be.

Wayne had suggested one solution to the transport. To the burial. Tarps and sleeping bags. Anne had suggested another. Her vacuum cleaner looked incongruous beside a prehistoric relic.

She had gathered a great deal of soil with her hands and sprinkled it on the one opened sleeping bag they had spread to the immediate right of the warrior. Now the men exchanged troubled glances. It would either work, or it wouldn't.

Some sort of canvas lay across the ribbing of cedar poles. Would it hold?

David stepped to the head of the burial, Blake to the right, Wayne to the left. With quiet, drill-like precision each bent and grasped the visible tarp. Anne watched quietly from the foot until they started to rise. Then she stepped closer and grasped the tarp. And Margaret moved to stand beside Wayne, also sharing the responsibility for disturbing the grave.

The contents shifted and slid as they lifted, and the ancient tarp ripped in places, threatening to tear completely, and sending dirt slithering down to the old wooden floor, but it held while they moved the few feet necessary and lowered it to the waiting bag.

The cats remained quiet.

Or maybe this was one of those times when they wouldn't hear them.

"Whatcha doin'?"

David jerked to his feet. Anne whirled around. The others seemed frozen in place.

Lilly. Four-year-old Lilly, who was supposed to be safely downstairs in her mother's care, stood at the opening from the closet.

All innocence, the girl came into the room and walked to Wayne's side. "Will you play hide and seek with me?" Trusting, totally ignorant of the danger she was in, she lifted her arms to Wayne to be picked up, and when he did she plopped her thumb in her mouth and looked down at the copper-covered skeleton.

"Did he get dead?"

Anne's eyes met David's, begging for guidance. Hell! How was he supposed to know what to do?

"Yes," he said. "But it was a long, long time ago."

"And it's a secret, Lilly. A big secret."

Lilly studied Anne's words. "Like the man who hurt my mama?"

"Yes, darling," Anne told her, finding words David couldn't. "But it's a secret even your mama doesn't know. A secret that she must not know. No one else must know."

"What you don't know can't hurt you?"

"What?"

Lilly slid her little arm around Wayne's neck. "My grandma told me. I'd ask her, and she'd say that. But it did. My mama kept saying she didn't know, but he didn't believe her. That kind of secret?"

Annie's smile almost faltered, but she managed to hold onto it. "Yes, darling. That kind of secret."

"Okay," she said, squirming. Wayne shrugged, but he let her down. What else could he do?

Lilly bent to the jumbled pile of grave goods. The crystal jaguar had shifted to the top of the pile. She picked it up. David sucked in a breath, but nothing growled or menaced, and after a moment, she put it down and looked at the copper mask covering the skull. "Will you put him someplace where nobody can hurt him again?"

He saw Anne's eyes close. In prayer? Maybe.

"Yes, darlin'," he promised her. "That's what we're doing now."

"Okay." She flashed him a brilliant grin. "I've got to go back to my mama now."

The five of them watched in stunned silence as she skipped from the room.

Blake broke the silence. "What will we do?"

"Nothing," Wayne said. "There's nothing we can do."

"Yes, there is." Annie picked up her vacuum cleaner hose and switched the machine on, sucking the spilled dirt into the clean bag.

Yes. There was. David recognized the wisdom of her actions. He reached for the second sleeping bag and shook it open over the burial, then knelt to connect the zippers.

It wasn't a perfect solution. The grave goods jostled together inside the combined sleeping bags, and Annie hadn't been able to get all of the soil. The floorboards had dried out over the years of darkness, had shrunk and separated, and now a generous portion of the grave dirt lay between them and the subflooring or the ceiling of the room below. But it was a solution.

The rear seats of the Suburban had already been removed by a previous owner in an attempt to convert a nine-passenger truck to a hunting camper. It all would fit. They'd make sure of that. Anne and David had decided they couldn't risk separating any part of it at this point, not even with the dirt. And they couldn't risk the lives of any of their friends by asking someone else to transport any of it. The three men maneuvered the sleeping bags into the back of the truck. The poles were the problem. But they, too, fit. Barely, by extending them over the back of the front seat and bracing them between the windshield and the rear cargo door.

David slammed the cargo door and turned to Anne. "We need to go."

"Yes."

But first there was something else that must be done. He went with Anne back into the house. The bedroom door was open. Lilly played quietly on the floor beside the bed where Nellie slept. Anne sat on the side of the bed.

"Nellie."

The young woman moaned and turned her head on the pillow.

"Nellie. Wake up. We need to take you to Gretta's now."

"Oh."

Nellie eased up against the headboard, grimacing and holding herself against her pain. "Now?" she asked.

"Now." Anne told her.

"Let me— I—" Nellie shook her head and then sucked in a sharp breath. "I was going to say, let me wake up, but I think that just did it." She fell quiet, breathing with deliberate care. "I don't think I can. Not just yet. In a little while, maybe. Probably."

"We have to leave now, Nellie."

Nellie bit at her lip. "I can call Gretta in a few minutes. I can ask her to come for me. I will. I promise I will."

Anne didn't look convinced, but she knew they had to go. She gave Nellie a gentle hug and Lilly a fiercer one. "Take care of your mama, cupcake. Do you know how to dial zero for help?"

"Of course."

Anne brushed her lips across Lilly's hair. "Of course. How silly of me."

"We had to leave her, Annie," David told her later, on their way to the mounds.

"I know."

"She'll be all right."

Anne looked at him over the barrier of the cedar poles separating them. "I know that, too."

Frances had told them where to park. A road ran along the east side of the park, back out of sight to a parking area where the archaeology students had camped the summer they helped excavate the Plaza. From there, half hidden now by briars, a stile crossed the fence and led to the north side of Craig Mound.

Blake led the way in his Jimmy, insisting they might need his police radio to summon help.

David and Anne followed in the Suburban.

Wayne and Margaret guarded the rear and brought the tarps and shovels they might need.

Frances met them at the stile. "We have freezing rain, maybe snow in the forecast for this morning."

Damn! Nothing about this was going to be easy.

But maybe it was. The tractor had started. And Frances had been busy. Very busy. She had already stripped sod from the back of the mound and stacked it neatly to one side and had opened a pit low in the back side of the mound. It was much lower than the relatively late burial of this man would have put him. But it was wide enough to accommodate the width of the poles and the litter burial, and it was long enough to accommodate his height.

They hurried. Even Anne, who'd visibly had to force herself to climb the stile and help carry the warrior into the park. The chances of being seen from the distant road were slim, and Frances argued that because she occasionally gave private tours she could explain their presence, if necessary.

They lay the poles in place over an all-weather tarp, lay the sleeping-bag-encased warrior on top of the poles, as he had been placed centuries before, straightening the bag even while knowing the goods would probably resettle themselves the way they had over the last fifty years, and finally they covered the entire burial with another all-weather tarp.

The six of them stood silently. David felt he ought to say something. His Catholic God was used to words at a time like this. He saw Anne's lips moving in familiar ritual and pulled her close with an arm over her shoulder. Each of them was having a similar problem.

Each of them was forgetting something very important. He looked around at the cluster of friends, so like mourners, who shared this moment. Six of them. Burying a fortune without one complaint about the loss of that fortune. Burying a man that none of them had known but who would forever be a part of their lives. "The words he would want to hear have already been said."

Anne smiled up at him through misty eyes. "Yes." She too looked around at the conspirators. "Thank you. All of you."

"One last thing." Frances pulled a plastic bag from her pocket and knelt beside the grave where she tagged the bag to a zipper pull.

"What?" Anne asked.

"Just a warning," Frances told her. "In case he's ever found, those who find him have to be warned to keep this burial together."

It was done.

All that remained was to close the grave.

Wayne commandeered the tractor, freeing Frances from this last, heavy work, and when the bulk of the soil had been replaced, they all took shovels and rakes and tamped and packed and filled, and eventually covered the raw wound on the mound with the waiting sod.

The snow started as they were gathering tools, preparing to leave. Frances looked up as the wet, fluffy flakes began drifting to the ground in rapid succession. "Thank you," she whispered.

She straightened and handed the shovel and hoe she had picked up to David. "Go now," she said. "These roads can get treacherous."

They went. At Fairview they all pulled into the parking lot at the sheriff's office. They looked at each other, but there didn't seem to be anything further to say. At least not now. Without speaking, Blake left his Jimmy and walked toward the courthouse, Wayne and Margaret turned toward an alternate route that would lead to their isolated mountain, and David and Anne headed for a purple house now emptied of its curse.

But maybe not quite.

◇ ◇ ◇

David had expected the eerie sensation that first warned him of something ominous in the house to be gone when they returned.

It wasn't.

Or maybe it was his own depression he felt settling over him as they reached the top of the driveway and he parked the Suburban. Depression caused by the knowledge that he still had nothing to offer Anne Locke.

He turned off the key and sat in the truck and looked at that damned blank wall that he had first seen—what?—ten days ago? Only ten days? Eleven now. It seemed as though this house and this woman had been a part of his life for years. If they had been, would David now be considering telling Annie they had no future?

He felt her hand on his cheek, turning him to face her. "Don't say it," she told him. "Don't even think it. Not yet. We have the rest of your month. Besides," she said with a tremulous smile, "we haven't necked in this wonderful truck yet."

He pulled her against him and buried his face in her glorious hair. *Annie, my Annie,* he cried silently. *I don't want to leave you. I never wanted to leave you.*

But he would.

It was inevitable.

Why?

The snow had followed them south and intensified in the higher elevations of the mountains surrounding Allegro. In the minutes since they had stopped it had gathered in the corners of the windshield and built up against the wiper blades, although it still melted when it touched the hood. He glanced around. The outbuildings were already dusted white.

"We'd better go in," he told her and watched his breath condense in the rapidly chilling air.

She rubbed her cheek against his chest and rested it a moment over his heart, but eventually she lifted her head and pulled away from him. A seductive smile softened her eyes and parted her lips. "Yes," she said. "I think we'd better."

They made it into the kitchen before she turned to him again. The door had been unlocked. He frowned at it, trying to remember if they had left it that way. Surely not, not with Nellie in the house. But Annie shrugged out of her jacket and dropped it to the floor, and she lifted her hands to peel him out of his.

Annie, an intentionally seductive Annie, was almost more temptation than he could resist. He caught her hands with his, stilling her. "Do you know what you're doing?"

She grinned at him. "I hope so. But if I don't, can you teach me?"

"It's called an affirmation of life, Annie."

She looked at him, all seriousness now. "I certainly hope so. But it's also called love, David. Something we're going to have to talk about. But not yet. Not just yet."

No. Please, God. Not yet. He wasn't ready to leave her yet. "Right. So what do you say to closing up the house, taking the phone off the hook, and locking ourselves in an upstairs bedroom for the next three weeks or so?"

She lifted her hands to his neck and stretched against him. "Sounds good to me."

"I'm afraid that will have to wait a while."

Anne's hands clenched on his neck. David jerked his head up to confront the menace in the words that had just echoed across the kitchen. She tried to turn, but he pressed her face against his chest and held her still.

Joe Hansom stood in the door to the butler's pantry. He looked as immaculate as the last time—the only time—David had seen him. From his black, western-cut leather coat, black denim jeans, black triple-stitched custom boots, to the .38 Colt revolver held in his black-leather gloved hand.

"This is not a good idea," David said, moving to place Anne behind him. He'd hidden his pistol inside a tin on the top shelf of a cabinet near the sink when he'd realized Lilly would be in the house. Fifteen endless feet away.

"Don't move."

Maybe not as immaculate. And definitely not as contained. There was a wildness about Joe, in his eyes and in the jerky motions of his head, that David had not seen at the café. And he was, after all, Crazy Marian's grandson.

"Is whatever you want worth this, Hansom?"

"I said don't move."

David opened his hands behind Annie's back, but he refused to release her. If necessary, he could spin with her held this way, turning to put himself between her and Joe.

"Step away from her. My argument's not with you."

"Oh, I think you just invited me into it."

"Hush, David," Annie murmured against his chest. "Don't antagonize him."

Tiny tremors worked their way through her in wave after wave. Oh, hell. It was Chicago all over again. She had to be thinking that. There was no way he was letting her go. "It's all right, Annie," he said softly. "It's all right."

"What is it, Hansom? What do you want?"

"I want to know if she's going to file charges. I want to know why you've been spending all this time with Blake Foresman. I want to know where that secret room is. And you're going to help me find it.

"It's all connected. I know that. I just had no idea it

was here, in the house. If she'd told me that in time, I could have bought it. I would have bought it. And then the two of you wouldn't have been snooping where you have no right to snoop.

"So move away from her and come on, slowly, carefully. It's upstairs. I know that much. I've been talking to that crazy old woman for years, and she finally gave me enough of the pieces to figure that much out.

"*Move!*"

"Annie," David said, feeling the shudder that wracked her at Joe's sharp command. "You can do this, darlin'." She nodded her head against his chest once, quickly, and raised her head. Maybe she could do it. And maybe this was the final straw that would send Anne Locke so far inside herself she'd never find her way out. "We can do it," he promised her, "together."

She took one step back from him, under her own power, and stood waiting. "Together," he said again.

"Upstairs," Hansom said. "Come on. Let's go."

David didn't know how Annie made it up the stairs unless it was by raw nerve. Each time David reached to help her, Hansom poked the gun in her back, far enough away that David had no chance of disarming him.

At the top of the stairs Hansom stopped them. "Now," he said, "where do you think my crazy grandmother would hide a secret room?"

Annie raised her head and looked at Joe with eyes that had already seen too much death to doubt what would follow. "Where do you think, Joe? Someplace where she could have easy access."

She was going to tell him. And why not. A protracted search might have given David more opportunities for a chance at overpowering Joe, but perhaps the shock of discovering he was only hours too late might do the same.

"You know!"

Anne drew herself tall. "Of course I know. But it will do you no good."

Joe gestured with the gun.

Damn it, Annie, David thought. Take your own advice. Don't antagonize him. Not now. Not until I can take advantage of it.

She led Joe directly to Marian's old room. Directly to the closet. Directly to the panel. Opened it for him. And stepped out of sight into the hidden room.

"Damn it!" Joe yelled. "Come out of there!"

"Don't you want to come in, Joe? Don't you want to see what your grandmother has kept hidden for fifty years?"

David's mind raced through a quick mental inventory of what was left in the room. A couple of barrels. A broken and discarded bed frame. A chest of drawers against the windowless wall. Anne's vacuum cleaner with its metal wand. Maybe. Maybe, if he could just get to it. If he could just make a moment for surprise. Don't do anything rash, Annie. He sent the thought silently. Please don't do anything rash.

She turned on the light.

Joe waved him forward and through the opening, but he followed too quickly for David to do more than reach Anne's side.

Inside the room the man stopped and stared at the siding visible through the windows, at the tattered floral wallpaper, at the dismal furniture and bare-bulbed light. He shook his head and turned in a wide circle, searching the room but never completely taking his attention from David or Anne.

"Where are they!?"

His cry rang through the room, shocking even him. He rocked back on his heels and took a deep breath. "Where are they?"

Yes, where were they? David wondered, but about something that had to be completely different. A pair of golden attack cats would come in handy right about now.

But they were gone.

Protecting the dead.

"This is all there is," David said. "This is what you have been paying for, for how many years, Joe?"

"No. You've found them. You've done something with them. But you haven't told Foresman. Not yet. I'd have known if you had. So there's hope. There's hope."

Was there?

"Found what, Joe?"

"Oh, no. No you don't."

And when Joe Hansom looked at them with Marian's eyes, David knew that there would be no escape. Not for both of them. But if he was careful, if he played the man just right, maybe Annie would live. Please, he prayed, to his God, to the god of the man they had just reburied, to any god who would listen. Please let Annie live.

David took a half-step forward. "Found what, Joe? Or who?"

Beside him, Anne sucked in a sharp breath and tensed. But she wasn't staring at Joe; she was staring past him.

Oh, God. He almost moaned. Lilly stood in the opening. There was no way he could tell her to run or hide without calling Joe's attention to her, and she did that herself, darting past him to run to Anne.

"What the—" Joe spun around and fired a shot that went wide. Wildly wide.

Now or never, David thought. I love you Annie. He sent that thought to her. Be safe. Please, God, be safe.

He felt the blow. It knocked him to his knees before he reached Joe. Too soon. Too soon.

And finally he heard the sound. Annie's body jerked as though she had been shot, too.

Beg, darlin', he tried to say. Do what you have to, but live. God, yes. Please live.

But Annie didn't beg. With a screech, she thrust Lilly behind her and ran at Joe. "You will not kill him," she screamed. "*You will not kill him!*"

He couldn't move. His legs wouldn't work. His knees wouldn't straighten. Not even his hand would raise. He could only watch as Annie, brave, foolish Annie, tackled a man with a loaded revolver and as Joe—two Joes now in his rapidly blurring vision—caught her and twisted her around, holding the gun at her throat, as a shadow—someone—edged from the opening into the room, swinging something . . . swinging something high and hard and connecting with the back of Joe Hansom's head as the noise echoed through David's and finally his knees gave out and he fell the rest of the way to the floor.

"Damned hard head."

"Hush, Blake."

David swam back to consciousness and a ringing in his head that resembled Big Ben at noon inside a closed car.

Consciousness.

He didn't die.

Annie leaned over him with a cloth in her hand. A bloody cloth. God. A head wound? How bad?

He could think. He could see. And even with that infernal clanging in his head, he could hear.

He could feel. Hands. Feet. Arms. Legs.

Annie's expression as she looked down at him was grave. But her eyes were clear. She had cried. He could see the evidence of that on her cheeks. But she wasn't crying now. And she was here, fully here, with him. Not locked inside herself.

"I don't believe it, Huerra," Blake said. "Yeah, I do. Pete said you were stubborn. Just thank your lucky stars that your skull's so thick and Joe was such a bad shot."

"Hush, Blake," Annie said again.

He'd been moved, stretched out on that hideous sofa in Marian's sitting room.

That was a good sign, wasn't it? He tested moving his tongue and his lips. "Lilly?" he croaked.

Anne's hand stilled on his head. Her eyes closed and her head bent forward. Almost touching his. Almost.

"She's fine," Anne said. "She came to tell us that she had dialed zero and told the operator that the bad man who hurt her mama was here, that Doc Anne needed Sheriff Blake right now, and that she'd found the key and let her mama out of the closet where Joe had locked her."

Joe. Damn! He was the one who had terrified Nellie. "Who— Who took him out?"

"Nellie." Anne's eyes filled with more tears and her voice caught. "She swears she's never going to cower from anyone or anything again as long as she lives."

"Is she—"

"She'll be all right." Annie answered before he had to force out all the words. "Margaret and Wayne are here. Margaret's with her."

"You?"

She touched her palm to his cheek. "I think I know how Nellie feels."

It was good—it was more than good—having her hovering over him, touching him with such tender care, if the damned bells would quit long enough for him to remember what had seemed so clear just before Lilly burst into the hidden room.

He shifted on the sofa and dragged himself up.

"Be still," Anne ordered.

"I'm fine."

She choked on a laugh. Or was it a sob? "You're not fine. You've very probably got a concussion."

"And a dashing bullet wound?" he asked. He had a feeling she would be leading him a merry chase for the rest of their lives. Hell, might as well play this damned headache for a little sympathy. It would probably be the last he got from her.

She shook her head. "Close, but no cigar."

He turned his head—bad mistake—to look at the bloody cloth she had stashed in the basin beside him and the suture tray beside it.

Once again she lay her hand against his cheek. Tears and laughter mingled in her eyes, but it was Foresman who spoke. "Hell, Huerra. The really spectacular wound came from hitting your head on Annie's vacuum cleaner when you passed out."

"No hospital."

He remembered saying those words, and apparently someone had listened, because when he awoke again, he was in bed. His and Annie's bed. He was alone, covered against the cold with the electric blanket turned on, staring at a buildup of fat, wet snow in the window ledges.

And the ringing—the *gong*ing—had stopped.

Damn! A head hard enough to deflect a bullet. And taken out by a vacuum cleaner. If Pete found out, he was never going to live this down.

But he was going to live. For a while there he'd been too damned sure he wouldn't. And Annie was going to live. With him.

He made a few tentative stretches with his legs. They

worked. They worked just fine. He eased himself to the side of the bed and sat up.

And he was still dressed, except for his boots and shirt. That simplified matters. He looked around the room and found his duffel bag. Carefully he knelt and rummaged through it until he came up with a pair of loafers. Better than boots anyway, right now. No tugging. No jarring. He slipped his feet into them and stuffed his arms in a soft, worn flannel shirt. Then he turned and came face to face with his bandaged, battered reflection in the dressing table mirror.

Matched bruises.

Damn.

If Joe had to shoot him in the head, why hadn't he had the decency to keep the bruise on the side that was already discolored? Now he really would look like an outlaw.

Joe. Joe. *Where are they?* Found what, Joe? Or who? *Where are they?*

And then he remembered what he had seen so clearly just before Lilly ran into the room.

"Oh, hell."

The cops were gone. Nellie and Lilly were gone. Everyone was gone except Wayne and Margaret, Blake, and Anne. David found them in the kitchen, still the only warm room in the house, all looking frazzled and about as bad as he felt.

"Caffeine," he said from the door to the hallway, remembering a morning only a few days before when he had teased and bullied Annie into feeding him and giving him coffee and letting him out of a trip to the hospital.

Anne jumped up from her chair and started toward him. Halfway across the room she stopped and frowned at him. "You belong in bed."

He grinned at her. "Go with me?"

Blake choked back a laugh.

David looked at the three still seated at the table. Now was as good a time as any, better than most. "I'm going to marry Anne Locke. The sooner the better. You're all invited."

Wayne smiled at Margaret and lifted his hand in salute. "Don't you think you ought to ask her?"

"Good idea. Annie, can I please, please have a cup of coffee?"

Anne closed her eyes, shook her head, and sighed. "Sit down," she insisted. "At least do that."

Gladly. Maybe he wasn't up to all that still had to be done. Nonsense. It *had* to be done. He pulled out a chair and eased himself onto it.

"Do me a favor, Huerra," Blake said. "Next time you decide you need a little peace and quiet, may I suggest Alaska for your vacation? Antarctica? Anywhere but my county? I'll be doing paperwork and fighting reporters over this day's work, and that's just the part we'll tell them about, clear up until time for reelection. What in the hell got into Joe? What *they* was he screaming about? He didn't see the cats, did he?"

Annie leaned against him, her arm over his shoulder. David drank in the warmth of her closeness. "Is it time for some more of those nice horse aspirin yet, Doc?"

Anne shook her head. "Don't press your luck. Blake can have an ambulance here in a heartbeat."

"Yeah." And the time for teasing had passed. "How about the county coroner?"

"What?"

David slipped his arm around Annie's waist and returned her hug. "Joe may have meant the burial and the artifacts, but I think the *they* he was talking about was much more current than the cats. I think he was talking about Walter and Lucy.

"I think Marian was holding him to her with more than the promise of a fortune, even a sizable one. That she was probably up to her old tricks of blackmail and coercion.

"With Joe's political aspirations and their family history, that wouldn't have been too difficult. And if bigamy or adultery or incest, take your pick depending on Marian's mood, wasn't enough of a scandal to keep him in line or was too far removed, why not throw in a couple of murders?"

"Marian killed them? Not the cats?"

"She never really said the cats killed them. Not to us. She quite pointedly didn't answer when I questioned her on that. What she said was the curse killed them. What she said was that they were trying to move the burial, maybe like we did, to keep it safe, but we'll never know for sure. That she returned the items that they had taken and picked up the cedar box to take it to the country with her and get rid of the woman's miniature, *too*. Remember, Anne?"

"Yes." She pulled a chair close and sank onto it. "But where are they? And why didn't anyone find them?"

"I think because no one was looking in the right place. She was in the hospital for weeks, Marian said, weeks and weeks and weeks. Ellie went with her. While they were gone, no one would have come up here, at least not after the original search, because of the story of Ralph and the curse, because of Marian's insistence on supernatural, killer cats. And when Ellie and Marian finally returned, no one could find Walter and Lucy.

"The car in the barn, Anne. The one your mother said Marian wouldn't let anyone drive. The car that sat through World War II with all its tires intact and the key in the ignition?

"I don't think Walter and Lucy went anywhere, because I believe Marian took her dive down the stairs before she had a chance to get rid of their bodies."

Blake and Wayne lifted the bar and opened the doors to the barn, but when they found the trunk lid on the old Ford coupe stuck, Wayne brought a pry bar from his truck and handed it to David.

The miasma of despair surrounding the car hadn't weakened. Beside him, Anne shuddered. Did she feel it, too? Or was he the only one?

He swallowed once—did he really want to do this?—and jammed the pry bar under the trunk lid, beneath the lock. It didn't budge; he simply didn't have the strength. Annie stepped aside as Wayne moved forward. He put his hands on the pry bar beside David's. "Let me help."

David searched Wayne's eyes and saw an acceptance of what was and what must be that was older than time. Yes. It was right for him to help. Together they bent over the bar, joining their efforts, until the old lock snapped and the lid popped loose.

"Blake?" David stepped back in acknowledgment of Blake's jurisdiction.

Blake fitted a towel under the edge of the trunk and lifted.

"Hell."

One syllable. Not three. But containing a wealth of emotion.

Annie clutched his arm. David dropped the pry bar and clutched her.

Was this the way she had felt when she grieved for the warrior? It felt as though it must be.

The two skeletons lay in the bottom of the trunk. Walter, for that was who it had to be, the larger of the two, lay on the bottom. The side of his skull that was visible clearly showed the fracture that had killed him. Lucy, smaller, almost tiny, lay draped over him, her arms and legs positioned awkwardly behind her as though she had been bound, but looking as though even in death she comforted him.

Annie burrowed her face against David's chest and moaned. Too much. This time it was too much for him. He turned, holding her tight and walked from the barn into the bright, harsh light reflected off the snow covering the yard, leaving the others there to deal with the reports and the realities.

He'd never be able to prove how Lucy Hansom died, but he knew. She'd died in the trunk of that car huddled over the body of the man she loved, hearing the cars and ambulance arrive for Marian and then the silence as she waited and no one came for her.

He stopped and grabbed Annie to him. "Whatever you want to do, Anne Locke, and wherever you want to live, I'm going to be there with you. City. Small town. Mountaintop. Deserted island. Somewhere. Anywhere. It doesn't matter anymore. Just as long as we're together."

Had he known all this on some level when he made his declaration in the kitchen? Somehow he thought he must have, that he must have known since the day he woke up on the side of a road and found her ordering him around and working her way into his heart. *Back* into his heart?

"And don't think you're getting out of this deal in thirty days," he warned. "This is forever, lady. Forever."

She turned her face up to his. Her eyes were washed with tears, but he saw enough love in them to last more than a couple of lifetimes. "Yes," she said. Just, "Yes."

It was more than enough.

Epilogue

1990

Katherine Maria Huerra, named for her two grandmothers, decided to be born the night before Thanksgiving, two weeks early, in Dallas, Texas, at the hospital where her mother, who had at long last found her career home in pediatrics, practiced medicine.

Anne had been busy at her workbench when she admitted to herself that Katie was determined to make an appearance. She'd had time to put the finishing touches on the latest of the engraved copper plates that once again fascinated her, and to stack it with the others she had been almost driven to complete during her pregnancy. And then she reached for the telephone to call David.

David had returned to the Dallas P.D. Pete Tompkins hadn't taken his badge. Instead, when Pete retired he'd recommended David for promotion, citing intuition, integrity, and common sense among his numerous qualifications for the job. Now he found himself more often corralling reports and officers than criminals. But that was okay. That job was a necessary part of police work, too. And if it bought him more time with Anne, it was better than okay.

David let himself into the house through the garage door before Anne finished dialing. He grabbed the bag they had already packed, bundled her into the car, and hurried her to the hospital. He didn't tell her that the reason he had come home early was that for the first time in five years, he had heard the cats. Grumbling, fussing, but not angry. Not this time.

He might never tell her that.

He thought more often than he wanted to admit about Walter and Lucy, and about the warrior they had reburied. All of those involved did. That was obvious from their silence about it when they got together at the Hansom house in Allegro for their annual Thanksgiving dinner.

Only Blake would be sharing the meal with them tomorrow. Because of Anne's advanced pregnancy, their regular dinner had been held a month early this year. At that time Frances had quietly given him a copy of the legislation that had been introduced the year before giving federal protection to Native American funerary and sacred objects. It was too early to tell just how this legislation would develop and how it would work in actuality, but maybe, just maybe if the warrior were ever found there would be protection in place for him and because of that, for those who found him.

Frances Collins, on leave from the University of Oklahoma where she taught anthropology, heard the wind rising and looked out the window of her grandmother's house, toward the line of trees that marked the curve of the river, then farther, to the lights of the lock and dam, and then to the west, toward the park where the warrior lay buried. Her stomach tingled. Something was happening. Something completely unrelated to her grandfather's funeral, which she had attended that morning. She felt it. And then she saw the glow. Golden. Hanging low over the mounds. Circling them.

Wayne Samuels looked up from his woodcarver's bench as wind rattled the windows in the glass-walled room adjoining the kitchen in the house he and Margaret had bought from Anne. He didn't like living in town, even one as small as Allegro. He might never like it. But here at least he could walk in the woods when people crowded him too much. And Margaret needed to be here. She still worked at the clinic, keeping it open for the doctor who came three half-days a week. There was talk—just talk so far—of the possibility of a nurse practitioner license for registered nurses in rural areas of the state. Maggie would like that. And because she would, he would.

The house was big, too big for just the two of them. So, surprising himself, he had suggested they invite Nellie and Lilly to share it with them while Nellie finished high school and then began work on a degree at the community college in Fairview. And Nellie, surprising herself, he suspected, had agreed.

But right now, the house wasn't big enough. Wayne put down his carving and walked to the back door. Something was happening. Something he had to investigate.

In Dallas, caught in the grip of a powerful contraction, Anne clutched her husband's hand. He was there for her. Always. As he had promised.

Near Spiro, Frances climbed over the stile into the park and walked toward Craig Mound. Yes. The cats were there. Visible. Pacing, but not anxious.

The wind whistled down from the river, lifting the edge of her coat, then hesitated and with a sigh, stilled. And the cats were gone.

In Allegro, Wayne followed the wind to the restored

barn on the rear of the lot. Lilly had discovered it and used it as a playhouse, coming and going through a loose board beneath the rear window. She thought no one else knew about it. He thought that maybe she was what he heard in the barn tonight.

But that couldn't be. Lilly had gone into Fairview with her mother and the young man Nellie was dating.

So what . . .

Wayne opened one of the doors to the barn and stepped inside. The wind followed him, grabbing the door and banging it back, then hesitated, and with a sound as gentle as a sigh, left the barn in silence.

In Dallas, at 11:59, Katherine Maria gave her first triumphant cry. The lights in the hospital flickered once, probably because of the wind that had whipped itself into an almost unheard of frenzy for Dallas in November, but then steadied. David took his daughter from the doctor and held her in trembling arms. Little Katie was as beautiful as her mother, and Anne was so beautiful he sometimes wondered how he could have been so blessed. Not trusting himself not to drop her, he lay her on her mother's breast. Anne lifted one hand to Katie's back and the other to David, asking for his touch. She smiled at her daughter and then at him through a shimmer of tears.

She heard them, too. He knew she did when her hand tightened on his and her eyes widened, but not in fear. Not this time. Maybe never again. Against the backdrop of the hospital noises, the conversation between doctor and staff in the room with them, the bleeps and gurgles and thunks of machinery, and their awareness of the tiny miracle of Katie, the two of them heard the unmistakable sound of the cats. Not angry. Far from it. Not even fussing. The sound they heard could almost be described, if ever they dared describe it, as a contented purr.

Let HarperMonogram Sweep You Away

❦

BURNING LOVE by Nan Ryan
Winner of the *Romantic Times* Lifetime Achievement Award
While traveling across the Arabian desert, American socialite
Temple Longworth is captured by a handsome sheik.
Imprisoned in *El Siif*'s lush oasis, Temple struggles not to lose
her heart to a man whose touch promises ecstasy.

A LITTLE PEACE AND QUIET by Modean Moon
Bestselling Author
A handsome stranger is drawn to a Victorian house—and the
attractive woman who is restoring it. When an evil presence is
unleashed, David and Anne risk falling under its spell unless
they can join together to create a powerful love.

ALMOST A LADY by Barbara Ankrum
Lawman Luke Turner is caught in the middle of a Colorado
snowstorm, handcuffed to beautiful pickpocket Maddy
Barnes. While stranded in a hostile town, the unlikely couple
discovers more trouble than they ever bargained for—and
heavenly pleasures neither can deny.

DANCING MOON by Barbara Samuel
Fleeing from her cruel husband, Tess Fallon finds herself on the
Santa Fe trail and at the mercy of Joaquin Morales. He brands
her with his kiss, but they must conquer the threats of the past
before embracing the paradise found in each other's arms.

And in case you missed last month's selections...

MIRANDA by Susan Wiggs
Over One Million Copies of Her Books in Print
In Regency London, Miranda Stonecypher is stricken with
amnesia and doesn't believe that handsome Ian MacVane is her
betrothed—especially after another suitor appears. Miranda's
search for the truth leads to passion beyond her wildest dreams.

WISH LIST by Jeane Renick
RITA Award–Winning Author

Only $3.99

While on assignment in Nepal, writer Charlayne Pearce meets elusive and irresistibly sensual Jordan Kosterin. Jordan's bold gaze is an invitation to pleasure, but memories of his dead wife threaten their newfound love.

SILVER SPRINGS by Carolyn Lampman

Only $3.99

Independent Angel Brady feels she is capable of anything—even passing as her soon-to-be-married twin sister so that Alexis can run off with her lover. Unfortunately, the fiancé turns out to be the one man in the Wyoming Territory who can send Angel's pulse racing.

CALLIE'S HONOR by Kathleen Webb

Only $3.99

Callie Lambert is unprepared for the handsome stranger who shows up at her Oregon ranch determined to upset her well-ordered life. But her wariness is no match for Rafe Millar's determination to discover her secrets, and win her heart.

Harper Monogram